DATE DUE

VIEWPOINTS IN
BIOLOGY

2

ENGLAND: BUTTERWORTH & CO. (PUBLISHERS) LTD.
                LONDON: 88 Kingsway, W.C.2

AFRICA: BUTTERWORTH & CO. (AFRICA) LTD.
                DURBAN: 33/35 Beach Grove

AUSTRALIA: BUTTERWORTH & CO. (AUSTRALIA) LTD.
                SYDNEY: 6-8 O'Connell Street
                MELBOURNE: 473 Bourke Street
                BRISBANE: 240 Queen Street

CANADA: BUTTERWORTH & CO. (CANADA) LTD.
                TORONTO: 1367 Danforth Avenue, 6

NEW ZEALAND: BUTTERWORTH & CO. (NEW ZEALAND) LTD.
                WELLINGTON: 49/51 Ballance Street
                AUCKLAND: 35 High Street

U.S.A.:   BUTTERWORTH INC.
                WASHINGTON, D.C.: 7235 Wisconsin Avenue, 14

VIEWPOINTS IN
BIOLOGY

2

Edited by

J. D. CARTHY

*Department of Zoology, Queen Mary College
London*

and

C. L. DUDDINGTON

*Department of Chemistry and Biology, The Polytechnic
Regent Street, London*

LONDON

BUTTERWORTHS

1963

Suggested U.D.C. number: 547(047.1)

Printed in Northern Ireland at The Universities Press, Belfast

INTRODUCTION

Viewpoints in Biology will publish broadly based reviews of biological subjects which may be extensively illustrated. These reviews should not only summarize the state of the subject but also indicate the direction in which progress may be expected, and stress unsolved problems. While putting a cogent, well-argued point of view the authors will, however, not necessarily be asked to give exhaustive documentations of all the work in the subject. Considerations of the theoretical aspects of biology, criticisms of well-established methods and discussions of material from an evolutionary point of view will all be welcome. Descriptions of the practical details of methods will not be accepted unless they are involved in the consideration of a subject of general biological interest.

As far as possible the reviews should be readily understandable to other scientists as well as biologists. With increasing specialization within biology as well as the sundering of science into departments, it is more and more necessary that the problems facing one sort of scientist should be presented in a way which is understandable to others, so that if their interests are aroused they can bring to bear their own specializations on to the problems of another department of science.

Contributions will be printed in English but may be submitted in French or German.

Suggestions for contributions should, in the first place, be sent in outline form to one of the editors:

J. D. Carthy, Department of Zoology, Queen Mary College,
Mile End Road, London, E.1.

C. L. Duddington, Department of Chemistry and Biology,
The Polytechnic, Regent Street, London, W.1.

A guide to authors and information on fees will be sent when a suggestion is acceptable.

The editors wish to thank all authors, societies and publishers for permission to reproduce diagrams and tables which have appeared in previous publications.

CONTENTS

CONTENTS

3. ARTHROPODS AS PREDATORS

John S. Edwards, *Department of Biology, Western Reserve University, Cleveland, Ohio*

4. ANATOMICAL AND PHYSIOLOGICAL ADAPTATIONS IN DIVING MAMMALS

R. J. Harrison and J. D. W. Tomlinson, *Department of Anatomy, The London Hospital Medical College*

5. KINETIC ASPECTS OF ION REGULATION IN AQUATIC ANIMALS

J. SHAW, *Department of Zoology, King's College, Newcastle upon Tyne*

6. PALAEOBOTANICAL TECHNIQUES

WILLIAM S. LACEY, *Department of Botany, University of North Wales*

MICRO-ORGANISMS AND FOOD

Arnold Fox

INTRODUCTION

THE subject of food microbiology[1,2] is so vast that it would require a very lengthy treatise to do full justice to it, even in a review article such as this. For this reason I have purposely omitted reference to the micro-organisms associated with the enrichment of soil nutrients, both by breaking down complex organic matter (heterotrophic organisms) and by utilizing inorganic substances (autotrophic organisms), in order to obtain their supplies of energy. Without these organisms in the soil the farmer would have an impossible task in trying to grow our basic food materials.

A brief mention only can be made of that vast group of microscopic plants and animals collectively termed plankton. These are found in the surface layers of natural waters, both fresh and marine, and are essential as food for larger aquatic animals such as fish.

What I do intend mentioning are those micro-organisms associated with the production of foods derived from more basic food materials, such as bread from flour, wine from grape juice, cheese from milk, *etc.*

A vast amount of food is wasted every hour of every day by the action of micro-organisms, and these will be discussed together with the various methods of food preservation used to counteract their activities.

Another topic covered in this article is food poisoning, the organisms associated with it, and the methods by which they are eliminated or eradicated from foods.

Since this article is not intended for professional food microbiologists, (although it is hoped that they will find it helpful), but for amateur and professional biologists, I have tried to reduce the number of specific references by indicating only the key papers from which further reading can be initiated.

ORGANISMS AS AIDS TO FOOD MANUFACTURE

The science of microbiology deals with all aspects of microscopic organisms, from true plants such as algae to obvious animals such as protozoa, by way of groups showing some characteristics of both kingdoms, *e.g.* bacteria, fungi, and slime moulds. Other groups such as viruses and Rickettsiae are among the smallest of all living matter, viruses being so minute that they cannot be seen under the most powerful light microscope but can only be photographed under the electron microscope; their size is measured in millimicrons (mμ).

The main organisms associated with food manufacture are bacteria and fungi. The microscopic forms of fungi are referred to as yeasts and moulds, to distinguish them from the larger fungi such as mushrooms, toadstools, morels, *etc*. Algae, those microscopic green plants forming much of the plankton of natural waters are, as yet, not used in the manufacture of food although much work has been done on the continuous cultivation of *Chlorella pyrenoidosa*. This organism grows at a very rapid rate when given adequate supplies of inorganic salts, carbon dioxide, water and good illumination. Since under varying conditions this alga can produce large quantities of protein (5–50 per cent of dry weight) or fat (5–75 per cent) its large scale production, especially in under-developed and over-populated parts of the world, could lead to a substantially increased food supply.

BACTERIA

These minute organisms, measured in microns are found practically everywhere in nature, from high mountains and oceanic depths to polar ice and hot springs. Their ability to withstand extremes of physical conditions can be attributed to their small size, simplicity of structure (compared with larger multicellular creatures), and to protective mechanisms and structures which many of them possess. Examples of the various shapes of bacteria are shown in *Figure 1.1*. It would be wrong to assume that the shape of any bacterial species is constant, since many bacteria exist in several morphological forms (pleomorphism) such as cocci, rods and filaments, depending on the life-cycle and environment of the organisms.

Many bacteria are motile, movement in a liquid being effected by hair-like projections (flagella) arising from the cytoplasm just internal to the cell wall (see *Figure 1.2*). Some organisms, although not possessing flagella, can move by flexing their bodies and so glide over solid surfaces (*e.g. Microscilla, Cytophaga*) or through liquids (*e.g. Borrellia*). Most bacteria, whether motile or non-motile, can be carried to other habitats by air currents, water, aerosols, surfaces of animals, food, *etc*. By these means the distribution of bacteria is world-wide.

Bacteria multiply by simple fission: *i.e.* when a cell has reached an optimum size it splits into two 'daughter' cells which then continue to grow and divide to form four, and so on. In this way under favourable conditions a single bacterial cell can divide every 20 minutes, so giving rise to millions of progeny within a day. This fact is utilized by bacteriologists to ascertain the numbers of living bacteria in a sample of food or other material. By dispersing a known volume of the aqueous food suspension in a nutrient medium containing a solidifying agent (agar-agar or gelatine) and incubating the culture at a suitable temperature, each viable organism will proliferate in the solid medium to produce a visible colony containing millions of bacteria. Colony characteristics such as size, shape, colour, contour, *etc*. are often used to help identify bacteria, since many form highly individual colonies on specific media.

Another very important criterion used in the classification of bacteria, is the ability of some of them to retain certain dyes (of the pararosaniline group) when stained according to the method of Christian Gram. These Gram-positive organisms appear purple under the microscope, whereas Gram-negative bacteria fail to retain the purple dye and are coloured red

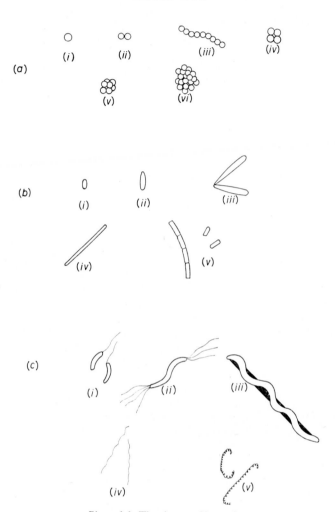

Figure 1.1. The shapes of bacteria

(*a*) The Coccus. (*i*) single coccus; (*ii*) Diplococcus; (*iii*) Streptococcus; (*iv*) *Gaffkya tetragena* (tetrads of cocci); *Sarcina*
(packets of 8 and 16 cocci); Staphylococcus (irregular
clusters of cocci).

(*b*) The Rod. (*i*) Small ovoid rod (*e.g. Serratia marcescens*);
(*ii*) Round-ended rod (*e.g. Escherichia coli*); (*iii*) Club-
shaped (*e.g. Corynebacterium diphtheriae* showing characteristic
'hinge' cells); (*iv*) Long slender rod (*e.g. Lactobaccillus*
species); (*v*) Square-ended rods (*e.g. Bacillus anthracis*).

(*c*) The Spiral. (*i*) 'Comma-shaped' (*e.g. Vibrio*); (*ii*) Simple
spiral (*e.g. Spirillum*); (*iii*) Long spiral surrounding central
axial filament (*e.g. Spirochaeta*); (*iv*) Slender spiral (*e.g.*
Treponema); (*v*) Slender coiled spirals (*e.g. Leptospira*).

(After Hawker, Lilian E., Linton, A. H., Folkes, B. F., and
Carlile, M. J., 1960. 'An Introduction to the Biology of Micro-
organisms'. Edward Arnold, London).

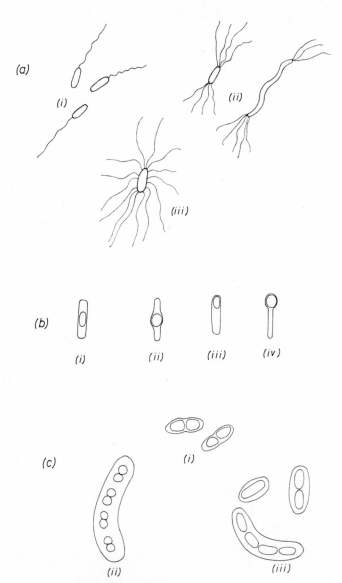

Figure 1.2. Flagella, Spores and Capsules

(*a*) Flagellated bacteria. (*i*) Single flagellum (Monotrichous); (*ii*) Tuft of flagella at each pole (Lophotrichous); (*iii*) Flagella surrounding cell (Peritrichous).

(*b*) Endospores. (*i*) Central (*e.g. Bacillus cereus*); (*ii*) Central spore causing cell to swell (*e.g. Clostridium* sp.); (*iii*) Terminal (*e.g. Bacillus coagulans*); (*iv*) Terminal, swelling the cell to form 'drumsticks' (*e.g. Clostridium tetani*).

(*c*) Capsules. (*i*) *Diplococcus pnemoniae* Type I; (*ii*) *Diplococcus pneumoniae* Type III; *Klebsiella pneumoniae*.

by the counterstain used (safranine, carbon fuchsin, *etc.*). There seems to be a fundamental difference in the two groups of bacteria based upon the presence or absence of magnesium ribonucleate in the surface layers of the bacterial cell. However, many bacteria lose their Gram-positive character with age, so that bacteriologists try to carry out this particular test with young actively-growing cultures.

'Acid-fastness' is another phenomenon associated with the staining of bacteria. Some organisms fail to stain with the normal procedures because the waxy substances present in the cell wall make entry of the stain very difficult. To stain these bacteria we have to resort to more drastic treatment, such as a more powerful stain and the application of heat to the preparation. When the cells have been stained by this method they cannot be decolorized by the action of acid (usually 20 per cent sulphuric acid) and are termed 'acid-fast' (the tubercle bacillus, *Mycobacterium tuberculosis*, is a good example of an acid-fast organism).

Biochemical tests are also undertaken to find out which sugars the organism ferments, whether it reduces nitrates to nitrites and/or sulphur-containing compounds to hydrogen sulphide, whether growth is encouraged by certain carbon and nitrogen sources, *etc.*

The ability to exist and even to multiply in apparently unfavourable conditions is due largely to one or a combination of a number of factors, both morphological and biochemical. These include the following:

(*a*) Spore formation. The presence of highly resistant endospores (*Figure 1.2.*) within the bacterial cell enables many organisms to withstand freezing, boiling, the action of disinfectants, *etc.* for varying periods of time, often measured in years. Spores are often formed as a result of an adverse change in the environment of the bacteria.

(*b*) Capsule formation. These structures (*Figure 1.2.*) are mucilaginous envelopes completely surrounding many bacteria and composed of long-chain polysaccharides and/or polypeptides. Not only do capsules protect the bacteria by making the entry of harmful substances into the cell difficult, if not impossible; but they are also associated in many pathogenic bacteria with the production of disease within a suitable host. Examples of pathogenic capsules are those surrounding *Diplococcus pneumoniae* (pneumonia) and *Bacillus anthracis* (anthrax). The cells which lack capsules are avirulent and produce rough-textured colonies as distinct from the smooth colonies of pathogenic forms.

(*c*) Enzyme systems. The internal biochemistry of the bacterial cell may be such that adverse external conditions are counterbalanced. Thus if *Escherichia coli*, a very common organism found in the gut of man and animals, is placed in an acid environment certain enzymes (carboxylases) are formed. These catalyse reactions leading to the removal of carbon dioxide from amino-acids with a consequent raising of the internal pH of the cell. On the other hand, if the cell is placed in an alkaline environment, other enzymes (deaminases) are produced instead of decarboxylases. These remove $-NH_2$ groups from amino-acids resulting in a more acid cell[3].

Many bacteria, because of their internal metabolism, are able to withstand such diverse conditions as the absence of air, presence of sulphur, iron, salt, *etc.* Some of these special habitats and nutritional requirements are

Table 1.1. Some physical and chemical requirements of bacteria

Requirement	Example	Descriptive term
A. Physical		
1. Temperature		
(a) Optimum below 20°C	Pseudomonas spp. Achromobacter spp.	Psychrophiles
(b) Optimum between 20°–45°C	Most bacteria including pathogens	Mesophiles
(c) Optimum above 45°C	Bacillus stearothermophilus, Clostridium thermosaccharolyticum	Thermophiles
(d) Capable of withstanding high temperatures	Spore-bearing bacteria	Thermoduric organisms
2. Acidity		
(a) Preference for pH below 4.5	Lactobacillus spp. Acetobacter spp.	Aciduric
(b) Preference for medium pH range	Most bacteria	
(c) Preference for alkaline pH above 8	Alcaligenes	
3. Light		
Illumination is essential	Rhodospirillum Chromatium	Photosynthetic bacteria
4. Osmotic concentration		
(a) Tolerant of high sugar concentrations	Leuconostoc mesenteroides	Osmophiles
*(b) Require 12–30% salt for growth	Halobacterium	Obligate halophiles
*(c) Tolerant of high salt concentrations	Staphylococcus aureus	Facultative halophiles
B. Chemical		
1. Oxygen requirements		
(a) Oxygen necessary for growth	Most bacteria	Aerobes
(b) Oxygen prevents growth	Clostridia	Obligate anaerobes
(c) Growth with or without oxygen	Escherichia coli	Facultative anaerobes
(d) Require low oxygen-tensions	Many lactic-acid bacteria	Micro-aerophiles
2. Other gaseous requirements		
(a) Nitrogen	Azotobacter, Klebsiella aerogenes†	Nitrogen-fixing bacteria
(b) Hydrogen	Hydrogenomonas	
(c) Carbon dioxide	Chlorobium	Photosynthetic autotrophes
	Thiobacillus	Chemosynthetic autotrophes
(d) Methane	Methanomonas	Chemosynthetic autotrophes
(e) Carbon monoxide	Carboxydomonas	Chemosynthetic autotrophes
3. Other inorganic sources		
(a) Ammonia	Nitrosomonas ⎱	Nitrifying bacteria
(b) Nitrites	Nitrobacter ⎰	
(c) Hydrogen sulphide, sulphur, thiosulphates	Thiobacillus spp.	Colourless sulphur bacteria
(d) Iron and manganese	Gallionella Sphaerotilus Ferrobacillus	Iron and Manganese bacteria
4. Organic compounds	Majority of bacteria	Heterotrophes

* Not entirely an osmotic phenomenon
† K. aerogenes fixes nitrogen under neutral or alkaline conditions.

6

given in *Table 1.1*. Many of the bacteria listed combine a number of special requirements, *viz.* lactobacilli are aciduric and anaerobic, and *Thiobacillus thio-oxidans* is aerobic, oxidizes elemental sulphur, and withstands acid down to pH 0.3 (normal sulphuric acid).

With such a wide choice of habitat it is, therefore, not surprising that many bacteria are able to preserve foods from putrefactive organisms by producing acids, such as lactic acid and acetic acid. Others aid in the production of characteristic flavours and aromas (*e.g. Pediococcus cerevisiae* in butter). On the debit side, however, many bacteria cause breakdown of food materials resulting in putrefaction, and others cause illness to the persons eating the food. A brief classification of bacteria commonly associated with food is therefore given here[4].

Lactic acid bacteria—Lactobacillaceae

Streptococcus—Spherical to ovoid cells (cocci) occurring in pairs or long or short chains. They are Gram-positive and non-motile. Only one small group (Lancefield's group N), consisting of *Strep. lactis* and *Strep. cremoris*, is used in the dairy industry, although the presence of other group members in foods indicates contamination with faecal or potentially pathogenic organisms.

Pediococcus—Gram-positive, non-motile cocci occurring singly, as tetrads, pairs or even short chains. It produces lactic acid from carbohydrates and is found in beer, sauerkraut and pickles. *Pediococcus cerevisiae* produces diacetyl, a substance which gives the characteristic aroma of fresh butter.

Leuconostoc—Gram-positive, non-motile cocci occurring singly or in short or long chains. *Leuconostoc mesenteroides* forms a slime from sugar, and is found in fermenting vegetable material and prepared meat products, as well as from sugar refineries.

Lactobacillus—Gram-positive, non-motile rods, often long and slender. Anaerobic to micro-aerophilic. The majority of species produce lactic acid from glucose (homofermentative) and are more tolerant of acid conditions than other lactic acid bacteria. Therefore they usually form the final bacterial flora of fermented milk, pickles, sauerkraut, *etc.*

Acetic acid bacteria

Acetobacter—Gram-negative rods occurring singly or in long chains. *A. aceti* is used in vinegar manufacture, and many other species are found in situations where ethyl alcohol is present *e.g.* in beer. These bacteria are highly oxidative and form a slimy pellicle or skin on the surface of liquid media, that of *A. xylinum* being composed entirely of cellulose, a polysaccharide rarely produced by bacteria but found in large amounts in plant cell walls.

Pseudomonas

These are gram-negative rods usually motile by means of a tuft of flagella. They are common in soil and water, and many are plant parasites. Most species can break down proteins (proteolytic) and many are psychrophilic, being able to grow at low temperatures. The slime on the surface of fish

2

and meat contains large numbers of these organisms. Many are characterized by the production of fluorescent diffusible pigments of varying colour.

Halobacterium

This group is placed in the same family as Pseudomonas and Acetobacter, namely the Pseudomonadaceae. It is unusual in that all species are halophilic since they cannot grow below a salt concentration of 12 per cent. They are frequently found in salted fish and meat, where their presence may cause an orange or red discoloration.

Achromobacter and Flavobacterium

These are Gram-negative rods with feeble powers of fermenting carbohydrates. They are often present in foods. *Flavobacterium*, as the name implies, produces a yellow pigment.

Enterobacteriaceae

Gram-negative rods; aerobes and facultative anaerobes; actively ferment carbohydrates.

Escherichia and Klebsiella—These two genera comprise the major group of 'coliform' bacteria, *i.e.* organisms able to ferment lactose to give acid and gas (CO_2 and H_2) in the presence of bile salts. *E. coli* type I is found in very large numbers in the gut of mammals, including man, and is, for this reason, the major 'indicator' of faecal pollution in water and foods. *K. aerogenes* is very widely distributed, occurring in soil, dust, foodstuffs, and the gut of mammals and man. It is often associated, together with other bacteria, in some fermented foods such as smoked sausage.

Salmonella—These motile rods do not ferment lactose although other sugars are fermented; they are parasitic in animals (including man) and cause typhoid, enteric fevers, and food poisoning.

Proteus—Highly motile, often forming 'swarming' colonies on solid media; lactose not fermented; urea broken down; common in all putrefying matter.

Serratia—Often produce large amount of red pigment (prodigiosin). *S. marcescens* (*Chromobacterium prodigiosum*) is sometimes found in milk and on bread, *etc.* to form a blood-red discoloration.

Micrococcaceae

Gram-positive, spherical cocci occurring in irregular masses, tetrads or packets.

Micrococcus—Irregular masses or tetrads of cocci; yellow, orange or red pigments produced by some species; saprophytes in dairy products and milk; non-pathogenic when parasitic.

Staphylococcus—Single or clusters of cocci; pathogenic strains are usually pigmented (*e.g.* the golden colour of *Staph. aureus*) and produce an enzyme, coagulase, which assists the clotting of the host's blood around the bacteria. Apart from causing pyogenic infections, abscesses, boils, *etc.* the production of a heat-stable toxin has led to many outbreaks of food poisoning.

Bacillaceae

The members of this family of Gram-positive, rod-shaped bacteria are all capable of forming highly resistant endospores; they may be motile and may occur singly or in chains.

Bacillus—This genus is aerobic; spores are usually no wider than the vegetative cell. The group contains parasites *e.g. B. anthracis* which causes anthrax, and may saprophytic species including thermophiles such as *B. stearothermophilus*, the cause of 'flat souring' of canned foods.

Clostridium—Anaerobic spore-forming rods; spores are spherical or oval and are often wider than the cell, causing swelling (see *Figure 1.2*); the position of the spore can be terminal, subterminal or central; many are pathogenic, *e.g. Cl. tetani* (tetanus) and *Cl. botulinum* (botulism); saprophytic species include many which are of industrial importance, *e.g. Cl. aceto-butylicum* used in the production of butyl alcohol, and many which cause spoilage of foods, *e.g. Cl. putrificum, Cl. thermosaccharolyticum* and *Cl. nigrificans*, the last two being thermophilic organisms causing spoilage of canned goods.

YEASTS[5,6]

These organisms are predominantly unicellular, and although they are true fungi, they are usually grouped separately from other moulds. They are microscopic but are larger than bacteria and require a slightly more acid environment for growth than bacteria. A typical yeast cell (shown in *Figure 1.3(a)*) is ovoid, spherical or sausage-shaped, has a fairly rigid 'fungal cellulose' cell wall, possesses a nuclear apparatus consisting of a nucleolus and a vacuole, and has various inclusion bodies scattered throughout the granular cytoplasm. Glycogen is the carbohydrate which is stored as an energy reserve material, and oil droplets are found in many older cells and in certain species of yeasts. 'Volutin' granules or 'mitochondria' are found in the cytoplasm and these are thought to be store-houses of enzyme systems.

Most yeasts reproduce asexually under good growth conditions, *i.e.* when supplied with sugar and air. This proliferation of the yeast is by budding or by splitting into two, *i.e.* fission.

Budding yeasts (Figure 1.3(b–d))

Most yeasts, including *Saccharomyces cerevisiae*, the brewers' and bakers' yeast, produce daughter cells by outgrowths or 'buds' from the parent cell. As the bud enlarges the nuclear apparatus divides into two, one half being passed to the daughter cell which constricts at the point of attachment to seal the cytoplasmic bridge. Although the two cells are now separate individuals, the daughter cell may remain attached to the mother cell, and it is quite common to observe masses of adhering yeast cells which have arisen from a single cell by successive budding (*Figure 1.3(c)*). In *S. cerevisiae* a bud can arise from any point on the cell wall (multipolar budding), but some yeasts, including some apiculate or lemon-shaped types, produce a bud at one or two points only (polar budding—*Figure 1.3(d)*). Where polar budding is successively in one plane the yeast may form a pseudomycelium, a fila-mentous multicellular structure which may be very difficult to distinguish from a true mould mycelium.

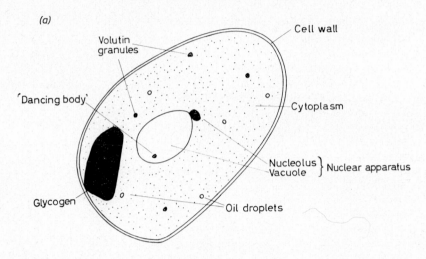

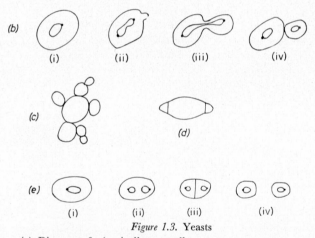

Figure 1.3. Yeasts

(*a*) Diagram of a 'typical' yeast cell.
(*b*) (*i–iv*) Stages in the formation of a 'bud'.
(*c*) Multipolar budding resulting in a mass of adhering yeast cells.
(*d*) Polar budding in an apiculate yeast.
(*e*) (*i–iv*) Cell division of a 'fission' yeast.

Fission yeasts

In this group the yeast cell after reaching an optimum size divides into two, by firstly a division of the nuclear apparatus, followed by the laying down of a cross-wall between the two nuclei. The two cells formed usually separate (see *Figure 1.3(e)*).

Pseudomycelial yeasts

Some pseudomycelia produce cells called blastospores which are capable of asexual reproduction by budding, whereas in other types the pseudomycelium fragments into its individual cell units, each being termed an arthrospore (*Figure 1.4(a)*).

Many yeasts carry out sexual reproduction when conditions are not favourable for normal asexual growth, and produce spores. These spores are not formed in the same way as bacterial spores, but are the result of a sexual process similar to the formation of ascospores by Ascomycetes. It is, in fact, thought by many mycologists that most yeasts are degenerate Ascomycetes, whose predominant phase is unicellular. All Ascomycetes produce sexual spores within a special sac or ascus, which may be naked as in yeasts, or enclosed within specialized fruit-bodies as in the larger members of the group, such as truffles and morels.

Saccharomyces cerevisiae is a diplobiontic yeast, *i.e.* its predominant phase is as a vegetable cell containing the double number of chromosomes (diploid). Under adverse conditions the nucleus divides by a reduction division (meiosis) resulting in the formation of four spores each containing the single number of chromosomes (haploid) within its nucleus. These spores when released from the ascus grow into haploid vegetative cells, which eventually pair up and fuse to form the diploid vegetative cell once again (*Figure 1.4(b)*).

Schizosaccharomyces octosporus is a fission yeast whose vegetative cells are predominantly in the haploid phase (haplobiontic yeast). These cells fuse together in pairs to form the diploid zygote, the nucleus of which divides by meiosis followed by a simple division (mitosis) to form eight haploid ascospores. These eventually germinate to form the haploid vegetative cells once more (*Figure 1.4(c)*).

Many sporing yeasts (or ascosporogenous yeasts) have characteristically shaped spores (*Figure 1.4(d)*), which aids in their identification. Not all yeasts produce spores, however, and the so-called asporogenous yeasts (degenerate Fungi Imperfecti?) include some of industrial and medical importance.

Asporogenous yeasts

(a) Fermentative yeasts. These actively ferment various sugars under anaerobic conditions, *e.g. Torulopsis*.

(b) Oxidative yeasts or film-forming yeasts. These yeasts utilize sugars aerobically but not anaerobically, and they form a film of yeast cells on the surface of the substrate, *e.g. Mycoderma*.

(c) Apiculate or lemon-shaped yeasts, *e.g. Kloeckera*.

(d) *Candida* (or *Monilia*) is a pseudomycelial yeast which produces blasto-spores as a means of asexual reproduction. *C. albicans* is important medically since it causes the respiratory infection known as 'thrush' in humans.

(e) *Brettanomyces*, like Candida, is pseudomycelial with blastospores but is not pathogenic. It is sometimes used for obtaining a secondary fermentation in stored beers.

(f) *Geotrichum candidum* (or *Oidium lactis*), often grouped within the Fungi Imperfecti, has a pseudomycelium which produces arthrospores. It is very common in the soil, in milk products, and in Bakers' yeast.

Yeasts, like all fungi, are aerobic and need a free access of air for the oxida-tive respiration of carbohydrates. The complete oxidation of these sugars

11

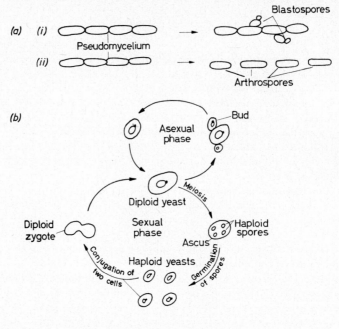

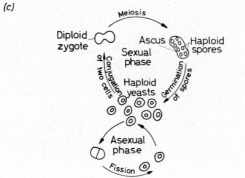

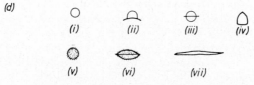

Figure 1.4.

(*a*) (*i*) Pseudomycelial yeast producing blastospores, *e.g. Candida intermedia;* (*ii*) Pseudomycelial yeast producing arthrospores, *e.g. Geotrichum candidum.*

(*b*) Diagram showing the life cycle of a diplobiontic yeast, *e.g. Saccharomyces cerevisiae.*

(*c*) Diagram showing the life cycle of a haplobiontic yeast, *e.g. Schizosaccharomyces octosporus.*

(*d*) The shape of ascospores in various yeasts

    (*i*) Spherical and smooth—*Saccharomyces*
    (*ii*) Bowler hat shaped—*Hansenula*
    (*iii*) Saturn-shaped—*Hansenula saturnus*
    (*iv*) Helmet-shaped—*Zygopichia*
    (*v*) Spherical and warty—*Debaryomyces*
    (*vi*) Walnut-shaped and warty with equatorial rim—*Schwanniomyces*
    (*vii*) Needle-shaped—*Monosporella*

((*d*) *i–iii* and *v–vii* after Ingram, ref. 5).

12

results in the formation of carbon dioxide, water and more important, the energy, which is utilized by the cell for all its metabolic activities.

Apart from oxidative respiration many yeasts, notably *Saccharomyces* species, are able to obtain energy from the incomplete breakdown of carbohydrates under anaerobic conditions. This fermentation of sugar leads to the formation of carbon dioxide gas and ethyl alcohol, as well as energy (although the energy yield is less than in oxidative respiration, it is still sufficient to enable good growth of the cell). These two chemical products are utilized industrially, *i.e.* carbon dioxide gas in bread making and ethyl alcohol in brewing, wine making and industrial alcohol production.

MOULDS[7]

The microscopic fungi, or moulds, are all heterotrophic organisms deriving their energy from the breakdown of organic material obtained from non-living sources (saprophrytic moulds), or from living plants and animals (parasitic moulds). They are characterized by the formation of a network of filaments, the mycelium, which may be septate or aseptate. Since they are highly aerobic organisms they are found on the surface of plants, food materials, *etc.* although they may penetrate deeper into the substratum if this is of open structure or if there is enzymic breakdown of the substrate.

Like yeasts, most moulds reproduce asexually to form spores, which are usually borne on specialized aerial hyphae. These spores may be enclosed within a sporangium or may be naked and the 'fruiting body' may be highly coloured, *e.g.* black sporangia of *Mucor* and *Rhizopus*, green spores of *Penicillium*, green, brown or black spores of *Aspergillus*, *etc.*

The classification of the fungi is based mainly upon the type of sexual spore and the structures associated with it. A very much over-simplified scheme is given here showing the moulds particularly concerned with foodstuffs.

Phycomycetes

Mycelium is aseptate and hyphae usually wider than in septate groups.

Oomycetes—Sexual reproduction is by passage of contents of male organ (antheridium) into the female organ (oogonium). Fertilization leads to the formation of thick-walled oospores.

Examples are *Phytophthora infestans* (Potato Blight), *Pythium debaryanum* ('damping off' in seedlings).

Zygomycetes—Sexual reproduction in most genera is by the fusion of gametangia of equal size (isogametes) arising from the same mycelium (homothallic) or from physiologically different mycelia (heterothallic). The fusion results in the formation of a thick-walled zygospore. Examples are *Mucor* and *Rhizopus* (*Figures 1.5(a)*, *1.6(a)*, *1.6(b)*) the 'pin-head' moulds commonly found on damp bread.

Ascomycetes

Sexual spores are endogenous, *i.e.* formed within a special sac-like ascus, usually eight spores per ascus. Asexual spores are often present and are very varied in form and arrangement.

13

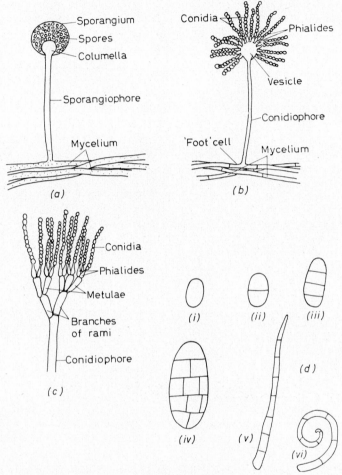

Figure 1.5.

(a) Diagram of Mucer showing sporangium.
(b) Aspergillus showing condiophore and 'fruiting head'.
(c) Diagram of a penicillus of *Penicillium*.
(d) Types of spore found among the Fungi Imperfecti

    (i) Amerospore *e.g. Botrytis*
   (ii) Didymospore *e.g. Trichothecium*
  (iii) Phragmospore *e.g. Dactylella*
  (iv) Dictyospore *e.g. Stemphylium*
   (v) Scolecospore
  (vi) Helicospore

Examples are Yeasts, *Aspergillus (Figure 1.5(b))*, *Penicillium (Figures 1.5(c)*, *1.6(c)*, *1.6(d))*.

Basidiomycetes

Sexual spores exogenous, *i.e.* formed on the outside of special cells, the basidia, each carrying four basidiospores attached by stalks or sterigmata. Examples are mushrooms, toadstools, and most larger fungi.

14

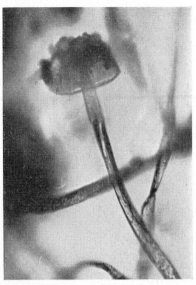

(a) *Rhizopus nigricans* showing dark spor-angia, and sporangiophores arising from a common node (slide culture ×100).

(b) *Rhizopus nigricans* showing the columella with adhering spores after dehiscence of the sporangium (×225).

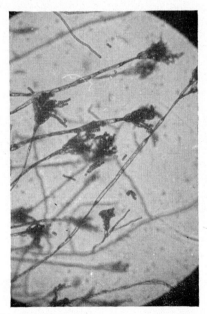

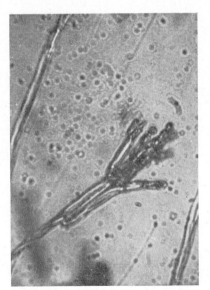

(c) *Penicillium* sp. showing many 'sporing heads' or penicilli (slide culture ×225).

(d) *Penicillium* sp. showing single penicillus (×500).

(Photographs by R. J. Callow)

Figure 1.6.

15

Fungi Imperfecti

This is an artificial group consisting of those fungi whose perfect stage or sexual phase is not known. Reproduction is by asexual spore formation, the spores are often large, multicellular and variously shaped (*Figure 1.5(a)*).

THE FOODS REQUIRING MICRO-ORGANISMS

Milk and Milk Products[8]

Milk has often been claimed as the 'perfect' food because of its great nutritional value in possessing protein, fats, carbohydrates, salts and various vitamins necessary for health. Because of its composition it is the natural habitat of those bacteria which are nutritionally exacting, *i.e.* needing proteins, carbohydrates and many different growth factors. Among these bacteria are members of the lactic acid group which produce varying quantities of lactic acid from the sugars present in the milk. This acid production is a natural and necessary method of preserving milk against breakdown by putrefactive organisms, and is the basis of the production of butter, cheese and fermented milks such as yoghurt.

Milk

Milk itself, however, is a commodity that is required in as fresh a condition as possible, and for this reason most milk bottled in the United Kingdom is given a heat treatment to destroy or drastically reduce the number of bacteria present. It is essential that the heat treatment given to the milk will destroy pathogenic bacteria such as the tubercle bacillus (*Mycobacterium tuberculosis*), *Brucella abortus* (causing contagious abortion in cattle and undulant fever in man), and food poisoning organisms, and for this reason Government regulations are in force[9] concerning the various methods of treatment. These are listed below.

Pasteurized milk

Holder method—Milk is placed in a large vat or tank and is heated to between 145° and 150°F, and retained at this range for at least 30 minutes. It is then immediately cooled to below 50°F.

H.T.S.T. method—The initials stand for High-Temperature-Short-Time, the temperature being not less than 161°F, and the holding time not less than 15 seconds. This is also followed by rapid cooling to below 50°F. Because of the shorter holding time this method can, and is, made a continuous process for pasteurizing milk, and is more popular than the older batch process necessitated by the Holder method.

U.H.T.S.T. or Ultra-high-temperature-short-time—This method results in the production of practically sterile milk free from any organisms. In this process the milk is heated, under pressure, to temperatures of 275–302°F for between 20 seconds to one second, followed by an immediate cooling. Any UHTST method must have the approval of the Ministry of Agriculture, Fisheries and Food, and the Ministry of Health, before sale to the public is permitted.

Sterilized milk

This type of milk is more correctly designated as intensively-heated milk because of the confusion between 'sterilized' and 'sterile'. This milk, after homogenization (dispersion of fat globules throughout the liquid), is boiled for varying periods of time within the bottle, this being sealed on or before the completion of the treatment. Boiling in this way may completely sterilize the contents, but it is more usual to find some highly resistant bacterial spores still present.

Raw milk

Raw farm-bottled milk is allowed to be sold to the public provided the cows are free from tubercular infection, as denoted by a negative tuberculin test. The milk is known as Tuberculin Tested milk and is safe to drink, as far as TB is concerned, although it may contain other pathogens.

Raw milk also contains various enzymes, including phosphatase, which is destroyed by temperatures slightly higher than those necessary to kill the tubercle bacillus. Since pasteurization temperatures are still higher, the heat-treatment should not only kill off the bacilli but should also destroy phosphatase. This is used as a test for the adequate pasteurization of milk, a negative phosphatase test signifying proper treatment, and a positive test showing either inadequate treatment or admixture of the treated milk with raw milk.

Butter

Much butter is made from ripened cream that has been soured with lactic streptococci. In the process of churning the cream there is a phase change from an oil-in-water emulsion, to one in which the continuous phase is oil with interspersed water droplets. The butter is then washed with water to remove nitrogenous substances, and this practice, provided water of drinking-water standard is used, will reduce the likelihood of proteolytic spoilage. Salting of butter with 1½–2 per cent salt results in a high salt concentration (10–15 per cent) in the water phase, reducing the chances of spoilage by *Pseudomonas* and enteric organisms. The aroma of butter is the result of diacetyl production by *Pediococcus cerevisiae* which is added, with lactic streptococci, to the pasteurized cream as a 'starter' culture. Other butter, *e.g.* from New Zealand and Australia, is made from sweet or un-ripened cream. The churning of this cream results in a butter less liable to go rancid, and which can be stored for longer periods than the ripened-cream butter, although this latter type (made in Holland and Denmark) has a better flavour.

Cheese

When milk is acidified or treated with rennet, the protein portion (casein) is coagulated, resulting in solid curd and liquid whey. Since bacteria present in the raw milk may hinder the cheese-making process, most of the milk is pasteurized. It is then inoculated with a 'starter' or pure culture of lactic acid bacteria, such as *Strep. lactis*, which converts milk sugar (lactose) into lactic acid. For the so-called acid curd cheeses such as cottage cheese or

17

cream cheese the coagulation process is completed by the bacterial acidification, and after removal of the whey the cheese is consumed within a fairly short period of time.

Most cheeses are rennet curd cheeses in which the enzyme coagulates the casein (acidity helps in this coagulation). The whey is removed and the curds are pressed with varying degrees of pressure resulting in soft to very hard cheese. Since additional pressure squeezes more moisture from the curds, the hardest cheeses contain the least amount of water. After pressing the cheese is allowed to ripen, by the action of bacteria, yeasts or moulds, or a combination of these organisms.

Soft rennet curd cheeses—Two examples are given below.

(*a*) Limburger. Ripening is initiated by *Strep. lactis*, but a mixed flora of bacteria and yeasts on the surface of the cheese continue the ripening process by secreting protein-splitting or caseolytic enzymes into the interior.

(*b*) Camembert. The final ripening of this soft cheese is carried out by a mould, *Penicillium camemberti*, following action by bacteria and yeasts (*Geotrichum candidum*). The mould spores may be added as a pure culture, but this is usually unnecessary because of the large number of mould spores already present in the cheese factory.

Hard rennet curd cheeses—These include cheddar and the blue-veined cheeses.

(*a*) Cheddar. After coagulation the curd and whey are heated about to 100°F and stirred until the curd settles to the bottom of the vat. The whey is drained off and the curd is cut into large pieces which are stacked or 'cheddared' to allow further drainage. After a few hours the curd is milled or ground into small pieces, mixed with salt, packed into presses lined with cheesecloth and pressed for several hours. The cheese is then bandaged in cloth and stored for a few months to ripen, mainly by the action of *Strep. lactis* and *L. casei*.

(*b*) Roquefort. This cheese, along with Stilton and other blue-veined cheeses, is mould ripened with *Penicillium roqueforti*. The mould is usually cultured on bread which is then ground and mixed with the curds before pressing. The mould, although aerobic, can also grow in the micro-aerophilic conditions found along the characteristic cheese cracks, and so the cheese is ripened by the proteolytic enzymes of the mould.

Other organisms used in cheese making include the propionic acid bacteria (species of *Propionibacter*) which form, because of gas production, the characteristic holes in certain Swiss cheeses.

Fermented milks[10]

Acidophilus milk—Pasteurized whole milk is inoculated with a starter culture of *Lactobacillus acidophilus* which converts lactose to lactic acid. The product is popular in the U.S.A., where it is often prescribed for the treatment of intestinal disorders.

Buttermilk—This resembles acidophilus milk in appearance, and is the acid by-product of the churning of sour cream into butter. Under natural conditions the cream is soured by a mixed variety of organisms but in the production of cultured buttermilk a pure starter culture of lactic streptococci is used.

Yoghurt—This type of fermented milk, common in the Balkan countries, relies on a lactic acid fermentation brought about by *Lactobacillus bulgaricus*. Whole milk from the cow, goat, sheep or buffalo is boiled to reduce its volume, cooled to about 45°C (the optimum temperature for this organism), and inoculated with some previously-made yoghurt. It is kept warm until it has clotted and become viscous.

Cultured yoghurt is produced industrially in many countries with a well-developed dairy industry, ripening being due to the addition of equal amounts of lactobacilli and streptococci to the milk.

Kefir—This sour-milk product is popular in the Caucasus and is the result of a mixed fermentation due to lactobaccilli, streptococci and a yeast (*Saccharomyces kefir*). Up to one per cent of alcohol may be present because of the activities of the yeast. Propagation of the product is by adding dried particles of clotted milk, known as kefir grains, to more milk. The grains contain all the organisms necessary for the successful fermentation already described.

A variety of kefir is Koumiss, which is made from mare's milk in some parts of Russia. Since this milk contains more lactose than cow's milk, the alcohol content of the final product is much higher, *i.e.* up to 3 per cent alcohol.

Pickles

Sauerkraut

This is fermented cabbage and is very popular in continental countries. In the home it can be made by shredding white cabbage and layering it, with salt, in a large glass jar. The layers of salted cabbage are firmly pressed down, the jar is topped up with water and then firmly closed.

Commercially, the cabbage is machine shredded and packed into large vats together with salt (about 2·5 per cent). A heavy lid compresses the mixture to exclude air.

Under anaerobic conditions, the naturally occurring lactic acid bacteria begin to ferment sugars. There is a succession of dominant types depending on the lactic acid tolerance of the organism. Thus the initial stage of fermentation is brought about mainly by *Leuconostoc mesenteroides* which, as the lactic acid concentration is increased, is replaced by *Lactobacillus plantarum* which in turn gives way to *Lactobacillus pentoaceticus*.

Cucumber pickles

Unripe, sound cucumbers are washed and placed in large brine tanks which, when full, are covered with weighted wooden boards. The planks keep the cucumbers submerged in the brine instead of floating on the surface. Water, sugars and other nutrients are removed from the vegetables by the action of the salt, and these substances form the substrates upon which the naturally occurring organisms grow. Lactic acid bacteria produce the acid which acts as a preservative, certain coliform bacteria ferment the sugars to form gases which escape through the gaps between planks, and yeasts produce some alcohol. During the 6–9 weeks curing process a surface scum of undesirable yeasts and moulds may be formed, but this can be largely prevented by measures including the thorough cleaning of sound cucumbers,

Figure 1.7. A battery of mash tuns or kieves in a modern brewery. (By Courtesy of Arthur Guinness Son and Co. (Park Royal) Ltd.)

Figure 1.8. Mash tun opened to show sparging of grist with hot water. (By Courtesy of Arthur Guinness Son and Co. (Park Royal) Ltd.)

irradiation of the surface of the brine with ultra-violet lamps, or the addition of fatty-acid preservatives such as propionic acid and sorbic acid.

Brewing

The main steps in the brewing of British-type beer are as follows.

Production of malt—Barley grains are soaked or 'steeped' in several changes of water to soften the tough seed coat or testa. After draining away the water the grains are spread over a stone or asphalt floor and allowed to germinate. This process is helped by a constant humidity and periodic turning of the grains to allow adequate aeration. Kilning, or hot-air drying of the barley, follows in order to arrest the further breakdown of starches by diastatic enzymes.

Mashing and sparging—The dried germinated barley or malt is lightly crushed between metal rollers to fracture the outer layers, and mixed with other unmalted grains and sugar. The resulting grist is heated to 150°F and placed into large metal vessels, the mash tuns or kieves (*Figure 1.7*), together with hot water at the same temperature. This allows the complete conversion of starch into simpler dextrins by enzyme action, after which the resulting wort is drained off through the false bottom of the tun and recirculated by a rotating sparge pipe. All the wort is drawn off and the grist is further sparged by hot water to remove most of the sugars, dextrins, *etc.* (*Figure 1.8*).

Boiling—The wort collects in a heated metal vessel known as the underback, from which it is pumped to the large steam-heated copper (*Figure 1.9*). Hops are mixed with the wort and the whole is boiled, more hops being added towards the end of the boil. The heat-treatment not only sterilizes the wort but stops further diastatic action, coagulates wort proteins, and extracts various resins from the hops. These humulones give to the beer its characteristic astringent flavour as well as acting as preservatives.

Fermentation—After boiling the wort is run into the hop back, a vessel with a false bottom like a mash tun. Here the hops and coagulated proteins settle to the bottom as a layer through which the wort is strained and further clarified. It is cooled to around 60°F through coolers before passing to the large fermenters where the wort is pitched (*i.e.* inoculated), with a culture of brewers' yeast, *Saccharomyces cerevisiae*. The whole process of fermentation, which may take $2\frac{1}{2}$–7 days according to the type of brew, is carried out at temperatures between 57 and 73°F. Yeasts ferment simple sugars to give alcohol, carbon dioxide and energy

$$C_6H_{12}O_6 \rightarrow 2C_2H_5OH + 2CO_2 + \text{energy (66,000 cals.)}$$

utilizing a complex series of enzymes collectively called 'zymase'. Left unchecked, a yeast will ferment the sugar completely, but the brewer aims at an incomplete fermentation of sugar (only 80–90 per cent) in order to leave some carbohydrate for a secondary fermentation during storage, and also to improve the flavour. The yeast, which is initially dispersed throughout the wort, is carried to the surface by the carbon dioxide to form a 'lathery' head which is eventually removed (*Figure 1.10*). *S. cerevisiae* is called a 'top yeast' because it rises to the surface, whereas *S. carlsbergensis* settles to the

Figure 1.9. A large Copper in which wort is boiled with hops.
(By Courtesy of Whitbread and Co. Ltd.)

Figure 1.10. Skimming the yeast from the fermented beer. (By Courtesy of Arthur
Guinness Son and Co. (Park Royal) Ltd.)

bottom of the vessel, *i.e.*, is a 'bottom yeast'. The latter organism is used to make continental beers and lagers.

Finishing operations—These include storage in large cooled vats (*Figure 1.11*), racking into barrels (*Figure 1.12*), carbonation, pasteurization, bottling and canning. Not all of these treatments are given to every beer; for example, beer in barrels is not pasteurized, to enable secondary fermentation to occur on the unfermented sugar, either originally present or added as sugar syrup or wort to the cask, whereas canned or bottled beer is usually pasteurized and carbonated.

Like all efficient industrial processes the modern brewing industry tries to avoid wastage of materials. For this reason CO_2 is used to form a gaseous 'blanket' above the fermenting liquor, thus inhibiting much bacterial growth. It is compressed and sold as solid carbon dioxide, and it is used for carbonating some of the brew. Similarly the bulk of the spent yeast is sold to manufacturers of yeast extract while some is retained to pitch the next fermentation. Because this subculturing technique has been going on for decades, the brewery microbiologist has to be ever watchful that the yeast has not become contaminated with harmful organisms and that its fermenting ability has not diminished.

Ginger beer

This can be made by fermenting a mixture of sugar (10–20 per cent) and ginger root with some 'ginger-beer plant'. This is a substance consisting of a mixed culture of bacteria and yeasts (*Bacterium vermiforme* and *Saccharomyces pyriformis*).

Wines

The making of wine is probably more ancient an art than the brewing of beer, since naturally occurring yeasts ferment the crushed grapes. The yeast, *Saccharomyces ellipsoideus*, is present on the grape skins, together with other types of yeast and bacteria. After crushing, the juice, together with skins and some stalks (*i.e.* the must), is poured into wooden or stone vats where fermentation takes place. A temperature range of between 70 and 90°F is needed and sulphuring the must with about 100 parts per million of sulphur dioxide may be necessary to inhibit undesirable organisms (*e.g.* acetic acid bacteria). After fermentation the wine is racked in wooden casks and allowed to mature, during which time yeast cells and other particles settle out as a sediment, and fresh wine is added to top up the cask which has lost some of the original liquid due to evaporation. The wine may be racked several times before final clarification with isinglass (prepared from the sturgeon's swim-bladder), agar or egg white.

Red wines are made from black grapes whereas most white wines are derived from white grapes, although some are made with black grapes, care being taken to exclude the skins from the juice to be fermented.

Baking

The organism of paramount importance to the baker is, of course, yeast, and the one used is a special strain of *Saccharomyces cerevisiae*. When dough is

3   23

Figure 1.11. Large temperature-controlled storage vats for the finished beer. (By Courtesy of Whitbread and Co. Ltd.)

Figure 1.12. Filling casks with draught beer. (By Courtesy of Whitbread and Co. Ltd.)

mixed with yeast and salt and allowed to stand for some hours at 70–80°F (the higher the temperature the shorter the time), fermentation of sugars present in the dough takes place. The products formed are alcohol and carbon dioxide, but it is the latter product which is important, since the gas makes the dough porous and raises it. After the period of 'proving' the dough is cut, shaped, and baked, a process which stops fermentation and drives off most of the alcohol as well as making the product fit to be eaten.

24

There are other types of bread in which various bacteria as well as yeasts promote fermentation, and these include:

(*a*) 'Sauerteig'. This is made from dough which has been seeded with fermenting organisms derived from a portion of a previous baking. Certain coliform bacteria produce characteristic acids and flavours resulting in the 'sour dough'.

(*b*) Black bread. Coarse whole-meal (wheat or rye) which is usually leavened with 'sauerteig'.

(*c*) 'Jamin-bang' is another coarse bread popular with the Indians of Brazil where the fermentation of the maize flour is carried out by a mixture of two yeasts and one bacterium derived from the maize or from the river water in which the grains are soaked.

Vinegar

Many acetic acid bacteria, or species of *Acetobacter*, are able to oxidize alcohol into acetic acid and water, the energy of oxidation being utilized for metabolic processes within the organisms as well as some being lost as heat. Vinegar-making is really a double process, consisting of the fermentation of sugars to form alcohol, followed by the oxidation of this to acetic acid. The sugary substrate can be sugar syrup, molasses, fruits and saccharified starchy materials, such as cereals. In this country most vinegar is made from the beer wort derived from fermented malt, whereas on the Continent it is made from the oxidation of wine; in America much vinegar is made from cider. The main methods of vinegar manufacture are given below.

Orleans method

This is one of the oldest industrial vinegar processes and was started in France. The alcoholic liquor used is wine (usually containing less than 10 per cent alcohol) which is added to vinegar in casks or long tanks, leaving an adequate air space above the liquor for aeration. Under these conditions the alcohol is oxidized to acetic acid by the vinegar bacteria, which form a continuous film or pellicle over the liquid. When the concentration of acetic acid has reached 12–14 per cent (usually after a week) some of the liquor is run off and more wine is added. Since it is essential that the bacterial film remains unbroken it is often supported by a wooden grating, and the wine inlet and vinegar outlet pipes are placed below the level of the pellicle. Although this method produces a very fine quality vinegar it is also very slow, and so the following two methods have been devised for speeding up the oxidation.

Quick-vinegar process

This is the main method of vinegar production in this country, and consists of the alcoholic fermentation of malt followed by acetification in large wooden cylindrical vessels. The production of wort is similar to that of the brewers' wort except that there is no boiling with hops, because the vinegar manufacturer requires as complete a conversion of sugars to alcohol as possible, and boiling will destroy the diastases which continue to break down dextrins. This sugary wort is fermented by pitching with a special strain of yeast (*S. cerevisiae*) and is continued until 6–7 per cent alcohol is formed. The liquor is sparged into the top of a large wooden acetifier, such as the Frings generator (*Figure 1.13*), where it trickles downwards over beech shavings while air rises from perforations in the false bottom of the tank. The shavings form a very large surface area on which the *Acetobacter* species form a slimy covering, and in this way maximum oxidation of alcohol is achieved. The warm acetified liquor falls to the bottom of the generator whence it is removed or cooled through a double tube and pumped to the top of the vessel for re-sparging. Other types of acetifier are packed with birch twigs, corn cobs *etc.* to give the large surface area required.

Figure 1.13. A group of wooden acetifiers in a large vinegar works. (By Courtesy of British Vinegar Ltd.)

Deep fermentation

This is a relatively new process in the vinegar industry although used extensively for antibiotic production. Instead of a large surface oxidation, the fermentation is carried out in deep tanks through which there is a controlled aeration with compressed air. Although still largely experimental, I believe there is a plant in operation in Switzerland, and also developments in other countries. One of the difficulties of the Swiss method is the high power cost involved, a factor of much less importance in a country of cheap hydro-electric power than in countries where electricity is much more expensive. There is no doubt, however, that deep fermentation methods will become increasingly used in the manufacture of vinegar.

Bean Fermentation

Cocoa beans

In the pod, cocoa beans are covered with pulp which is difficult to remove by mechanical means. The best method of removal is by fermentation carried out by a combination of yeasts and bacteria. The pulp is not only removed but the colour, flavour, and aroma of the cocoa is affected.

Soya beans

A mould, *Rhizopus oryzae*, has been shown to be essential in the production of 'Tempeh', a fermented soybean food common in Indonesia. The organism, provided it is given sufficient air, a high humidity, and a favourable pH range (4–5) at the right temperature (37°C), will ferment the beans by enzymic action, removing the tough skins and producing characteristic flavours.

Micro-organisms as Food

Food yeasts

Because yeasts contain appreciable amounts of protein and vitamins of the B complex, attention has been given to their utilization as food supplements. Because of its rather strong flavour *Saccharomyces cerevisiae* is not usually used for adding to food or animal fodder although, since there is a vast amount of unwanted yeast grown by the brewer, various methods are adopted to remove bitterness caused by the hops; the yeast is then dried and powdered. The yeast which is most frequently used is *Candida utilis* (*Torulopsis utilis*) since its flavour is quite pleasant and it gives good yields of protein and B vitamins.

The production of food yeast follows the same pattern as for the manufacture of bakers' yeast, *i.e.* a suitable strain of yeast is maintained in the laboratory as a pure culture, and this is used for each batch of commercial yeast. The initial stage in the production is the formation of the 'seed' yeast which provides the inoculum for the very large industrial fermenters. This 'seed' is the result of successive subcultures (usually four or five), starting from a small inoculum grown in a flask of molasses wort containing various salts, nitrogen and phosphate, to large volumes of substrate (3,000 gallons) housed in large stainless-steel vats. At each stage of growth the yeast is given correspondingly more nutrients and, since the maximum amount of yeast cells are required, not the production of alcohol or carbon dioxide, aeration is necessary, slow at first but increasing to a continuous stream of sterile compressed air. This incremental or logarithmic addition of sugar and other nutrients is continued when the 'seed' is transferred to the very large fermentation tanks, which may be up to 30,000 gallons capacity. All nutrients must be added as sterile solutions and the concentration of sugars should never exceed about 0·0004 per cent, facts which call for great skill in the design of the plant and the continuous maintenance of sterility. Growth of yeast proceeds for about 12 hours at a temperature range of 24–30°C, and pH of 3·5–4·5. The yeast cells are separated from the wort by means of centrifugation, washed, dried in a filter press and packed as 1 lb. blocks in greaseproof paper. This compressed or block yeast remains viable for several weeks if stored below 40°F in a refrigerator.

Vitamins

These substances are not, strictly speaking, foods, but accessory food factors necessary for the maintenance of good health. Many yeasts produce good yields of vitamins of the B group which include thiamin or aneurin (vitamin B_1), riboflavin (vitamin B_2), nicotinic acid, pantothenic acid, biotin, pyridoxine, and folic acid. By varying the strain of yeast and the growth conditions, the vitamin of choice can be obtained. For example, thiamin can be produced by many yeasts, including brewers' yeast, when grown on grain wort and given a restricted air supply, and riboflavin is prepared commercially by utilizing the yeast-like mould *Eremothecium ashbyii* grown in a protein-rich medium.

Vitamin D, which prevents the bone condition known as 'rickets', is made from yeasts by irradiating the cells or cell extracts with ultra-violet rays. These activate the ergosterol present in the cell to form vitamin D.

Fat production[11]

Many yeasts and moulds produce large amounts of fat when grown under appropriate conditions, and use has been made of these organisms during war-time scarcity of fats. Yeasts giving a high yield of fat include the pink *Rhodotorula gracilis* (up to 50 per cent dry weight of fat), *Lipomyces lipofera* (25–33 per cent) and *Trichosporon sp.* (up to 38 per cent); other fat-forming moulds include *Geotrichum candidum* (*Oidium lactis*), *Endomycopsis vernalis* and various species of *Mucor, Aspergillus* and *Fusarium*.

Various substrates have been used to grow the cultures, including glucose, maltose, molasses, and sugars derived from straw. In this latter case it has been estimated that, using a strain of *G. candidum*, 100 tons of crude straw would give 31 tons of utilizable sugar, 15 tons of fat-containing mycelium, and 5 tons of fat[12]. Extraction methods include treatment with acids or fat-solvents such as ether or methanol.

It is a great pity that only in times of war do governments spend money on industrial plant for the biological production of fats, *etc*. Micro-organisms could play a very important part in supplementing the nutritional needs of millions of undernourished people, if only the governments concerned or a supra-national body could finance suitable projects.

Algae

Many algae produce considerable amounts of fat or protein when grown under suitable conditions, *e.g. Chlorella pyrenoidosa* can produce up to 50 per cent protein or 75 per cent fat. The advantage of utilizing these micro-scopic green plants is that, unlike yeasts and moulds, they do not require pre-formed organic materials as energy substrates. Since they are photo-synthetic autotrophes they can build up carbohydrates within the cell from sources such as carbon dioxide, water and inorganic salts, in the presence of sunlight.

Experimental work carried out during the last war indicated the practicability of growing these algae in large economic quantities, although costs became higher if protein or fat extraction was carried out. The partially dried and pressed cells could easily be incorporated into animal feeding stuffs, even though the product proved unpalatable and indigestible to humans. This source of fat and protein could be of great value to over-populated countries, especially as these usually have excellent natural sunlight.

ORGANISMS CAUSING FOOD SPOILAGE

Dairy Products

Milk

We have seen how in this country most bottled milk is given a heat treatment to kill off pathogenic bacteria such as *Mycobacterium tuberculosis*, *Brucella abortus* and *Staphylococcus aureus*. Unless, however, the bottling, storage, and distribution of the milk is carried out hygienically, the bacteria may drastically cut the effective storage 'life' of the product. The normal flora of lactic acid bacteria will sour the milk, and species of *Pseudomonas* will break down the milk proteins, causing putrefaction, even at refrigerator temperature. Other defects of milk include gassiness due to coliform bacteria, ropy milk caused by capsulated bacteria (*Alcaligenes* and *Klebsiella aerogenes*), and 'sweet curdling', due to spore-bearing bacteria. These latter organisms, especially members of the *Bacillus cereus* group, sometimes cause trouble when the Holder method of pasteurization is used.

The keeping quality of raw and pasteurized milk largely depends on the number of bacteria present. For this reason the best method of assessing the keeping quality is to carry out a viable plate count using Yeastrel Milk Agar. However, since not all laboratories and dairies are equipped for performing bacteriological tests, the statutory method is the Methylene Blue test, which is based upon the reduction of the blue dye to the colourless form, leuco-methylene blue, by the action of bacteria. There is a rough correlation between the number of organisms and dye reduction, approximately 100,000 organisms per millilitre of milk will reduce the dye within 30 minutes when incubated at 37°C. Other tests can be carried out to detect any post-pasteurization contamination *i.e.* the coliform test about which much more will be said, and tests for the presence of psychrophilic bacteria.

Evaporated and condensed milk

Evaporated milk is made by heat-treating raw milk (higher temperatures than for pasteurization are usually used), homogenizing and evaporating it. After cooling to 4°C the milk is filled into cans which are sterilized or processed in order to destroy thermophilic spores. If treatment is inadequate, or if contaminated cooling water leaks into the can after processing, spoilage bacteria of the spore-bearing type may lead to 'blown' cans or to the coagulation of the milk.

Sweetened Condensed Milk is not given a final sterilization treatment because the concentrated sugar solution with which it is mixed immediately before or during evaporation, acts as an osmotic barrier to the growth of most bacteria. After evaporation the product is cooled to about 12°C and filled into cans, which are sealed but not sterilized. If the sugar solution has not been given a heat treatment (a minimum of 90°C) osmophilic yeasts and micrococci may cause spoilage of the final product.

Dried milk

This product is made by pasteurizing whole or skimmed milk, and then drying by passing a thin layer of milk over heated rollers (Roller-dried method) or by spraying the milk through the top of heated vessels (Spray-dried method). If, at any stage during the manufacture, the milk is allowed to stand in a warm atmosphere, there may be a considerable build-up of bacteria in the dried product. Several outbreaks of food-poisoning have been caused by the build-up of toxin-producing staphylococci in this way.

Cream

The heat-treatment given to cream is higher than for ordinary milk, *viz.* holding temperatures of 145–155°F for 60–30 minutes, or a high-temperature-short-time process at 180°–190°F for 10 seconds, which is repeated after 24 hours cold storage at 40°F. Insufficient treatment or recontamination may lead to souring caused by coliform organisms and various cocci; the spore-bearing organisms *Bacillus subtilis* and *B. cereus* sometimes causes 'bittyness' in cream.

Butter

Taints of butter include rancidity due to the activities of lipolytic bacteria (*Pseudomonas spp.* and butyric acid bacteria), breakdown of protein caused by caseolytic organisms, and mould growth on the surface.

Cheese

There are two main faults associated with the starter culture used in cheese making; these are:

(*a*) Over acidity due to the too-rapid development of the starter.

(*b*) Lack of sufficient acid due to the poor growth of the organisms. This may be caused by the killing of bacteria infected with bacteriophage particles (bacterial viruses specific to one organism or group of organisms), or by the inhibiting effect of antibiotics such as penicillin (used to treat the cow for various infections) and nisin (produced by various lactic streptococci).

The presence of large numbers of coliform organisms may lead to gas formation in the cheese, because lactose is completely broken down. *E. coli* and some yeasts (*e.g. Torula* spp.) may cause 'fruitiness', proteolytic organisms such as *Proteus* will lead to liquefaction, while slimy cheese is caused by caseolytic bacteria and a mould, *Mucor*. Other defects include rancidity (butyric acid bacteria), 'open-ness' (the yeast *Torula cremoris*), 'black spot' (*Bacillus subtilis* var. *niger*), 'stinking cheese' and 'blowing' of processed cheese (both caused by species of *Clostridium*).

Ice cream

A fairly typical ice cream mix contains about 12 per cent fat, 10·5 per cent milk solids other than fat, 13 per cent sugar and 0·5 per cent stabilizer such as gelatin or sodium alginate. The ingredients are weighed and then mixed with water, after which the mix is homogenized and pasteurized. The heat-treatment given is more rigorous than for pasteurized milk, *i.e.* holding at 160°F for 20–30 minutes or not less than 175°F for 15 seconds (H.T.S.T method), followed by cooling to 45°F or below within one hour. The cooled mix is usually allowed to 'age' for several hours in large refrigerated vats before being piped to the freezers, where air is beaten into the liquid and the aerated mix is hardened to form a pliable product. This may be extruded into waxed cartons or cups, cut into blocks, or bulk dispensed in cans. The wrapped ice cream is then frozen hard, often by a blast of cold air in a hardening tunnel, and then stored in a deep freeze conservator until sold to the final consumer.

Although during the last war the fat used in ice cream was of vegetable origin, dairy fats are again being used in increasing amounts, and the products sold at higher prices!

Because of the statutory regulations[13] governing the heat-treatment of ice cream, coupled with the frozen nature of the product, ice cream in this country is singularly free from serious taints. Flavour changes may occur owing to overheating some mixes containing full cream milk, and shrinkage occurs when ice cream thaws slightly and is then refrozen (as may happen in cinemas and theatres). Many frozen confections contain fruit syrup or purée (e.g. strawberry ice cream, iced fruit lollies and fruit-flavoured ice cream lollies), which, if stored under faulty conditions, may allow yeasts to develop, causing off-flavours.

Meat and Meat Products

The blood and tissues of living animals are usually free from micro-organisms, although the intestines and skin are heavily contaminated. Invasion of the tissues from these sources can be very rapid if the animals are killed and butchered in an unhygienic manner, and this leads to putrefaction and/or slime formation. Slime is formed by members of the Pseudomas-Achromobacter groups, and since many of these are psychrophilic, spoilage may occur even during cold storage.

Temperature and humidity are the main factors influencing the growth of micro-organisms in meat, and it is found that at relative humidities below 90 per cent most bacteria are inactivated. This figure does not, however, hold true for moulds since an R.H. of 70 per cent or less may be necessary. Some fungi grow on meat chilled to 0°C at a constant R.H. of 90 per cent, and cause taints such as 'whiskers' (*Thamnidium* and *Mucor*), 'white spot' (*Sporotrichum carnis*), and 'black spot' (*Cladosporium herbarum*). Cold storage under an atmosphere of carbon dioxide prevents much spoilage, but the concentration of CO_2 should not be above 10–12 per cent, because loss of colour, changes of flavour, and the promotion of staphylococci may result.

Minced meat

When meat is minced in the preparation of the popular 'Hamburger steak', there is a much greater surface area of meat available for contamination. Also any localized pocket of bacteria within the meat can be quickly spread throughout the minced product, eventually causing putrefaction. Among organisms that cause this type of spoilage are species of *Proteus* and *Escherichia coli*.

Sausages

The sausage is composed of ground meat bound with a starchy product, (e.g. soya flour), and seasoned with various spices, the mixture then being extruded into a sausage casing. This latter is traditionally an animal intestine (usually the small intestine) which has been cleaned, washed, and brined. The length of sausage is twisted at intervals to give the characteristic 'string' of sausages which may be wrapped and sold raw, (*e.g.* beef and pork sausages), or treated by smoking and cooking, (*e.g.* Frankfurters, salami, *etc.*).

A recent development is the use of plastic sausage casings instead of natural ones. Apart from the reduction of contamination the use of these artificial skins enables manufacturers to give the sausages a light cooking treatment after which they are extruded from the casing and pre-packed as 'skinless sausages'.

Defects of sausage include the growth of certain yeasts (particularly *Debaryomyces*) occurring as white spots on the skin, 'slimy sausage' caused by various bacteria on the surface, 'ropiness' due to capsulated micrococci, and the formation of green rings often caused by bacteria able to oxidize various haem pigments.

Flour and Bread

Because of the nature of the product it is only to be expected that flour will contain a variety of micro-organisms, and in practice many mould spores (*Aspergillus* and *Penicillium* species predominate) and bacteria are found. If storage conditions are favourable for mould growth (*i.e.* R.H. of 80–90 per cent at room temperature) they may cause mustiness and rancidity.

Bacteria which are nearly always present in flour are members of the *Bacillus mesentericus* group. These spore-bearing organisms, if present in large numbers and if the centre of the loaf has not been adequately baked, may cause a defect known as 'ropy bread'. The capsulated bacteria produce an off-white to brown discoloration in the bread, which can be pulled away as a sticky strand.

Another organism which may cause trouble is the pigment-producing bacterium *Serratia marcescens* (*Chromobacterium prodigiosum*) which gives a blood-red colour. A pink colour is formed by various moulds such as *Monilia sitophila* and *Fusarium spp.* Other moulds such as *Mucor* and *Rhizopus* give a woolly growth with black 'pin-heads', and *Penicillium* and *Aspergillus* form colonies of varying texture and colour.

The wrapping of bread in moisture-proof material has increased the risk of mould growth because of the higher humidity within the package. Another source of contamination is the machinery used to slice bread before wrapping. If the cutting blades are infected with mould spores, the developing taints may not be noticed until the slices are removed from the wrap, even if this is a transparent film.

Fish[14]

Fish are very susceptible to spoilage, because the larger number of bacteria in the intestines and over the surface invade the tissues after death. Surface slime is very common and consists of *Pseudomonas* and *Flavobacterium*, many of these bacteria being psychrophilic. Spoilage can be delayed by hygienic handling and gutting, cold storage in ice or chilled brine, salting *etc.* Red discoloration on fish may be due to the halophilic bacteria *Micrococcus morrhuae* and *Halobacterium salinaria*.

32

Shellfish are also very prone to spoilage and autolysis, the 'filter-feeders' (oysters, mussels, cockles, and scallops) being potentially more dangerous than 'browsers' (whelks and periwinkles) because they may retain typhoid, paratyphoid, and food-poisoning organisms in the gut, derived from polluted water. If oysters and mussels are placed in salt water made free from harmful bacteria (by chlorine/dechlorination treatment or ultra-violet irradiation of the water[15]) they get rid of any original intestinal pathogens within 48 hours. This method of cleansing bivalves is carried out in the U.K., and a check on the bacteriological condition of these shell-fish is made by the Fishmongers' Company on the fish coming in to Billingsgate Market[16].

Eggs

The virtually sterile egg as laid by the hen is rapidly contaminated by soil, faeces, nesting material, *etc.* Although the shell membrane and albumen (containing lysozyme) are physical and chemical barriers to some bacteria, they cannot cope with the vast number of organisms which penetrate the porous shell, if this is soiled and moistened. Penetration is always hastened by wetting, and therefore the practice of washing eggs is not to be recommended.

Spoilage taints of shell eggs by bacteria are known as 'rots'; 'white', 'mixed', and 'black rots', being successive stages in decomposition caused by proteolytic bacteria. Growth of moulds, particularly *Cladosporium herbarum* and *Penicillium glaucum*, occurs when eggs are stored under humid conditions.

A great deal of egg material is preserved in a frozen or dried condition in order to give a constant source of supply to bakers, restaurants, *etc.* Frozen whole egg is prepared by breaking the eggs into clean metal containers, mixing the bulked eggs with a mechanical mixer, and dispensing into metal cans of 28 lb. capacity. The closed cans are rapidly frozen to below $-10°C$ until despatched to the customer. Liquid egg yolk and albumen can also be frozen in a similar manner after the whites have been separated from the yolks. Defrosting for long periods at warm temperatures will greatly increase the numbers of bacteria in the product which, in any case, may be heavily contaminated. Many people are actively campaigning for Government heat-treatment regulations, so that all liquid egg is pasteurized before freezing. Two methods which kill the food-poisoning Salmonella organisms are:

(1) heating to 148°F for $2\frac{1}{2}$ minutes, or
(2) 6–7 days at 127–130°F.[17]

The efficiency of pasteurization can be assessed by the destruction of the enzyme α-amylase (*cf.* phosphatase test of pasteurized milk).

Whole egg can be dried by spraying into a chamber at 400°F, and although this method may lead to a great reduction of bacteria, faulty methods of reconstitution and storage may result in the multiplication of pathogens.

Before drying albumen it is necessary to remove glucose from the egg white to prevent a blackening of the product. In China a natural fermentation by coliform organisms is allowed to reduce the sugar content, whereas other producers may utilize yeasts, bacteria (*e.g. K. aerogenes*), or various enzymes.

It has been suggested that a colicine-producing strain of *Escherichia coli* would not only ferment the sugar but also kill any Salmonella organisms in the product[18].

Sugar and Confectionery

The extraction of sucrose from sugar cane and sugar beet, and the subsequent refining process involve heat treatment, and this kills off the majority of organisms present in the raw materials. Some thermophiles may, however, survive to cause spoilage when the sugar is used by canners, *e.g. Bacillus stearothermophilus* and *Clostridium nigrificans*. Infection of the cooled extract and finished product with osmophilic organisms may lead to a serious loss due to fermentation and inversion of the sucrose. *Saccharomyces rouxii* and *S. mellis* are two osmophilic yeasts which can thrive in sugar syrups with a sucrose concentration in excess of 60 per cent. *Leuconostoc mesenteroides* is a bacterium which can cause trouble to sugar refiners because it forms a sticky gum, dextran, which may block pipes. Personal hygienic habits are also important, since *Streptococcus salivarius*, which is usually present in human saliva, produces another type of gum called levan.

Boiled sweets and other sugar candies are usually free from visible defects, because the high sugar concentration does not favour the growth of micro-organisms. This does not necessarily mean that the product is sterile since it has been shown by several workers that pathogens can be carried by these sweets, particularly if unwrapped goods are handled. Salmonella organisms could be derived from ingredients that are incorporated into the product such as nuts and desiccated coconut, although food-poisoning outbreaks attributed to this type of confectionery are extremely rare.

Chocolate-coated fondants or chocolate creams have been known to burst owing to gas formation by osmophilic yeasts or saccharolytic anaerobes of the genus *Clostridium*. Chocolate itself, and especially milk chocolate, may contain many viable organisms such as spore-bearing bacilli and coliform bacteria. Because this product is often stored for long periods in a liquid condition at about 100°F, a build-up of these bacteria may occur giving poor bacteriological results to, for example, chocolate-coated ice cream.

Canned Foods[19]

Since 1810 when the Frenchman Nicholas Appert invented this method of preserving food, the canning industry has enormously increased, both in the range and quantity of foods processed. The basic idea of canning is simple—it is to cook food inside a non-toxic metal container so that air is driven off and pathogenic and spoilage organisms are killed. The sealed can is then cooled, thus causing a vacuum in the head-space of the pack, and provided there is no leakage, the food will remain wholesome for many months, years or even decades.

The closed cans are heated in large pressure cookers or retorts where steam under pressure raises the temperature of the food to a level at which spores of *Clostridium botulinum* are destroyed. This anaerobic bacillus is the most virulent food-poisoning organism known, and largely because of the effective heat-treatment given during the processing of foods, it is also the rarest cause of poisoning. In practice the canning technologist will allow cooking times and temperatures in excess of those necessary to destroy these spores, although even more resistant bacterial spores may survive. In low and medium acid foods (of pH above 4·5) the heat-resistant spores of thermophilic bacteria may cause spoilage if the cans are stored under warm conditions (around 55°C). Three types of thermophilic spoilage have been described, namely:

(a) 'Flat-sour' spoilage due to the formation of acids from sugars in the food, without the production of gas. Such cans do not appear to be different from normal ones and only by smelling or tasting the food can it be detected. *Bacillus stearothermophilus* is an organism causing this type of spoilage, and *B. thermoacidurans* is found in many acid foods such as tomatoes (pH 4·5–3·7).

(b) 'Blown cans' or 'swells' are usually caused by the action of thermophilic sugar-splitting clostridia which produce gas, causing the ends of the can to swell. Since a considerable pressure is built up, careless opening of the can may lead to a shower of butyrous food material. *Clostridium thermosaccharolyticum* is the best-known of these organisms.

(c) 'Sulphide' spoilage is caused by the production of hydrogen sulphide (H_2S), which although a gas, dissolves in the food and blackens it, but does not cause the can to swell. *Clostridium nigrificans* is a cause of this spoilage.

An interesting type of spoilage of canned and bottled fruits, particularly strawberries, is due to heat-resistant ascospores of the mould *Byssochlamys fulva*. Soft fruits are not given the drastic heat treatment afforded to soups, *etc.* because the flesh would disintegrate under these conditions. It is not always possible, therefore, to destroy the resistant spores which eventually lead to a general softening of the fruit.

Although heat resistant spores may remain viable during processing, much more contamination may arise after the heating operation when the cans are cooled. One method of cooling (*i.e.* pressure cooling) is to fill the retort with cold water under pressure (this is to ensure equal pressures inside and outside the can, thus avoiding strain), but if this water is contaminated bacteria could enter the can. It has been shown that the number of spoiled cans increases with the degree of contamination of the cooling water, and for this reason only bacteriologically clean water should be used[20].

Soft Drinks[21]

Under this heading come fruit syrups, juices and squashes, and mineral waters. Fruit syrups have a fairly high sugar content and so spoilage is usually due to osmophilic organisms such as certain yeasts, *Leuconostoc mesenteroides*, *etc.* Squashes and juices have less sugar than syrups, but the acid conditions and/or the presence of carbon dioxide help to preserve them even if no additional chemical, such as sulphur dioxide or benzoic acid, is present. There have been some instances of spoilage, however, due to certain yeasts which were tolerant to benzoic acid.

Some fruit juices are treated by filtration or 'cold sterilization' in order to remove micro-organisms, although citrus juices cannot be filtered. They are given a heat treatment instead, in order to inactivate enzymes which could clarify the juice.

The other principal ingredient of soft drinks besides sugar, fruit juice and citric or tartaric acid, is, of course, water. This must be of at least drinking-water standard, and be free from metallic and bacterial contamination.

THE CONTROL OF FOOD SPOILAGE

The methods available for the control of microbial attack are numerous and varied, and a food manufacturer may use a combination of methods, depending on the nature of the food. A few of the techniques used to preserve foods are given below.

Aseptic Handling of Food

If freshly gathered or harvested food is handled in a hygienic manner there is much less chance of contamination by spoilage organisms and pathogens. Foods which benefit from aseptic metho dsare fruits, vegetables, and eggs.

High Temperatures

Pasteurization

This method of treatment aims at the complete destruction of possible pathogenic organisms in the food without altering its flavour or nutritional value. While any pasteurization process destroys many bacteria apart from pathogens, it is not claimed, nor does it intend, to kill all micro-organisms within the product. The Holder method where milk is heated to 145°F for 30 minutes has been virtually superceded in this country by the H.T.S.T. method of heating to 161°F for 15 seconds. This latter method has the advantages of being a continuous process and of producing less change in the flavour and quality of the milk. U.H.T.S.T. methods (*e.g.* 275–302°F for 1–20 seconds) give a virtually sterile milk, but unless this sterility is absolutely essential, the capital cost involved and the extra precautions necessary during bottling may not make the process economically attractive.

Milk and various milk products such as cream, ice cream, yoghurt, *etc.* are usually pasteurized, as well as some beer, vinegar and, soft drinks.

Boiling

This cooking treatment results in the total destruction of vegetative cells, although some heat-resistant bacterial spores may still survive. Sterilized milk is given this treatment, as are steamed puddings.

Processing

To obtain steam temperatures above 100°C, pressure is used. Most canned foods are given a pressure-cooking treatment in large retorts where, as the steam is passed into the enclosed vessel, the pressure increases and the temperature rises. The aim is to kill the spores of *Clostridium botulinum* (a temperature of 115°C for 10 minutes is required to kill these spores in buffer solution) without unduly altering the texture, flavour, and nutritional value of the food. In practice the amount of heat given (a combination of temperature and time) to a food depends on many factors, such as:

(*a*) The nature of the food *i.e.* liquid soups, solid meat, or combinations of liquid and solid (vegetable soups, *etc.*).

(b) The effect of prolonged heat on the food may make it unsaleable although sterile, e.g. large pack apples or apple chunks as sold to caterers may be too soft and 'stewed' for their intended use.

(c) The size of the can is important because heat penetration will take longer for a large can than for a smaller one, and hence the processing will have to be increased.

(d) The acidity of the food is important because less processing will be required for acid foods.

All these points make it necessary to find out the rate of heat penetration for every product in all the regular can sizes. A thermocouple is inserted into the can at the point of greatest temperature lag, and potentiometer readings are taken throughout the processing to give a heat-penetration curve. This graph, together with a knowledge of the thermal death rate of *Cl. botulinum* spores, enables the canning technologist to work out the safest processing times and temperatures for the product.

Low Temperatures

Refrigeration

Domestic refrigerators usually maintain a temperature of 5°C, at which most mesophilic and thermophilic organisms do not grow. Psychrophiles, however, will flourish at this temperature and may cause spoilage of the food. Such organisms, which may grow down to $-10°C$, include the bacteria *Pseudomonas*, *Micrococcus*, *Flavobacterium*, and *Achromobacter*, yeasts of the *Torulopsis* type, and moulds such as *Penicillium*, *Cladosporium*, *Mucor*, and *Thamnidium*.

Freezing

At temperatures below $-10°C$ the growth of all micro-organisms is stopped, and although a percentage may be actually killed by freezing, many are only in a state of 'suspended animation' being able to grow when the food is thawed. For example, viable pathogenic bacteria have been found in strawberries kept at $-18°C$ for 6 months.

Quick freezing of foods is now taken for granted by the British housewife, but its rapid growth has taken place only since the last war. The process is based upon the fact that when cellular foods are frozen rapidly to about $-18°C$, the contained water freezes as minute crystals of ice which do not rupture the cells. Slow freezing results in large ice crystals and the food, on thawing, will soften owing to tissue damage.

Apart from the enormous variety of quick-frozen foods, other products relying on low temperature storage include meat, fish, eggs, ice cream, etc.

Gas storage

Carbon dioxide—Gas storage of fruits such as apples and pears is successfully carried out under an atmosphere of CO_2. In combination with refrigeration, CO_2 is used in the preservation of chilled beef (10 per cent CO_2), fish (20 per cent), eggs, and soft fruits such as blackcurrants.

Ozone—This powerful oxidizing agent tends to cause rancidity of fats, and therefore its use needs careful control. Very small amounts are needed for

37

effective lengthening of the storage times for chilled beef (intermittent use of 3 parts per million of ozone) and eggs when stored at fairly high humidities (0·6 p.p.m. ozone prevents mould spoilage at 31°F at an R.H. of 90 per cent).

Limitation of moisture

Sugar—When sugar is added to a food its osmotic concentration increases, resulting in a decrease of available water. Since most bacteria cannot grow below 90 per cent R.H., and the minimum R.H. for mould growth is about 74 per cent, the addition of sugar to foods is a very effective method of preservation. Some osmophilic yeasts can tolerate as much as 80 per cent sugar and many moulds are liable to grow on jam, *etc.*, if a drop of moisture condenses on the surface causing a reduction in osmotic concentration at that point.

Dehydration—The drying of food is one of the oldest methods of food preservation, and fish and strips of meat are still dried in the sun by primitive tribes. The most successful dried foods are derived from liquids *e.g.* instant coffee and tea, milk powder, dried egg, *etc.* Although flavour is changed, the dehydrated food has advantages in bulk and weight reduction.

Freeze-drying—This is essentially a dehydration method carried out in two stages. The first operation is to quick-freeze the food material, after which it is placed between heated metal plates in a vacuum chamber. The water in the product after freezing is in the form of minute ice crystals, but when heat is applied the ice sublimes *i.e.* the solid ice is converted to gaseous water vapour. Provided the vapour can easily pass through the food to the heated surface and then be carried away by the vacuum system, the food material loses water without a reduction in bulk. In other words, a freeze-dried lamb chop still looks like the genuine article apart from a slight loss of colour, and of course, the drastic reduction in weight. The material is very porous and takes up water of reconstitution very quickly. Although still largely in the experimental stage some foods such as instant coffee and tea are already being marketed in this country, and many more varieties are found in the United States of America.

Salt

High concentrations of salt also increase the osmotic effect and decrease the available water although, unlike the effect of high sugar content, other factors play a part, such as pH, temperature, protein content, *etc.* Water is also necessary because it is the concentration of salt in the water phase and not the amount in the food as a whole that is important. For example, although salted butter contains only 1½–2 per cent by weight, the concentration in the water phase is appreciably higher, 10–12 per cent.

Some bacteria, moulds and yeasts can tolerate concentrated salt solutions up to 25–30 per cent salt. Such organisms may cause spoilage to salted fish and pickled vegetable brines, as was mentioned in the previous section.

Acids

The inhibiting effect of mineral acids is due to the hydrogen ion concentration, and for organic acids the undissociated molecule or anion is important. Most bacteria cannot develop below pH 4·5 although there are exceptions such as *Lactobacillus spp.* and *Clostridium butyricum* which can grow down to pH 3·5. Yeasts and moulds grow best in a slightly acid environment (pH 5–6) and can tolerate pH 2 or lower.

Acetic acid—This is used widely in the manufacture of sauces, pickles, mayonnaise, *etc.* where the concentration may vary from 1·5–4 per cent.

Lactic acid—This is the natural product of sugar fermentation by lactic acid bacteria, and is used for the preservation of sour milks, sauerkraut, and other lactic pickles.

Citric and tartaric acids—Both are used in the manufacture of soft drinks, where the presence of sugar and/or carbon dioxide enhances the inhibitory effect.

Fatty acids—Propionic acid and its salts are very effective fungistatic compounds, inhibiting mould growth on butter (0·1–0·5 per cent), fruit jellies, and similar products. It also inhibits the germination of 'rope' spores in bread.

Sorbic acid, found naturally in rowan-berries, is even more effective than propionic acid for inhibiting mould growth. 0·1 per cent inhibits the surface growth of yeasts and moulds during cucumber fermentation, and 0·05 per cent has been successfully used to prevent mould growth on cheese by dusting the wrapper with the substance.

A recent report on the subject of food preservatives has recommended the inclusion of propionic acid and sorbic acid in any forthcoming Government regulations on this question[22]. The 1962 Preservatives in Food Regulations have, in fact, adopted these recommendations.

Curing

Many meats are pickled in brines containing nitrates or nitrites because of the attractive colour and pleasant flavour of the products after cooking. The brine is a 20–28 per cent solution of salt containing about one-tenth by weight of sodium nitrate, and this is injected into the meat before immersion into the brine tank. At a temperature of 5°C the halophilic bacteria present (particularly species of Micrococcus) convert the nitrate to nitrite. This latter gives a source of nitric oxide which combines with the muscle pigment myo-haemoglobin to form nitric oxide myoglobin, which on cooking becomes stabilized as the red pigment nitric oxide myochromogen.

Smoking

Many meat and fish products are smoked after pickling and brining by exposing them to smoke generated by smouldering hard woods (oak, ash, elm, *etc.*). The food is hung over the wood, or smoke from a smoke generator is ducted into the food chamber. The effect of this treatment is to heat and dry the surface of the product, and also more important, incorporates into the surface various bactericidal substances (aldehydes and phenols among them). This combination of effects drastically reduces the number of bacteria present, although it may have very little fungistatic effect. The residual substances from the smoke and also the dry salted surface of the product help to preserve it against further bacterial contamination.

Spices

Many spices and herbs exert a toxic effect on yeasts and bacteria owing to the presence of certain essential oils. Cloves, cinnamon, and mustard, show the greatest effect, with garlic, onion, and cassia following on behind them. The concentration of spice necessary to inhibit micro-organisms may be too great for a palatable product, and so the full effect is rarely attained.

Permitted chemical preservatives

The addition of foreign substances to food in this country is jealously guarded by various statutory regulations, and it is not surprising that there are so few chemicals allowed as preservatives apart from natural substances such as salt, sugar, spices, acetic, and lactic acids, *etc.*

(*a*) Sulphur dioxide (including sulphites) can be used in certain foods but only in restricted amounts *e.g.* 450 p.p.m. in raw sausage meat, 3,000 p.p.m. in fruit pulp, and 70 p.p.m. in ready-to-drink fruit drinks. SO_2 has a marked bactericidal action in acid media but in the presence of sugars it may form complexes, thus reducing the amount of free undissociated acid.

(*b*) Benzoic acid (and benzoates) may be used in the same foods (apart from sausage meat) mentioned in connection with SO_2, but only as an alternative to sulphur dioxide. It is effective, under acid conditions, against yeast and mould spoilage of fruits and fruit juices, although some yeasts are able to ferment benzoates and so cause trouble in soft drinks, *etc.*

(*c*) Diphenyl is permitted in limited amounts in imported citrus fruits, derived from the wrapper impregnated with this volatile substance. It is a very effective mould inhibitor, and losses due to this type of spoilage have been greatly reduced.

(*d*) Sodium nitrite can be added to bacon, ham, and cooked pickled meats, the amount remaining in the latter group being not more than 200 parts per million.

Filtration

A very satisfactory method of removing unwanted micro-organisms is by filtration. This method, although used extensively for bacteriological culture media which may be sensitive to heat, has but a limited application in the food industry. Some clear liquids such as non-citrus fruit drinks are 'cold sterilized' in this way by forcing them through special pads made from asbestos and cellulose. The assembled filter is sterilized before use by steaming for 10–20 minutes, and the sterile liquid is aseptically dispensed into germ-free containers.

Irradiation

Ultra-violet rays[23]—Strong sunlight has long been known to exert an inhibitory effect on micro-organisms, owing to its ultra-violet component of wavelength below 300 mμ. Low pressure mercury vapour lamps give a high output of ultra-violet radiation at 253·7 mμ which is very close to the maximum lethal value of 260 mμ. However, because of their poor penetrating power, ultra-violet rays are used only for sterilizing surfaces or thin layers of clear material. Ultra-violet lamps have been successfully used to prevent scum formation during cucumber fermentation, to prevent spoilage during the tenderization of meat at 13–18°C, for air purification in bottling and food-processing plants, and for the control of surface mould growth on cheese and baked products.

Gamma (γ) *rays*[24]—These high energy electromagnetic waves are emitted from radioactive elements and have a lethal effect on micro-organisms. Experimental work is still being carried out into the commercial possibilities of sterilizing food materials in this way, although the high capital costs involved may be prohibitive.

Antibiotics

Antibiotics are substances which are produced by some micro-organisms and which have inhibitory effects on other organisms. The classic example, of course, is penicillin, an antibiotic produced by species of the mould *Penicillium* (*P. notatum* and *P. chrysogenum*) which is lethal to many pathogenic bacteria without adversely affecting the patient. Food microbiologists also look for antibiotics which will destroy or inhibit certain types of spoilage bacteria without being toxic to the consumer of the food.

The tetracyclines—This group of antibiotics, which includes aureomycin, has a marked inhibitory effect on many Gram-negative bacteria such as *Pseudomonas* and *Achromobacter*. For this reason much research has been carried out, particularly in Canada and the U.S.A., on the effect of incorporating these substances into the brine or ice used for fish storage. It was found that as little as 7–10 p.p.m. of the antibiotic resulted in a much longer storage 'life' because it delayed the onset of slime formation. Eviscerated poultry can also be dipped into chilled brine containing the antibiotic with equally good results. In North America preservation of these commodities with antibiotics is permissible, provided the amount of residual antibiotic in the food after cooking is no greater than a stated maximum value. This method has also been successfully used to preserve whale meat.

Tetracyclines as preservatives have recently been approved in the U.K. for raw fish (up to 5.p.p.m.) and its restricted use is mainly because of the possibility of inducing resistant strains of pathogenic bacteria. It is well known that with the almost indiscriminate use of penicillin a large number of resistant organisms, particularly staphylococci have become the dominant infecting organisms in hospitals, sanatoria, *etc.* On the other hand, the advocates of this method of food preservation state that the substances are present in only very small amounts in the uncooked food, and are virtually undetectable when the food is properly cooked. Airing a personal view I would think that the greatest danger in this method is not the breeding of resistant pathogens but the growing of resistant spoilage organisms, which could lead to serious food losses.

Nisin—This antibiotic is produced by certain strains of lactic streptococci and is found naturally in many types of cheese. Its effect is to kill clostridia and to lower the heat-resistance of bacterial spores, so that it could prove of great value to the canning industry. In fact its use was recommended by the Food Standards Committee, for the preservation of cheeses against gas-forming clostridia and for the control of thermophilic spores in certain canned goods which are given sufficient processing to kill off *Cl. botulinum* spores. Nisin is now permitted in cheese, clotted cream, and any canned food.

Colicines—The possible use of these substances has already been mentioned in the destruction of salmonellae in albumen by colicine-producing strains of *E. coli*. Much more work will have to be done, however, before these antibiotics can be safely used in foodstuffs.

FOOD POISONING[25]

There are many types of poisoning caused by the eating of certain food-stuffs, but the term 'food poisoning' is usually reserved only for those ailments associated with bacteria or bacterial toxins present in the ingested food. Other causes are usually of a chemical nature, such as poisoning with metallic contamination, pesticide residues, ptomaines or products of food breakdown, *etc*. Some people may be genuinely allergic to certain foods and others may produce a psychological response, such as vomiting or diarrhoea. Whichever is the real reason for a particular 'upset tummy', Medical Officers of Health and Food Bacteriologists have to become detectives in the search for truth.

Food Poisoning Bacteria

Fortunately, although the number of food poisoning bacteria is extremely large, the number of types is small, and it will be more convenient to discuss them by type.

Staphylococci

Many strains of *Staphylococcus aureus*, the organism found in boils and the pus of wound infections, produce an enterotoxin which is secreted from the cells. This toxin is rather heat-stable and is the substance which causes the onset of sickness and/or diarrhoea fairly soon after eating contaminated food (sometimes as little as 30 minutes after the meal). Even though the food may have been cooked sufficiently to destroy all the bacteria, provided the numbers of these present before heating were great enough to build up the toxin, this latter would cause poisoning.

Salmonellae

This group of enteric organisms includes the typhoid bacillus (*S. typhi*), paratyphoid bacilli (*S. paratyphi* A and B), and several hundred strains of food poisoning bacteria, often known by the name of the locality which first isolated it, *e.g. S. london, S. montevideo, S. dublin, etc.* The most prevalent in this country is still *S. typhi-murium* which accounted for 45 per cent of all reported cases in 1960, other salmonellae numbering only 16 per cent of the total[26].

This motile, Gram-negative, rod-shaped bacillus produces an endotoxin within the cell, and a treatment which destroys the organism will also destroy the poison. To produce symptoms of diarrhoea, *etc.* living bacteria must be ingested with the food, small numbers requiring a longer incubation period within the host than larger numbers of bacteria (from 12–24 hours).

Clostridium welchii

Certain ultra-heat-resistant strains of this anaerobic spore-bearing organism give rise to food-poisoning. Toxins are produced but, unlike *Staph.*

aureus, the living organism must be present before the illness can occur. Like staphylococci, however, it caused about 2 per cent of known outbreaks during 1960.

Clostridium botulinum

Botulism, caused by the toxin of this organism, is usually a fatal illness, which may begin as diarrhoea, but rapidly attacks the central nervous system, leading to paralysis of the throat and thorax. Even small amounts of the toxin, one of the most potent poisons known, can cause serious illness necessitating a very long convalescence. Fortunately, rigorous control of the processing of foods liable to give trouble has reduced the risk in this country to negligible proportions.

Other organisms

On rare occasions bacteria other than those already mentioned have caused intestinal disturbances. They include species of *Streptococcus*, *Escherichia*, *Proteus*, *Bacillus*, and *Clostridium*.

Sources of Contamination

Salmonellae are intestinal organisms found in the gut of man and many animals. It is easy to see how even scrupulously hygienic methods of slaughtering animals can lead to some contamination of the carcases. Although these bacteria will be destroyed by cooking, they could easily be transferred to products which will receive no further heating (*e.g.* cooked meats), by careless handling in the butcher's shop. This cross-contamination would be greater if animals were slaughtered in filthy and unhygienic abbatoirs.

Egg products may also be heavily contaminated with salmonellae, many outbreaks of food poisoning in recent years having been caused by eating non-heated foods containing Chinese dried-egg albumen. This product was traditionally fermented before drying in order to remove sugars. As the organisms concerned were a mixture of many types, salmonellae were often included, and these remained viable on the dried product. Another food material which had been incriminated in this way was desiccated coconut from Ceylon, although this material is now safe owing to control measures in the country of origin.

Careless handling of food by people with unhygienic personal habits, those recovering from intestinal disorders, or persons who are symptomless carriers of these bacteria, could all lead to contamination.

Staphylococci are found in the noses of a large percentage of healthy people, as well as in boils, pimples, and septic cuts. It follows from this that any careless handling of food or exposure of food to coughs and sneezes could lead to heavy contamination. This is particularly the case where 'milky' products such as custard, blancmange, and synthetic creams are exposed in shops or canteens. Another source of staphylococcal food poisoning has been from corned beef processed in East Africa; 13 out of 21 outbreaks from this type of product during 1960 were derived from that part of the world.

Clostridium welchii is a common soil organism and is also present in animal and human intestines, although not all strains can give rise to food poisoning. This particular strain is a member of the so-called 'Group A', of which the gas gangrene organism is the prominent member. Any inadequate cooking or processing of non-acid foods may result in numerous viable spores of this organism. Such foods *e.g.* stews, meat pies, *etc.* may be re-heated sufficiently to allow these spores to germinate, so that large numbers of bacteria are present when eaten. It is the ingestion of the living organisms which results in the unfortunate symptoms of diarrhoea, *etc.*

Clostridium botulinum is another soil organism which forms resistant spores. If these are allowed to develop in non-acid foods, enough toxin may be produced to cause botulism. Fortunately food manufacturers rely on a very large safety margin, by giving canned and bottled food much greater heat treatments than the minimum required to destroy these spores.

In general we can say that the foods which are more prone to harbour food poisoning bacteria are cooked meat products. To quote a recent report of the Public Health Laboratory Service, 'of the 165 outbreaks in which the vehicle of infection was identified, 143 were associated with meat, nearly always with processed or made-up meats'. This is a sad reflection of the state of awareness to the problem shown by most sections of the public.

The Detection of Food Poisoning Bacteria

When there is an outbreak of this particular illness the local Medical Officer of Health is immediately informed, and it is he and his staff who have to act as detectives. They try to find out the item or items of food which all the affected persons consumed, they take specimens of faeces for examination to see if there is an organism common to all patients, and try to prevent a spread of the infection.

The bacteriologist who receives the food samples for examination has at his disposal a number of tests which help to identify the organisms present. Usually the first stage is to make a 10 per cent suspension of the macerated food in sterile diluent (physiological saline or tap water are often used), although in some cases the food may be directly inoculated into specific media. From the suspension the following tests should be made.

Total microscopic count

A known volume of the suspension is evenly spread over a known area of a clean sterilized glass slide, and the preparation is dried, fixed by rapidly passing it through a flame, and stained using the Gram technique. With a given microscope system of known magnification, each organism observed will represent a certain number of bacteria originally present in the sample. For example, if 0·05 ml. of a 10 per cent suspension is spread over 5 sq. cm, when viewed under a 1/12" oil-immersion lens and a $\times 10$ monocular eyepiece, each bacterium would represent 5 million organisms per gram in the sample. This technique, known as the Breed Method, gives a good indication of the total number of organisms present, both living and dead.

Staphylococci

If present, Staphylococci can be isolated by enrichment in a nutrient broth containing 10 per cent salt. They are tolerant to this concentration, which inhibits most other bacteria in the food. After overnight incubation at blood heat (37°C) the culture can be streaked over various solid media such as Nutrient Beef Agar (for golden-coloured colonies of *Staph. aureus*), Phenolphthalein Phosphate Agar (for the detection of phosphatase), Mannitol Salt Agar (acid production), and various other media, to be further incubated at 37°C. Confirmatory tests are then made with various sugars and to find out whether the coccus is haemolytic and produces the enzyme coagulase. Phage-typing of the organism is the final test and this is usually only carried out in large central reference laboratories.

If staphylococci are not detected, the Breed count may give some indication of the number of dead cocci in the sample before processing. Of course this does not prove that these cocci were harmful, but it is a general indication to be weighed with all the other evidence available.

Salmonella

When Salmonella organisms are present in food they are usually found in small numbers, so that a large sample (at least 50 g) should be examined. Enrichment is also necessary using Selenite Broth and Tetrathionate Broth, followed by sub-culture on to solid media, such as Wilson and Blair's Bismuth Sulphite Agar (for characteristic shiny black metallic colonies) and Desoxycholate Citrate Agar (for colourless colonies). Suspect colonies are then examined further by various biochemical tests, and by agglutination with type-specific or polyvalent H- and O-antisera. Actual identification of the strain of *Salmonella* is not usually possible in most laboratories, and for this reason most positive identifications are carried out at the Salmonella Reference Laboratory, which is part of the Central Public Health Laboratory at Colindale.

Clostridium welchii

When grown anaerobically in Litmus Milk, *Clostridium welchii* forms a characteristic 'stormy clot' *i.e.* the milk proteins are coagulated and the red acid clot is ruptured by the formation of gas. Since most strains of the organism are able to produce this effect, a pre-treatment is necessary in order to increase the chance of isolating the food poisoning strain. Since we know that the spores of this strain are ultra-heat-resistant and can withstand boiling for one hour, we cook the sample suspension in this way before inoculating the medium. Production of a 'stormy clot' will be a strong indication that the food poisoning variety is present, although a confirmatory test using specific antiserum would still have to be performed.

In addition to the four tests already mentioned, others are usually carried out as a matter of routine, and these are given below.

Total viable count at 37°C

Serial dilutions in sterile diluent are made from the original suspension, and aliquots are plated out in sterile Petri dishes, into which are poured molten medium (at about 45°C). The contents of each dish are thoroughly but carefully mixed and the medium is allowed to set before the plates are incubated at 37°C for 48 hours. The total colony count on the plate multiplied by the dilution factor will indicate the total number of living mesophilic bacteria in the sample.

Total viable count at 22°C

The technique is the same as for the 37°C count although the dilutions may be lower and the incubation is at 22°C for 72 hours. The same medium can be used for both counts *e.g.* Yeastrel Agar, Nutrient Agar, Yeastrel Milk Agar, *etc.*

Presumptive coliform count

Members of the coliform group are able to ferment lactose in the presence of bile salts, and these are the two basic ingredients of MacConkey's Broth, which is used in the primary isolation of the organisms. Serial tenfold dilutions of the suspension are inoculated in triplicate or quintuplicate tubes of the medium and incubated for 48 hours at 37°C. Positive tubes showing an acid reaction (a colour change from purple to yellow when bromocresol purple is the indicator) and gas formation (shown in a small inverted Durham tube present in the tubed medium) are presumed to contain coliforms, and further confirmatory tests are then carried out to establish their identity. The numbers of organisms can be assessed by noting the positive tubes and looking up the relevant entry in a set of statistical tables, the Most Probable Number (M.P.N.) tables.

Faecal E. coli count

Escherichia coli type I is the commonest indicator of faecal pollution in water and foods, and is detected initially by the Eijkman test. In this, all positive tubes in the Presumptive Coliform Test are subcultured into fresh tubes of MacConkey Broth and incubated at 44°C for 48 hours. At the same time tubes of peptone water are inoculated and placed in the same water bath at 44°C. Acid and gas formation in the lactose broth and indole production in the peptone water (shown by a red coloration when drops of Kovac's reagent are added) strongly indicate the presence of *E. coli.*

The significance of the last four tests outlined above will be discussed in the next section.

FOOD HYGIENE[27]

There are certain facts concerning food hygiene which anyone who thinks about the subject will immediately appreciate. We all realize, for example, the importance of personal cleanliness, keeping pets and pests away from food, covering refuse bins, *etc.* but these precepts are very often thought of in relation to other people, and not ourselves. Without realizing it a housewife might endanger her own family by faulty hygiene just as much as the insanitary practices which may occur in public eating places. Thus hygiene, like charity, should begin at home.

General Do's and Don'ts

1. Buy and prepare fresh food whenever possible.
2. Eat the food soon after cooking, but if this is not convenient, cool it rapidly and store it in a refrigerator or cold larder.
3. Never leave food exposed to flies, dust, coughs, and sneezes, *etc.*

4. Wash your hands after using the toilet and after handling raw meat or fish, to prevent contamination of other foods and utensils.

5. Do not use a soiled cloth for wiping cutlery and crockery. It is far better to wash up in warm, soapy water, then rinse in very hot water (160–180°F) and allow the crockery to dry by itself on a clean surface.

6. Cover all cuts, burns, and boils on exposed parts of the body with a waterproof dressing.

One could fill a book with hints of this kind, but if I were to choose just one 'do' it would be to 'think before you act'. With a little vigilance, we could all catch ourselves out and prevent the odd bad habit, such as wiping cutlery with our hands, touching the jelly to see if it has set, sampling from a communal ladle before re-stirring the soup, *etc.*

Hygiene in Food Manufacture

We have seen from earlier sections of this article how the food manufacturer can utilize many kinds of physical and chemical agents to prevent the ingress and growth of unwanted micro-organisms in food. It is, however, far better to supplement any such treatment with hygienic practices which result in products of low microbial content. Strict adherence to the instructions laid down in the Food Hygiene Regulations is not enough; for example, the management must not only provide adequate washing facilities but should also actively encourage their use.

Cleanliness of food machinery is very important and a regular routine of washing, sterilizing, and rinsing should be carried out by trained personnel (see *Figure 1.14*).

Hygiene in Food Distribution

All the points previously made apply to restaurants, canteens, and retail food shops. In recent years, the customers have become increasingly aware of chipped and dirty cups, exposed food, and the more obvious bad habits of food handlers *etc.*, and what is more important, they are less frightened of exposing these malpractices. This has led to a general, albeit a gradual, consciousness of food hygiene, although there are still too many 'traditional' bad habits being practised 'behind the scenes' in restaurants and canteens.

Modern methods of sales presentation, such as self-service stores and automatic vending (*Figure 1.15*), have encouraged the wrapping of foods which were traditionally sold in the unwrapped condition. This pre-packing of food gives the manufacturer a greater measure of control over his product, since handling en route to the customer is less important. Covered and refrigerated display cabinets are also increasingly fashionable, although a warning note should be sounded about the latter equipment. Unless adequately maintained and regularly de-frosted, these cold cabinets may, in fact, do more harm than good. A practical survey of cold storage temperatures being undertaken by the author in collaboration with various local authorities, shows a very wide range. One cabinet, in fact, gave a higher temperature at a certain point than in the rest of the shop!

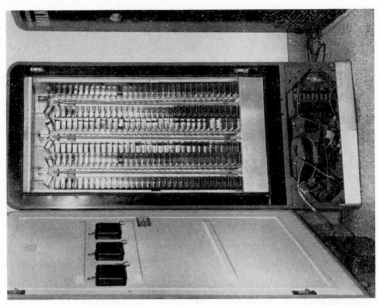

Figure 1.15. The interior of an automatic vending machine containing wrapped ice-cream. (By Courtesy of Joseph Sankey and Sons Ltd.)

Figure 1.14. Cleaning machinery at a modern food factory. (By Courtesy of Kraft Foods Ltd.)

Hygienic Significance of Microbiological Tests

There is no doubt that an organism which acts as an 'indicator' to the possible presence of enteric pathogens is a boon to the bacteriologist. In the examination of drinking water the presence of *Escherichia coli* type I, even in the low concentration of 1 organism per 100 ml of water, makes the latter unsatisfactory. This is because we know that the organism occurs in vast numbers in human and animal faeces, and also that it dies out rapidly in water, so that its presence must indicate recent pollution with faecal matter which might possibly contain pathogens, such as typhoid and paratyphoid bacilli.

In foodstuffs, however, *E. coli*. I may not be such a clear cut indicator of recent pollution or even of direct contamination with faecal matter. This is because it grows rapidly in a variety of foods stored at room temperatures. It does have some value, however, since we know that *E. coli* behaves very much like *Salmonella* in its rate of growth in many foods, and hence a high *E. coli* count may increase the microbiologist's efforts to detect salmonellae.

Coliform organisms, other than *E. coli*, are found in soil, dust, *etc.*, and their presence in certain foods might indicate inadequate cleansing of the plant. Such foods include pasteurized and processed products (milk, ice cream, canned foods, *etc.*), where these organisms would be destroyed by the heat treatment.

High bacterial counts on foods may indicate inadequate cooking or contamination during storage and dispensing of the product. A high 22°C with a much lower count at 37°C may indicate everlong storage of the product.

The diffidence I have tried to show in my generalizations outlined above are deliberate. A bacteriologist cannot examine a sample of food and tell you, in ninety-nine cases out of a hundred, how it came to be contaminated with a particular organism. He needs other information concerning the age of the sample, method of preparation, handling of the food, *etc.*, before he can adequately report his findings. What I am trying to say is that the interpretation of bacteriological results on many foods, and especially on meat products, is extremely difficult. Each sample has to be dealt with individually, which makes the provision of bacteriological standards for meats a very tricky problem indeed[28,29].

FUTURE TRENDS

Microbiology is an ever-changing science like all others. As one problem is solved, others appear, and it is not easy to see what lies in store for Food Microbiology in the future. However, there seem to be certain trends of research which will be pursued with more vigour.

The effects of packaging foodstuffs in plastic materials are being investigated to see what changes take place in the microflora. Much more research on the use of antibiotics and other preservatives will be made, as will the effects of new methods of selling foods, such as the hygiene of automatic vending machines, mobile soft ice-cream plants, *etc.*

Above all, I hope to see a greater awareness of the problems of the food scientist which I have tried to outline. I hope also that universities and industry will collaborate to form Schools of Food Science, concentrating on really practical problems of wide significance.

Acknowledgements

I wish to thank all the industrial organizations which have supplied me with photographs and other literature, and also express my gratitude to Mr. R. J. Callow for the many hours he spent in preparing photomicrographs.

Two recent publications have been of great help and are recommended for further reading for those seeking a general introduction to this subject: they are 'Micro-organisms and Foodstuffs' by L. D. Galloway[30] and 'Micro-organisms as Allies' by C. L. Duddington[31].

An especial 'thank you' is due to Dr. Duddington for his helpful criticism, encouragement, and above all, his patience.

REFERENCES

1. TANNER, F. W.   *Microbiology of Foods* 2nd edn: Garrard Press, Illinois, 1944
2. FRAZIER, W. C.   *Food Microbiology* McGraw-Hill, New York, 1958
3. GALE, E. F.   *The Chemical Activities of Bacteria* 3rd edn: University Tutorial Press, London, 1951
4. BREED, R. S., MURRAY, E. G. D., and SMITH, N. R.   *Bergey's Manual of Determinative Bacteriology* 7th edn: Bailliere, Tindall and Cox, London, 1957
5. INGRAM, M.   *An Introduction to the Biology of Yeasts* Pitman, London, 1955
6. LODDER, J. and KREGER-VAN RIJ, N. J. W.   *The Yeasts—A Taxonomic Study* North Holland Publishing Co., Amsterdam, 1952
7. SMITH, G.   *An Introduction to Industrial Mycology* 5th edn: Edward Arnold, London, 1960
8. DAVIS, J. G.   *A Dictionary of Dairying* 2nd edn: Leonard Hill, London, 1955
9. Statutory Instruments 1960 No. 1542. *The Milk (Special Designation) Regulations, 1960* H.M.S.O., London
10. *Joint FAO/WHO Expert Committee on Milk Hygiene—Second Report* WHO Technical Report Series No. 197. WHO, Geneva, 1960
11. PRESCOTT, S. C., and DUNN, C. G.   *Industrial Microbiology* 2nd edn: McGraw-Hill, New York, 1949
12. WOODBINE, M.   'Microbial fat: Micro-organisms as potential fat producers' in *Progress in Industrial Microbiology Vol. I* (Ed. D. J. D. Hockenhull) Heywood, London, 1959
13. *The Ice Cream (Heat Treatment, etc.) Regulations, 1947–1959* H.M.S.O., London
14. D.S.I.R. Food Investigation Leaflet No. 3 *The Care of Trawler's Fish* H.M.S.O., London, 1953
15. WOOD, P. C.   The Principles of Water Sterilisation by Ultra-violet light, and their Application in the Purification of Oysters *Fishery Investigations. Series II Vol. XXIII. No.* 6 1961,
16. KNOTT, F. A.   *Memorandum on the Principles and Standards Employed by the Worshipful Company of Fishmongers in the Bacteriological Control of Shellfish in the London Markets.* Fishmongers' Company, London, 1951
17. HELLER, C. L., ROBERTS, B. C., AMOS, A. J., SMITH, Muriel E., and HOBBS, Betty C. 'The pasturization of liquid whole egg and the evaluation of the baking properties of frozen whole egg'. *J. Hyg., Camb.* **60,** 135, 1962
18. MICKELSON, M. N. and FLIPPIN, R. S. 'Use of Salmonellae antagonists in fermenting egg white'. *App. Microbiol.* **8,** 371, 1960

19. BAUMGARTNER, J. G. and HERSOM, A. C. *Canned Foods—an Introduction to their Microbiology* 4th edn: Churchill, London, 1956

20. BASHFORD, T. E. 'Microbiology in relation to the quality of canned foods'. *J. R. Sanit. Inst.* **67,** No. 5, 1947

21. CHARLEY, V. L. S. *Recent Advances in Fruit Juice Production.* Commonwealth Agricultural Bureaux, London, 1950

22. *Food Standards Committee Report on Preservatives in Food.* H.M.S.O., London, 1959

23. CHARLETT, S. M. 'Ultra-violet irradiation in the food industry'. *Food Trade. Review* **25,** No. 6, 1950

24. HANNAN, R. S. 'Scientific and technological problems involved in using ionising radiations for the preservation of foods'. *DSIR Food Investigation Spec. Rep. No.* 61. H.M.S.O., London, 1955

25. HOBBS, Betty C. *Food Poisoning and Food Hygiene* Edward Arnold, London, 1953

26. 'Food poisoning in England and Wales, 1960'. *Monthly Bull. Ministry of Health & Pub. Health Lab. Service, 20* 160, 1961

27. HARVEY, W. C. and PERRY, H. A. *Food Hygiene Handbook.* Heywood, London, 1953

28. INGRAM, M. 'Microbiological standards for foods'. *Food Tech., Lond.* **15,** 4, 1961

29. ELLIOTT, R. P. and MICHENER, H. D. 'Microbiological standards and handling codes for chilled and frozen foods. A review'. *App. Microbiol.* **9,** 452, 1961

30. GALLOWAY, L. D. 'Micro-organisms and foodstuffs'. *Food Processing and Packaging* **28** and **29,** 1959

31. DUDDINGTON, C. L. *Micro-organisms as Allies* Faber and Faber, London; The Macmillan Company, New York, 1960

2

FUNGICIDES

D. Priest

INTRODUCTION

For several hundred years man has protected his crops against the ravages of pests. The scope of his early efforts was restricted to dealing with the more obvious depredations of insects and animals. More subtle but none the less important were the losses caused by fungi. The first use of fungicide was probably accidental, for the blackening of wheat grains and the blighting of crops was something that man could not then understand though he attempted remedies both physical and metaphysical.

Prévost[1] was one of the first people to appreciate that a fungus was the cause of bunt in wheat, and from that point the effective study of fungicides may be said to originate. This realization of the relationship between fungal pathogen and disease symptom laid the foundation for our present knowledge of fungicides. In the last sixty years a wide spectrum of compounds has been evaluated for fungicidal activity. A large number of the compounds tested have contained sulphur in organic or inorganic form, and their introduction and application is a direct consequence of the effectiveness of elemental sulphur as a fungicide. In the nineteenth century, sulphur and Bordeaux mixture which had been 'discovered' by Millardet[2] in 1882 were used to protect grape foliage against downy mildew. By 1900 formaldehyde was used as a seed treatment for wheat smut, and in 1913 Riehm[3] introduced organic mercury compounds for the same purpose. In 1934 Tisdale and Williams[4] discovered that derivatives of dithiocarbamic acid were fungitoxic and this subsequently led to the introduction of metallic dithiocarbamates, thiuram sulphides and bisdithiocarbamates. Kittleson[5] in 1952 described a new class of organic fungicides arising from the reaction of perchloro-methylmercaptan with the alkali-metal salts of amides and imides. These contributions may be regarded as outstanding landmarks in the history of fungicides.

The use of elemental sulphur as a fungicide and the introduction of organic sulphur compounds stimulated research in mechanisms of toxicity. These studies are primarily directed to obtaining relationships between chemical structure of the fungicide and biological response of the fungus, and include observations on mitosis, morphology, growth and metabolism. Considerable data have been obtained from *in vitro* tests using fungal mycelium or spores, and fungicides. The germination of fungal spores on glass slides in the presence of fungicide is a convenient means of screening large numbers of fungicides. Mathematical treatments of spore germination tests have been extensively considered by Bliss[6], McCallan and Wilcoxon[7], and Litchfield and Fertig[8]. An alternative technique is to introduce the fungicide into melted agar prior to solidification, or into liquid media. The effect of the fungicide is observed from the growth rate of the fungus in the poisoned environment. The technique of growing fungi on poisoned media in Petri-dishes was quantitatively examined by Falck[9]. The activity of the fungicide may be expressed in terms of the days required by the fungal colony to reach a given diameter, or by the colony diameter obtained in unit time.

Application of fungicides to crops and materials is an important aspect of protection. There are many ways in which fungicides may be applied but the primary object is to place the fungicide where it may be effective. The fumigation of seeds and materials depends upon several factors but the main requirement is a high vapour pressure of the fumigant. Dusting of crops suffers from the fundamental disadvantage that the fungicide particles usually acquire a negative charge when discharged from a machine, and the small particles are then repelled by the negatively charged leaf. Spraying is more suitable for crop protection, as the larger droplet size overcomes electrostatic repulsion. A further factor associated with spraying is the wettability of leaf surfaces. Certain leaves are not easily wetted and consequently the droplets roll off the surface. The addition of wetting agents to the spray improves the chance of the droplets remaining on some leaf surfaces but is unsuitable for easily wetted leaves.

An important consideration in the field of fungicides is the acquisition of resistance or adaptation by fungi to fungicidal action. In the field of plant pathology the extensive use of fungicides reflects attempts at control and therapy, but a potential threat to these efforts lies in this acquired resistance. Laboratory studies have shown that resistant strains of many fungi are produced by subjection to sub-lethal doses of toxic substances. This relationship between organism and toxic substance is shown in several fields of biology. At present, however, the realm of fungicides appears relatively free from serious failure of fungicides under field conditions due to adaptation.

From a chemical viewpoint fungicides may be divided into several groups though certain compounds overlap; thus *N*–trichloromethylmercapto–4–cyclohexene–1,2–dicarboximide (Captan) may be considered either as an organic sulphur or heterocyclic nitrogen fungicide. In this article fungicides are considered under a number of general headings and the inclusion of a fungicide in one group rather than another, though associated with mechanism of toxicity, is largely a matter of convenience.

METALS

Numerous inorganic compounds have been used as fungicides over the past three hundred years. Woolman and Humphrey[10], summarizing the literature on bunt of wheat in 1924, mentioned the use of sodium chloride by Remnant in 1637 and the subsequent introduction of arsenic, mercuric chloride, and copper sulphate in the eighteenth century as remedial chemicals for this disease. Although many metals have been used as fungicides, copper, mercury, and zinc have attained pre-eminence. Horsfall[11] arranged metal cations in the following order of descending toxicity: $Ag > Hg > Cu > Cd > Cr > Ni > Pb > Co > Zn > Fe > Ca$. Somers[12] obtained similar results from experiments on the toxicity of metal salts to *Alternaria tenuis* and

Botrytis fabae, but found the position of Pb and Ni interchanged. Silver salts are the most toxic but cost precludes their economic application.

The introduction of Bordeaux mixture, a product of copper sulphate and calcium hydroxide, in the nineteenth century, and its successful and extensive use over the last eighty years has focused considerable attention on copper salts as fungicides. Two fundamental problems arose from a study of Bordeaux mixture. One was concerned with the exact chemical nature of the complex, and the other with mechanism of toxicity. In the early part of the twentieth century it had been considered that Bordeaux mixture was tribasic copper sulphate and this view is currently accepted. The mechanism of toxicity has fostered numerous theories, arising form the fact that Bordeaux mixture is practically insoluble in water. The various theories proposed have all been directly or indirectly concerned with presenting the copper in a soluble form to the fungal spore or mycelium. McCallan and Wilcoxon[13] found that fungal spores exuded acids, among them malic acid, capable of bringing copper from Bordeaux mixture into solution, presumably by formation and dissociation of the copper salt. The studies of Wain and Wilkinson[14] enhanced this concept. They considered that dissociation of copper salts such as copper malate enabled the toxic copper cation to become available to fungal spores. Copper, chromium, and arsenic have been incorporated in fungicides in anionic form as cupri malates and tartrates, chromates, and arsenites. Martin, Wain, and Wilkinson[15] compared the toxicity of copper in cationic form and in complex anionic form. They found that copper was more toxic in an anion complex than as a cation. However, the field of metallic anion toxicity is still relatively unexplored and little is known about the mechanism of activity. The original copper and mercury fungicides were inorganic salts, but a disadvantage of inorganic mercury fungicides was their high mammalian toxicity. Inorganic copper salts have been retained as fungicides but inorganic mercury has been replaced by organic mercurials. Riehm[3] in 1913 introduced chlorophenol mercury as a seed treatment for cereals, and Tisdale and Cannon[16] later used ethylmercuric chloride for the same purpose. The only organic copper complex that has achieved repute as a fungicide is copper oxinate which was given field trials by Meyer[17] in 1932.

The site of activity of metals has been considered by several workers. As early as 1896 Kahlenberg and True[18] showed that the toxicity of metal poisons was correlated with ionization, and that the active agent was the cation rather than the molecule. Since ions penetrate fungal spores less readily than molecules, this suggested that copper toxicity was due to surface activity of the cations. Conversely Goldsworthy and Green[19] showed that spores soaked in copper sulphate revealed the presence of copper within the spores and implied that copper exerted its toxicity at some internal site. If cation toxicity is associated with surface activity, the adsorption of cations on cell surfaces must be a fundamental physico-chemical aspect of that toxicity. In 1930 Bodnar and Terenyi[20] found that the uptake of copper from solution by spores of *Tilletia tritici* followed the Langmuir adsorption isotherm. On the other hand McCallan[21] obtained experimental data on the uptake of copper by spores of *Alternaria oleraceae* and *Monilinia fructicola* that did not fit the Langmuir isotherm. Miller *et al.*[22] used various radioactive cations and found that fungal spores took up many more cations than could be explained on the basis of a single adsorbed layer. In addition they showed that pretreatment of fungal spores with either cerium chloride or silver nitrate did not interfere with uptake of the other cation. This indicated that uptake of these cations was not solely associated with adsorption. Evidence on cation adsorption and penetration provides a basis for speculation on site of activity but the two spheres of activity, internal and external, are not necessarily mutually exclusive. Both adsorption and penetration probably contribute to the observed toxicity of any cationic species.

The mechanism of metal toxicity at surface site is not clearly understood. Surface activity may be due to binding or inactivation of anionic sites essential to the existence of the cell, or due to deleterious effects on cell permeability. The way in which metals may exert their toxicity at some internal site was investigated by Janke, Beran, and Schmidt[23]. They considered that heavy metals reacted with sulphhydryl —SH groups present in living cells in compounds such as cysteine and glutathione. This reaction was either concerned with a catalytic autoxidation of the sulphhydryl group, or led to the formation of mercaptides and disturbed protein metabolism, or enzyme action. They also showed that cysteine and thioglycollic acid reversed the toxicity of mercuric chloride, phenylmercuric acetate and copper sulphate to spores of *Tilletia tritici*. Metals such as copper and mercury have been shown to inhibit a number of enzyme systems including those concerned with carbohydrate metabolism; thus their mechanism of toxicity is not specific. In this respect the view of Macleod and Snell[24], that toxicity arises because certain metals are structurally analogous to those essential for fungal metabolism, is a more acceptable concept.

Inorganic salts and organic metal complexes have frequently been used in poisoned food techniques and strains of fungi resistant to different metals have been obtained. The literature, however, contains few records of the appearance of strains resistant to inorganic fungicides under field conditions, though Horsfall[11] stated that to achieve the same control of *Phytophthora infestans* on potato along the Atlantic seaboard of America with Bordeaux mixture required a threefold increase in spraying compared with that of sixty years ago, and considered that this indicated the existence of strains resistant to copper. The spore germination studies of Taylor[25] have also shown that spores of *Physalospora obtusa* from orchards continually sprayed with Bordeaux mixture are more resistant to copper than those from unsprayed orchards. There are a number of laboratory studies on adaptation. Stakman *et al.*[26] investigated the adaptation of monosporidial lines of *Ustilago zeae* to arsenic. A threefold increase in tolerance for sodium arsenite was obtained after ten transfers on media containing arsenic, and the ability to grow on arsenic media of the same concentration increased with successive transfers. The resistant variants rapidly reverted to the parent susceptibility when grown on arsenic free media. Mader and Schneider[27] 'trained' cultures of *Monilinia fructicola* to increased concentrations of copper sulphate in agar media. The variants produced differed in their ability to rot fruit and, when transferred to fungicide free media, the acquired resistance was retained by some variants but lost by others. Similar Studies by Wilson[28] demonstrated the development of increased resistance to sodium arsenite by *Sclerotium rolfsii* and *Sclerotium delphinii*. Jurkowska[29] investigated the adaptation of *Aspergillus niger* to copper sulphate. After several sub-cultures on agar media containing copper sulphate, a resistant strain was obtained which tolerated concentrations which were toxic to the parent; this resistant strain was also resistant to normally toxic levels of zinc, nickel and manganese salts. Greathouse *et al.*[30] obtained a strain of *Aspergillus niger* resistant to copper oxinate but susceptible to oxine, which indicated that the resistance was to the copper moiety. Arakatsu *et al.*[31] investigated the adaptation of yeasts to cupric salts and found that a resistant strain, in contrast to the parent, was able to synthesize glutamic and aspartic acid when grown on media containing copper. It appeared that the fungitoxicity of copper was due to a direct inhibition of glutamic and aspartic acid synthesis. Bartlett[32] obtained strains of *Penicillium roqueforti* resistant to high concentrations of phenyl mercuric acetate and sodium azide, but the majority of these strains were unstable and rapidly reverted to the parent susceptibility when grown in drug free media. These studies have shown that under laboratory conditions fungi may be 'trained' to tolerate normally toxic levels of metallic fungicides. They have also shed some light on the mechanism of toxicity, but the general instability and reversion of resistant strains suggests that the phenomenon of adaptation is not likely to detract from the use of metallic fungicides under field conditions.

SULPHUR

Sulphur is one of the ancients in the field of pesticides. It has been used for about 2,000 years as a crop protectant, though not specifically as a fungicide. Forsyth[33] in 1803 appreciated that sulphur was an effective fungicide and recommended its use for the healthy management of fruit trees. Later, Robertson[34] in 1824 stated that sulphur was specific for powdery mildew of peach. The mode of fungitoxic action of sulphur has aroused considerable interest, mainly because the concept arose that sulphur particles themselves could not, or would not, penetrate fungal cells. The corollary to this hypothesis was that some oxidized or reduced derivative of sulphur was the active toxicant. Oxidation products of sulphur, pentathionic acid, sulphur dioxide and sulphur trioxide were at one time suggested as the active toxic agents. In 1884 Mach and Portele[35] proposed sulphur dioxide, Marcille[36] in 1911 favoured sulphur trioxide, and later Young[37] in 1922 suggested pentathionic acid. These views were supported by the observation of Doran[38] in 1922 that oxygen enhanced the toxic action of sulphur on germinating spores. These concepts of sulphur toxicity were later undermined by Roach and Glynne[39] and Wilcoxon and McCallan[40] who showed that the toxicity of oxidation products of sulphur was correlated with their hydrogen ion concentration in aqueous solution.

Hydrogen sulphide was suggested as early as 1875 by Pollacci[41] as the active reduction toxicant of sulphur. This view was supported by the work of Marsh[42], McCallan and Wilcoxon[43], and Sokoloff[44]. Their studies showed that hydrogen sulphide was toxic to fungal spores and mycelia. This general observation, associated with the knowledge that fungal spores could reduce sulphur, presented the hydrogen sulphide theory in a favourable light. The theory, however, has not survived the test of further critical experimentation. In 1948, Yarwood[45] showed that, in a closed system, when reduction products of sulphur were removed by an active oxidant, such as potassium permanganate, sulphur still had fungicidal value against powdery mildew on infected leaves. Miller, McCallan and Weed[46] suspended fungal spores in water containing sulphur particles. Nitrogen was bubbled through the suspension and the hydrogen sulphide formed was removed by absorption in zinc acetate solution. It was found that the rate of hydrogen sulphide production depended upon the fungus and the particle size of the sulphur, colloidal sulphur being most effective. Spore viability of different species under these conditions was not directly associated with the rate of hydrogen sulphide production. Active producers of hydrogen sulphide were not less viable than moderate producers after given test periods. A direct comparison of the toxicity of hydrogen sulphide and colloidal sulphur in a closed system to fungal spores, showed that, of the species tested, sensitivity to sulphur was invariably greater than that to hydrogen sulphide. The theory that particulate sulphur, or sulphur vapour was fungitoxic had been suggested by Sempio[47] in 1932. Earlier, Eyre and Salmon[48] found that hydrogen sulphide was not toxic to powdery mildews but that sulphur itself was an effective fungicide. Sempio and Castori[49] demonstrated that sulphur vapour was toxic to conidia of *Erysiphe*. Yarwood[50] also contributed to this aspect of vapour toxicity by showing a marked temperature variable in sulphur inhibition of mildew growth. Allotropic forms of sulphur and particle size were also shown to affect toxicity. In 1928 Goldsworthy[51] showed that sulphur particles were detectable in hyphae of *Tranzchelia prunosa* treated with polysulphides. This suggested that the fungal wall was permeable to sulphur. The theories that oxidized or reduced compounds of sulphur are responsible for toxicity have now been discarded. Sciarini and Nord[52] showed that in *Fusarium*, sulphur substitutes for oxygen in respiratory pathways and presumably interferes with hydrogen transfers. However, the precise mechanism of sulphur toxicity is still elusive. Fundamentally it appears that sulphur exerts its toxicity by functioning as a hydrogen acceptor in fungal respiration.

ORGANIC SULPHUR COMPOUNDS

The discovery by Tisdale and Williams[4] that derivatives of dithiocarbamic acid

$$\text{H} \diagdown \underset{\text{H}}{\diagup} \text{N} - \overset{\overset{\text{S}}{\|}}{\text{C}} - \text{S} - \text{H}$$

were fungitoxic, and the introduction by the Standard Oil Development Co. in 1949 of fungicides containing the *N*-trichloromethylthio, —NSCCl₃ group are the outstanding contributions in the field of organic sulphur fungicides.

The dithiocarbamic acid derivatives fall into three distinct groups: metallic dithiocarbamates, thiuram sulphides, and bisdithiocarbamates.

The metallic dithiocarbamates include cadmium, ferric, sodium, and zinc salts, of which the ferric and zinc salts are the most important:

$$(CH_3)_2 \cdot N - \overset{\overset{S}{\|}}{C} - S - Fe \underset{S - \overset{\|}{C} - N \cdot (CH_3)_2}{\overset{S - \overset{\overset{S}{\|}}{C} - N \cdot (CH_3)_2}{}}$$

Ferric dimethyldithiocarbamate

$$(CH_3)_2 \cdot N - \overset{\overset{S}{\|}}{C} - S - Zn - S - \overset{\overset{S}{\|}}{C} - N \cdot (CH_3)_2$$

Zinc dimethyldithiocarbamate

The most important thiuram sulphide is tetramethyl thiuram disulphide (TMTD):

$$(CH_3)_2 \cdot N - \overset{\overset{S}{\|}}{C} - S - S - \overset{\overset{S}{\|}}{C} - N \cdot (CH_3)_2$$

Tetramethyl thiuram monosulphide (TMTM) also possesses fungitoxicity, but has been less extensively used than the disulphide. Three bisdithiocarbamates are important, the disodium, zinc, and manganous salts of ethylene bisdithiocarbamate:

$$\begin{array}{c} CH_2 - \overset{\overset{H}{|}}{N} - \overset{\overset{S}{\|}}{C} - S - Na \\ | \\ CH_2 - N - C - S - Na \\ \overset{|}{H} \quad \overset{\|}{S} \end{array}$$

Disodium ethylene bisdithiocarbamate

$$\begin{array}{c} CH_2 - \overset{\overset{H}{|}}{N} - \overset{\overset{S}{\|}}{C} - S \\ | \qquad\qquad\qquad \searrow Zn \\ CH_2 - N - C - S \nearrow \\ \overset{|}{H} \quad \overset{\|}{S} \end{array}$$

Zinc ethylene bisdithiocarbamate

$$\begin{array}{c} CH_2 - \overset{\overset{H}{|}}{N} - \overset{\overset{S}{\|}}{C} - S \\ | \qquad\qquad\qquad \searrow Mn \\ CH_2 - N - C - S \nearrow \\ \overset{|}{H} \quad \overset{\|}{S} \end{array}$$

Manganous ethylene bisdithiocarbamate

The original contribution of Tisdale and Williams[4] showed that dithio-carbamate derivatives were toxic to a wide range of organisms. Tetramethyl thiuram disulphide was first used by Muskett and Colhoun[53] as a seed treatment for flax. In 1941 Goldsworthy et al.[54] used a number of metallic derivatives of dithiocarbamic acid in field trials, and in 1943 Dimond et al.[55] demonstrated the promising fungitoxic properties of disodium ethylene bisdithiocarbamate under field conditions. Analysis of field trials and labora-tory tests on dithiocarbamic acid derivatives has revealed differences in disease control. A comparison of zinc ethylene bisdithiocarbamate and zinc dimethyldithiocarbamate shows that the former controls both *Alternaria* and *Phytophthora* on potato, but that the latter controls only *Alternaria*. These results indicate different modes of toxic action of dithiocarbamates based on alkyl diamines, *e.g.* zinc ethylene bisdithiocarbamate; and those based on dialkyl amines *e.g.* zinc dimethyldithiocarbamate. Klöpping and van der Kerk[56] suggested that the toxicity of dialkyl amine derivatives was associated with ionization of the molecules. Davies and Sexton[57] were of the opinion that the molecules of certain dithiocarbamic acid derivatives were themselves responsible for toxicity. Dimond et al.[58] in 1941 reported an unusual dosage–response relationship between fungal spores and dosage of tetra-methyl thiuram disulphide. They found that as dosage increased toxicity increased, declined, then increased again, giving a polymodal dosage–response relationship. This phenomenon was also recorded by Parker-Rhodes[59] for the dithiocarbamates. Van der Kerk and Klöpping[60] considered that this dosage–response relationship was confined primarily to dithio-carbamate derivatives of dialkyl amines. If the whole molecule theory is correct it implies that either the dithiocarbamates penetrate fungal cells or that toxicity derives from surface action and prevents uptake of nutrients from the external environment. Dimond et al.[58] proposed that the poly-modal dosage–response relationship shown by tetramethyl thiuram disulphide and dialkyl dithiocarbamates was a reflection of the activity of the whole molecule at high concentrations and of the dithiocarbamate ion at low concentrations. Parker-Rhodes[59] considered that under test conditions dialkyl dithiocarbamates are converted to thiuram disulphides. Klöpping and van der Kerk[56] suggested that the thiuram disulphides dissociated to give dialkyl dithiocarbamates. These two suggestions are not irreconcilable. If either compound was added to fungal spores, an equilibrium would be established between the thiuram disulphide and the dialkyl dithiocarbamate. This provides a satisfactory explanation for the polymodal dosage–response curves shown by both compounds. Horsfall[11] suggested that the action of the dithiocarbamates was associated with chelation, *i.e.* the production of a highly stable complex between the molecule of the fungicide and essential metals. Considerable information on this aspect of toxicity has been realized from experiments with fungal enzyme systems and fungicides, in the presence of compounds able to bring about reversal or antagonism of toxic action. Sijpesteijn and van der Kerk[61] found that L-histidine inhibited the toxicity of TMTD and TMTM to spore germination of *Botrytis cinerea*, but not to mycelial growth. This effect was more apparent at high pH than at low pH. Further investigations by Sijpesteijn and van der Kerk[62] on the antagonistic action of certain imidazole derivatives to the fungitoxicity of dimethyl-dithiocarbamates showed that L-, and D-histidine and imidazole-4-pyruvic acid were able to antagonize the inhibitory action of sodium dimethyl-dithiocarbamate to spore germination of *Botrytis allii*. The antagonistic action of imidazole-4-pyruvic acid was greater than L-, or D-histidine, and was not due to conversion to L-histidine. They suggested that imidazole-4-pyruvic acid prevented interaction of sodium dimethyldithiocarbamate with some essential enzyme system. Van Raalte[63] found that addition of copper sulphate to nutrient media containing sodium dimethyldithiocarbamate on which *Fusarium caeruleum* was growing inhibited the toxicity of this fungicide. He also observed that under similar conditions *Aspergillus niger* produced pallid conidia, a copper deficiency symptom. The inference drawn from these experiments was that the dithiocarbamate formed a chelation complex with copper. An extension of this concept was proposed by Goksøyr[64] to explain the polymodal dosage–response shown by dialkyl dithiocarbamates. He suggested that the dimethyldithiocarbamate ion, [DDC]$^-$, combined with traces of copper in the medium to give a half chelate

$$[DDC]^- + Cu^{2+} \rightleftharpoons [DDC]Cu^+$$

which was toxic. With increased concentrations of dithiocarbamate a full chelate was formed which was less toxic:

$$[DDC]Cu^+ + [DDC]^- \rightleftharpoons [DDC]Cu[DDC]$$

At higher concentrations of the dithiocarbamate, increased toxicity was due to binding of further essential metals. Owens[65] studied the effects of a series of dithiocarbamates and bisdithiocarbamates on polyphenol oxidase, a copper prosthetic enzyme found in fungi. All dithiocarbamic acid derivatives, except the copper salts, caused some inhibition of this enzyme. Considerable experimental evidence has accumulated on the emanation of toxic vapours from sodium ethylene bisdithiocarbamate under laboratory test conditions. This compound is not in itself fungitoxic, as can be shown by spore germination tests in a low oxygen tension, but it is unstable and water soluble, and exerts its fungitoxic effect in the presence of oxygen. Various breakdown products have been postulated as the effective fungicidal agent. Barratt and Horsfall[66] suggested hydrogen sulphide and Lopatecki and Newton[67] also considered that the evolution of hydrogen sulphide observed under acid conditions was partly responsible for fungitoxicity. Rich and Horsfall[68] using a closed system investigated the nature of the toxic emanations from sodium ethylene bisdithiocarbamate, and their effect on spores of *Stemphylium sarcinaeforme* and *Monilinia fructicola*. Spores of *M. fructicola* released hydrogen sulphide from the pure chemical, and toxic vapours from sodium ethylene bisdithiocarbamate solutions killed *S. sarcinaeforme* spores. However, these vapours killed the spores far below predetermined concentration levels for hydrogen sulphide. Their conclusions were that liberated hydrogen sulphide was not directly associated with the toxicity of these vapours. They suggested that ethylene di-isothiocyanate

$$CH_2-N=C=S$$
$$|$$
$$CH_2-N=C=S$$

was responsible for the observed fungitoxicity, and this hypothesis was confirmed by the investigations of Klöpping and van der Kerk[69]. Later Ludwig and Thorn[70] showed that under aerobic conditions disodium ethylene bisdithiocarbamate liberated a highly toxic product, ethylene thiuram monosulphide:

$$
\begin{array}{ccc}
\underset{\displaystyle \text{CH}_2-\overset{\displaystyle \text{H}}{\text{N}}-\overset{\displaystyle \text{S}}{\text{C}}-\text{S}-\text{Na}}{\underset{\displaystyle \text{CH}_2-\text{N}-\text{C}-\text{S}-\text{Na}}{}} & \rightarrow & \text{etms}
\end{array}
$$

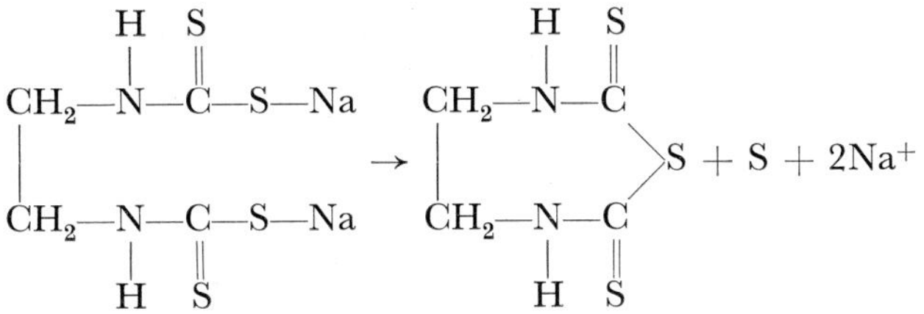

Further investigations by Ludwig et al.[71] showed that ethylene thiuram monosulphide may break down to give ethylene di-isothiocyanate:

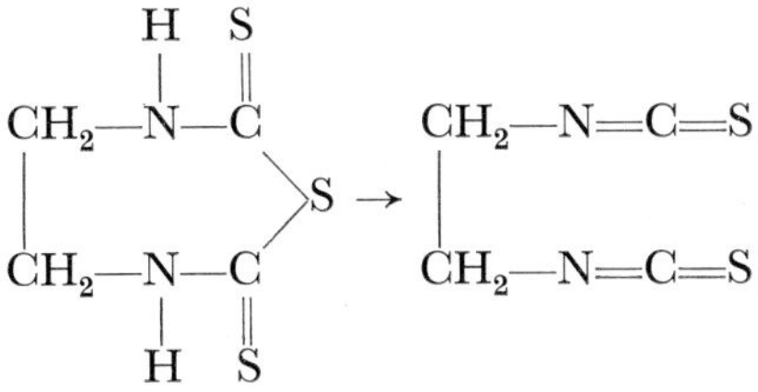

The problem of how the breakdown products of disodium ethylene bisdithiocarbamate actually kill fungi is still unsolved, but it appears that one or more of the postulated products interfere with sulphhydryl systems essential to the well-being and function of fungal metabolism.

The other outstanding organic sulphur fungicides are those containing the N-trichloromethylthio group. Sixteen compounds containing this group were initially synthesized, and one of these N-trichloromethylmercapto-4-cyclohexene-1,2-dicarboximide (Captan)

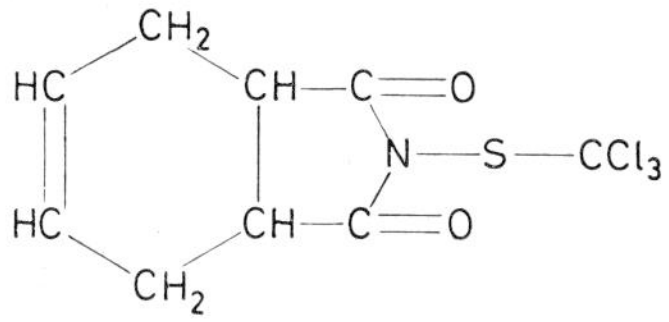

marketed and tested under the code name 'SR 406', was found to possess exceptional fungicidal activity. Captan has been applied to a wide variety of plant diseases with conspicuous success. Horsfall and Rich[72] found Captan was very effective against *Stemphylium sarcinaeforme* and they considered the following structural features could be involved in its fungitoxicity; the $-\text{CCl}_3$ group, the sulphur bridge, the diketone, and the carbon atoms alpha to the ketone. Hochstein and Cox[73] studied the fungicidal action of Captan on the respiration of growing and non-growing conidia of *Fusarium roseum*. Conidial germination and mycelial growth was observed in the

61

presence of Captan. Their manometric studies suggested that Captan inhibited growth in fungi by interfering with decarboxylation reactions requiring thiamine pyrophosphate as coenzyme. Rich[74] also studied the chemistry of the fungitoxicity of Captan. Various chemicals were tested for their ability to antagonize the toxicity of Captan in liquid media to *Monilinia fructicola*. Captan at 3×10^{-5}M completely inhibited the growth of the test organism; this toxicity was reversed by 10^{-2}M L-histidine, and 10^{-2}M L-cysteine. The former was effective if added 24 hours after the Captan, and the latter after 6 hours, but not 24. It was concluded from these observations that *M. fructicola* could by-pass every system poisoned by Captan, except those needed for synthesis or utilization of histidine. Captan was considered to react with sulphhydryl groups present in such compounds as cysteine to produce thiophosgene:

The thiophosgene formed was the active toxicant and exerted its effect by combining with free sulphhydryl, amino or hydroxyl groups within the fungal cell, indicating that the toxicity of Captan was attributable to the —SCCl₃ group. Uhlenbroek and Koopmans[75], however, have reported compounds containing this group which are non-toxic. It would appear that thiophosgene production is not the complete answer for Captan toxicity. Although the dithiocarbamate derivatives and *N*-trichloromethylmercapto compounds appear to be the most important organic sulphur fungicides, a number of other sulphur containing fungicides, including rhodanines, *p*-toluene sulphonamides, thio- and dithiocyanates have been shown to possess marked fungicidal potential.

   Few instances of acquired resistance to complex organic sulphur fungicides either under field or laboratory conditions have been reported. Gattani[76] 'trained' *Alternaria spp.* to Arasan (containing tetramethyl thiuram disulphide) by successive transfers to increasing concentrations of fungicide incorporated in potato dextrose agar. Parry and Wood[77] similarly obtained strains of *Botrytis cinerea* resistant to ferric dimethyldithiocarbamate and Captan, and these resistant strains did not revert to the parent susceptibility when grown on fungicide free media. At present it does not appear that adaptation of fungi under field conditions to Captan or dithiocarbamic acid derivatives has arisen to impair their pre-eminence among organic sulphur fungicides.

HETEROCYCLIC NITROGEN COMPOUNDS

These are fungicides which incorporate one or more nitrogen atoms in a five or six membered ring. Many heterocyclic nitrogen compounds have been tested for fungicidal activity. Prior to 1951 Horsfall and Rich[72] had examined over 150 compounds in spore germination tests for toxicity to *Monilinia fructicola* and *Stemphylium sarcinaeforme*. Captan, which was considered in the organic sulphur section, is perhaps the most outstanding heterocyclic nitrogen fungicide, but many others have shown promising potential, both under laboratory and field conditions. In general most nitrogen heterocycles appear to be fundamentally toxic. Horsfall and Rich[72] found that an unsubstituted heterocyclic nitrogen nucleus such as pyridine

was usually non-toxic, though there were exceptions such as pyrrole:

The introduction of a lipophillic substituent, either an alkyl or an aryl group, into the molecule conferred toxicity to non-toxic heterocycles and enhanced toxicity in toxic nitrogen heterocycles. The introduction of a lipophillic substituent, *i.e.* one that increases fat solubility, is directly associated with solubility of the fungicide in the fungal protoplasmic membrane. The addition of polar groups such as —NH$_2$, —NO$_2$, and —OH was also found to improve the toxicity of nitrogen heterocycles. These general observations agree in principle with the Overton-Meyer theory of drug action; that there should be a lipophillic substituent to confer lipoid solubility and a polar group to ensure a reactive centre. One of the best examples of a lipophillic 'tail' conferring toxicity is shown below. 2-Methyl-2-imidazoline

is not fungitoxic. When the methyl, —CH$_3$, group is replaced by theh eptadecyl, —C$_{17}$H$_{35}$, group the resulting compound 2-heptadecyl-2-imidazoline

is an active fungicide. The fungicidal potential of this compound was first reported by Wellman and McCallan[78], and a related compound 2-heptadecyl-2-imidazole acetate has been shown to be an effective fungicide against apple scab. Maximum fungitoxicity of 2-imidazoline derivatives appears to be associated with straight chain alkyl substituents in the 2 position of the ring, of between 13 to 17 carbon atoms. Similar observations have been reported on other heterocyclic nitrogen nuclei. Rader *et al.*[79] considered the derivatives of pyrimidine:

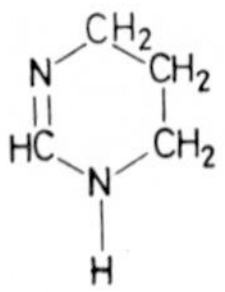

They found that fungitoxicity was greatly improved by substitution of methyl groups in the 4,4,6-positions. This toxicity was also intimately associated with the nature of the substituents in the 2-position. A straight carbon chain of 17 atoms conferred maximum toxicity to the 4,4,6-trimethyl substituted pyrimidine nucleus, and the resulting compound 1,5,5,6-tetra-hydro-2-heptadecyl-4,4,6-trimethylpyrimidine

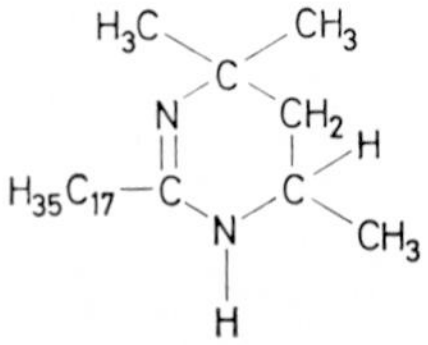

showed marked fungicidal properties.

The fungicidal properties of substituted pyrazoles was investigated by McNew and Sundholm[80]. 3,5-Dimethylpyrazole

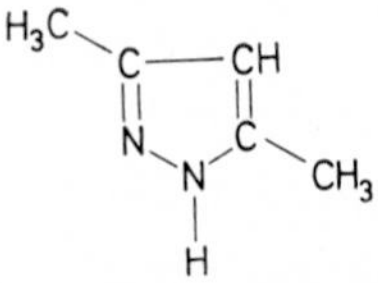

was found to be weakly fungicidal. Introduction of a nitroso, $-N=O$, group and a *p*-chlorophenyl, $-C_6H_4Cl$, group gave the highly reactive 1-(*p*-chlorophenyl)-3,5-dimethyl-4-nitrosopyrazole:

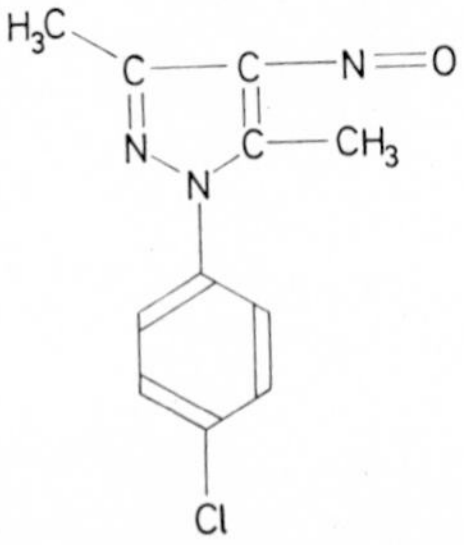

Investigations of heterocyclic nitrogen compounds have shown that their toxic mechanisms differ considerably. Rich[81] considered that nitroso-pyrazoles and tetrahydropyrimidines acted as physical toxicants. West and Wolf[82] showed that certain compounds, guanine and xanthine, were able to reverse the toxicity of 2-heptadecyl-2-imidazole, and believed that 2-imidazolines were competitive inhibitors of enzymes.

Heterocyclic nitrogen compounds are a promising source of fungicides. There are, however, certain disadvantages to their practical application. Several of them are skin irritants, especially those compounds which possess a nitroso group, while others are too toxic to plant life to be used commercially.

QUINONES

Certain quinones have been found to be valuable agricultural fungicides. Two chlorinated quinones commonly used are tetrachloro-1,4-benzoquinone (Chloranil):

and 2,3-dichloro-1,4-naphthoquinone (Dichlone):

The fungicidal potential of Chloranil was first suggested in 1938 by ter Horst and Felix[83]. Horsfall[11] demonstrated the toxicity of this compound to spores of *Stemphylium sarcinaeforme*, and successful field trials were carried out in 1939 by Cunningham and Sharvelle[84] who found that it was an effective seed protectant for lima beans. Chloranil has been found to be particularly effective as a seed treatment for legumes, but has not been successful as a foliage protectant, though Eddins[85] reported that it controlled cabbage downy mildew. It appears that Chloranil is generally innocuous as a foliage fungicide owing to conversion in sunlight to 2,5-dichloro-3,6-dihydroxy-1,4-benzoquinone:

This compound, chloranilic acid, was shown by Owens[86] to be much less fungitoxic than Chloranil to spores of *Monilinia fructicola*.

The search for a light stable quinone, suitable as a foliage fungicide, led to the introduction of Dichlone in 1943. This compound was found to be much more stable in light than its precursor and has since been extensively used against certain fungal diseases of plants, particularly apple scab. Collectively, quinones show activity against a wide range of organisms. The bactericidal property of quinones had been commented upon in the early part of this century, but prior to Chloranil an effective quinone fungicide had not emerged from this general observation. McNew and Burchfield[87] reviewed the fungitoxicity of quinones and reported that fungitoxicity increased in the order anthraquinone < *p*-benzoquinone < phenanthro-quinone < 1,4-naphthoquinone. Halogenation of these quinone nuclei increased toxicity but diminished solubility. Generally speaking the toxicity of halogenated compounds increases in the order iodine < bromine < chlorine < fluorine. This effect has been observed for a number of pesticides. Tehon[88] applied this halogenation principle to 1,4-benzoquinone and examined the fungicidal potential of fluorinated 1,4-benzoquinones. He found that 2,5-difluoro-1,4-benzoquinone

was the most effective in preventing the germination of *Stemphylium sarcinae-forme* spores, and showed that when fluorine was replaced by chlorine or bromine, fungitoxicity was markedly diminished. Other structural modifications to the benzoquinone nucleus have also been shown to affect fungitoxicity, phytotoxicity and water solubility. Byrde and Woodcock[89] examined a number of quinones based on the 1,4-naphthoquinone nucleus:

Certain esters such as 2,3-dichloro-1,4-diacetoxynaphthalene

were found to be as effective as the parent quinone when applied in aqueous acetone solutions to spores of *Monilinia laxa*, *Botrytis fabae*, and *Cladosporium fulvum*. These investigations led to the formation of a relationship between fungitoxicity and ease of hydrolysis. It was suggested that 2,3-dichloro-1,4-diacetoxynaphthalene was not in itself toxic but that this compound was hydrolysed to 2,3-dichloro-1,4-hydroquinone by a fungal esterase. The hydroquinone was then oxidized to the corresponding quinone which was the active fungicide:

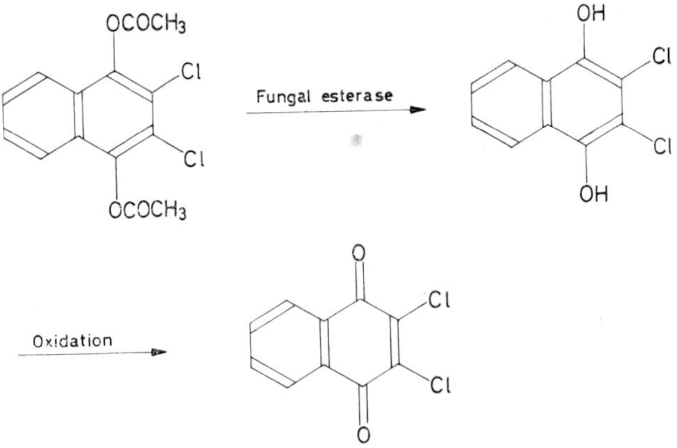

Several other quinones have been tested for fungicidal activity. Horsfall[11] showed that 9,10-phenanthrene quinone

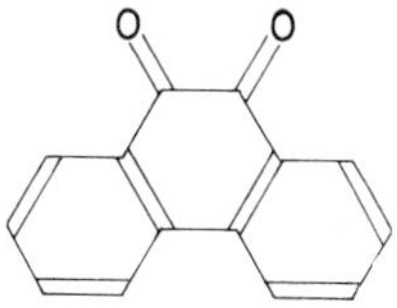

is a particularly active unsubstituted quinone which showed selective toxicity towards two common test organisms. Spores of *Stemphylium sarcinae-forme* but not those of *Monilinia fructicola* were killed by this quinone. This phenomenon was considered to be associated with permeation. The mechanism of toxicity of quinones has been considered from several viewpoints. Quinones are present in fungi as naturally occurring products and arise either as by-products of fungal metabolism, or are vital chemicals in normal metabolic pathways. In the latter respect certain quinone fungicides may act by interfering with normal quinonoid metabolism.

Quinones may be regarded as α,β-unsaturated ketones, *i.e.* they contain an unsaturated bond between the α and β carbon atom:

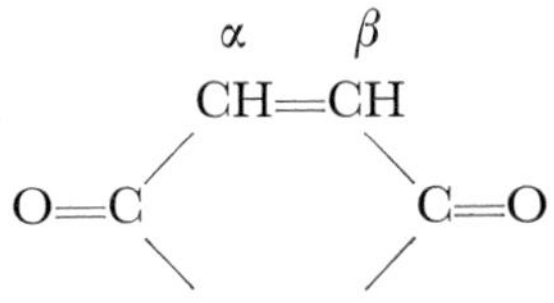

Owens[65] considered that this chemical characteristic enabled quinones to kill fungal spores by forming addition compounds with amino and sulph-hydryl groups. Wooley[90] showed that vitamins of the K group (K_1, K_1

67

oxide, K_2–K_7), reversed the toxicity of Dichlone. Vitamins of the K group, as illustrated by vitamin K_1

show a structural resemblance to Dichlone, and this structural resemblance is no doubt intimately associated with toxicity.

There are a number of other α,β-unsaturated ketones which have been shown to possess fungicidal activity. Brian[91] reported on the biological activity of griseofulvin, a complex α,β-unsaturated ketone. This compound, however, will be discussed more fully in the section dealing with antibiotic and systemic fungicides.

8-QUINOLINOLS

8-Quinolinols or oxines, in particular oxine, copper oxinate, and 8-quinolinol sulphate, with the following formulae

Oxine   Copper oxinate

8 – Quinolinol sulphate

possess exceptional fungicidal activity. Oxine has been known and used as a fungicide and bactericide for several years. Copper oxinate has been used extensively in the preservation of textiles to prevent rots and mildews. The fungicidal properties of 8-quinolinol sulphate were first reported by Fron[92] and it was suggested as a fungicide for the control of vascular wilts by Stoddard and Dimond[93]. A related compound, 8-hydroxyquinoline benzoate, was used by Dimond et al.[94] for the treatment of Dutch elm disease. Oxine is regarded as the classical example of fungicides which are thought to exert their toxicity by chelation with essential metals. This view, that oxine exerts its effect by chelation, was first proposed by Zentmyer[95]. There is, however, conflicting evidence on this point. Mason[96], showed that metallic oxinates were more toxic than oxine itself, and Anderson and Swaby[97] found that oxine in copper deficient media was considerably less toxic than in copper sufficient media. The investigations of Block[98] showed that the fungitoxicity of copper oxinate could be reversed by excess copper or oxine, whereas Manten et al.[99] found that trace elements such as Zn, Cu, and Mn, were unable to reverse the fungitoxicity of oxine to *Aspergillus niger* and considered that oxine did not exert its effect by chelation. This conflicting experimental evidence may to a certain extent be reconciled with Zentmyer's original proposition if the hypothesis is adopted that chelatory compounds possess toxic properties other than their ability to combine with essential metals. These relationships were further considered by Albert et al.[100] in 1953. They suggested that the toxic complex was a half chelate and that it exerted its toxicity at some internal site. In the presence of excess oxine the formation of the half chelate within the cell was inhibited. Reversal by excess metal was caused by inhibition of the full chelate in the circumambient solution. The conjecture was that the species most capable of penetrating the cell was the full chelate. Within the cell the most toxic species was the half chelate and this arose by dissociation or enzymic breakdown of the full chelate. There are certain observations to reconcile with this proposal. Greathouse et al.[30] found that unchelated oxine readily penetrates cells, and Block[101] found that lipoid solubility was associated with the toxic phenomena shown by chelated compounds. The latter worker showed that spores poisoned by oxine in a metal deficient medium could be revived by washing with water, but that dilute hydrochloric acid was necessary to revive spores poisoned by copper oxinate. It was considered that this showed the high lipoid solubility of copper oxinate, and low lipoid solubility of oxine. This lipoid solubility was correlated with site of attack. Zentmyer and Rich[102] showed that L-histidine or L-cysteine were able to reverse the toxicity of oxine and copper oxinate to mycelium of *Aspergillus niger* growing on solid media. This reversion of toxicity was due to the fact that these amino acids competed for the copper and liberated oxine. One probable explanation of the toxicity of copper oxinate and oxine which arises from these studies is that a chelated complex is able to penetrate the cell or cell site, but that toxicity is due to the liberation of copper which acts as a metal poison. Although chelation and lipoid solubility are generally regarded as essential considerations of oxine and oxinate toxicity, other proposals have been made regarding their mode of action. Sexton[103] considered that the phenolic properties of oxine were responsible for toxicity, and the studies of Gale and Folkes[104] on staphylococcal cells indicated that a portion of the oxine nucleus structurally resembled and competed with metabolic components.

PHENOLS

Phenols have shown exceptional qualities as bactericides, but as fungicides their use has been restricted. Phenols have been chiefly applied to textiles and woods as preservative fungicides, but have also been used as soil fungicides and seed treatments. Derivatives of cresol and *o*-phenyl phenol

have been mainly used as preservatives although *o*-phenyl phenol itself is used as a treatment for citrus fruit wrappings. The bisphenols are a particularly interesting group of phenolic fungicides. Marsh and Butler[105] found that bis(5-chloro-2-hydroxyphenyl)methane

was highly toxic to mould fungi and effectively prevented mildews developing on cloth. This compound was also recommended by Goldsworthy and Gertler[106] as a peach foliage fungicide. Horsfall and Rich[107] reported on the fungicidal potential of the corresponding thiobisphenols and found that bis(5-chloro-2-hydroxyphenyl) sulphide

was effective as a foliage fungicide against apple scab. Several workers have examined the relationship between structure and toxicity of phenolic compounds. Gruenhagen, Wolf, and Dunn[108] found that chlorination of simple phenolic nuclei increased fungitoxicity and confirmed the earlier observations of Bechhold and Ehrlich[109] on general biological activity of chlorinated phenols. Shirk[110] found that alkylation of the positions adjacent to the phenolic hydroxyl group reduced fungitoxicity. Earlier Walker and Link[111] examined the toxicity of phenolic compounds to *Colleototrichum circinans*, *Botrytis allii*, *Aspergillus niger*, and *Gibberella saubinettii* growing in Czapek's solution. With dihydric phenols, toxicity increased with increasing molecular weight when the hydroxyl groups were arranged in the ortho position to one another, but decreased when in the meta position. Structural modifications to the bisphenols affecting fungitoxicity have been considered by Cade and Gump[112]. Halogenation increased or decreased activity according to the position in the ring substituted. One interesting aspect of phenol poisoning is that fungi often produce abnormal spores and swollen hyphae. Wolf and Wolf[113] showed that when 3-methyl-6-isopropylphenol and 2-methyl-5-isopropylphenol were applied to *Aspergillus niger* swollen spores were produced. This suggests that phenolic compounds may exert their fungitoxicity by altering cell permeability. Certain phenols have also been shown to inactivate oxidases, and this represents an alternative way in which they may exercise toxicity.

QUATERNARY AMMONIUM COMPOUNDS

The development and introduction of these compounds as fungicides stems from the investigations of Domagk[114], who found that certain surfactants, *i.e.* compounds capable of altering the surface behaviour of a system, possessed strong bactericidal properties. The quaternary ammonium compounds which have been introduced as fungicides are alkyl pyridinium halides and alkyl trimethyl ammonium halides. These are cationic surfactants, *i.e.* they dissociate into a large cation radical carrying a positive charge, and a small anion radical carrying a negative charge. Rosella and Chabert[115] investigated quaternary ammonium compounds for their ability to inhibit the development of *Botrytis cinerea* inoculated into sterile grape must, and found that the greatest activity was shown by dimethyl benzyl alkyl ammonium chloride. Anson[116] reported that surfactants were able to split protein, and this suggests that the mode of surfactant toxicity is associated with disturbance of polypeptide chains. Quaternary ammonium compounds, however, have not been widely used as commercial fungicides and their practical application seems limited.

HALOGENATED AND NITRATED AROMATIC COMPOUNDS

For convenience, fungicides in this section have been arbitrarily divided into two groups; halogenated aromatics including those with one or more nitro groups, and non-halogenated but nitrated aromatics. The former group will be discussed first.

The chlorinated nitrobenzenes were introduced as fungicides in 1935 by Brown[117]. The initial experimentation of Brown[117] and Smieton[118] was concerned with the control of *Botrytis cinerea* on lettuce by trichlorodinitrobenzene. Subsequently Brown and Smieton[119] used pentachloronitrobenzene (PCNB)

for the same purpose, and also found that this compound controlled *Plasmodiophora brassicae* on cabbage and cauliflower. PCNB was developed and introduced by I.G. Farbenindustrie in the late 1930s and originally marketed as a fungicidal dust under a number of trade names for use as a seed treatment of wheat against bunt, and as a soil fungicide. Last[120] found that PCNB and 2,3,5,6-tetrachloronitrobenzene (TCNB) were effective in controlling *Botrytis* disease and *Rhizoctonia* attack of lettuce. 2,3,5,6-TCNB was also used by Foister and Wilson[121] to control *Fusarium* dry rot of potatoes. The fungicidal potential of two other isomers, 2,3,4,5-TCNB and 2,3,4,6-TCNB

was examined by Brook[122]. The three TCNB isomers were found to control *Botrytis* disease of lettuce to different extents, but also independently affected plant growth.

A chlorinated nitroaniline introduced in recent years, 2,6-dichloro-4-nitroaniline (Allisan) has been used to control *Botrytis* disease of lettuce, and Finger *et al*.[123] reported that 1-fluoro-3-bromo-4-,6-dinitrophenol was a potent fungicide, but in general halogenated nitrobenzenes and nitrophenols have not found a wide application in agriculture.

Non-halogenated nitro-aromatics invariably possess other chemical substituents than the nitro group. A well known example is 2,4-dinitrophenol

which was used over fifty years ago as a wood preservative. These compounds unfortunately have a high mammalian toxicity and their use is therefore restricted. Little is known about the mode of action of halogenated and nitrated aromatic compounds. Rich[81] considers that halogenated aromatic compounds owe their toxicity to the ability to release nascent halogen. The mechanism of toxicity of 2,4-dinitrophenol is thought to be associated with its ability to disrupt phosphorylative reactions. 2,4-Dinitrophenol has also been used as an enzyme inhibitor, and Shirk and Byrne[124] have shown that analogues of this compound are active inhibitors of fungal respiration.

There has been little speculation on the mode of action of chlorinated nitrobenzenes. These compounds exert their effect in the vapour phase and tend to inhibit mycelial growth and spore germination rather than kill fungal cells. Hewlett[125] established by paper chromatography the presence of ribose in extracts of *Botrytis cinerea* treated with 2,3,5,6-TCNB, and suggested that this was due to nuclear poisoning. Further evidence of nuclear disturbance by a chlorinated nitrobenzene was shown by Carey and McDonough[126], who found that spindle formation in onion was inhibited by paradichlorobenzene. Rich[81] considers that PCNB and TCNB

72

isomers act as competitive inhibitors for inositol, a growth factor in micro-organisms. The chlorinated nitrobenzenes have been shown to possess unusual attributes. Differences in their biological activity were reported by Brook[122]. As fungicides they are active in suppressing growth and sporulation in some fungi but appear innocuous against others. Their main point of interest lies in their ability to induce the formation of resistant strains in fungi originally susceptible to their action. There are a number of laboratory studies on this aspect of adaptation to chlorinated nitrobenzenes,

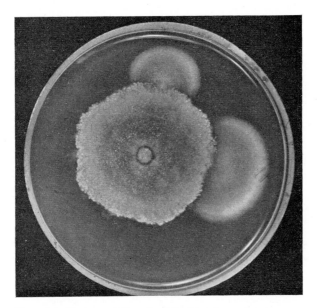

Figure 2.1. Variants of *Botrytis allii* arising in, and resistant to, the vapour of 2,3,4,5-TCNB.

particularly to the three TCNB isomers. Variants of *Botrytis cinerea* were first reported by Roy[127] and later by Reavill[128]. Similar studies have been described by Brook and Chesters[129], Parry[130], and Priest and Wood[131]. McKee[132] showed that *Fusarium caeruleum* mutated in the presence of 2,3,5,6-TCNB and became resistant to it. These studies have shown that when the parent strain is grown on nutrient media in Petri dishes in the presence of TCNB vapour, resistant strains generally arise spontaneously and appear as rapidly growing fan shaped mutants at the colony edge (see *Figure 2.1*). Priest and Wood[131] showed that in many instances the vegetative growth of the variants was comparatively unaffected by the TCNB vapours, in contrast to the slow growth and hyphal abnormalities shown by the non-resistant mycelium. These variants produced were also resistant in varying degrees to other chlorinated nitrobenzenes, and in general resistance to one compound conferred some measure of resistance to other similar compounds. The resistant strains retained their resistance after periods of growth, 6 to 18 months, in the absence of fungicide. These observations on resistance are in contrast to the majority of observations on resistance to fungicides which have been mentioned in previous sections.

In common with many other fungicides, PCNB and isomers of TCNB retard fungal growth but do not kill mycelia or spores, and are thus fungistatic rather than fungitoxic. In this article, however, no distinction has been drawn between fungistatic compounds and fungicides, as the former may be considered to exert sub-lethal toxicity.

In view of the poor laboratory performance of PCNB and isomers of TCNB against *Botrytis allii* and *Botrytis cinerea*, and the appearance of resistant strains, it is surprising that these compounds are effective under field conditions, though Way and Keyworth[133] noted that chlorinated nitrobenzenes sometimes fail to give satisfactory control of *B. cinerea* on lettuce. One possible explanation of their effectiveness under field conditions is that chlorinated nitrobenzenes may favourably modify the host, so that a balance is retained between ease of infection and naturally occurring resistant strains. In this respect, Brown and Reavill[134] showed that high concentrations of PCNB and TCNB radically altered the growth of certain plants.

The adaptation of fungi to fungicides is a serious potential threat to agricultural economies. The behaviour and response of certain fungi to chlorinated nitrobenzenes, though under somewhat artificial conditions, is a disturbing thought for the future.

SYSTEMIC FUNGICIDES AND ANTIBIOTICS

Systemic fungicides are those which are taken up by the plant and translocated within the plant system. They exert their effect in a number of ways. The compounds may themselves be fungicidal, or be capable of conversion into active fungicides. In this manner they may directly prevent attack of pathogenic fungi or restrict established pathogens. Alternatively they may chemically alter the host so that resistance to attack is increased, as was suggested for the chlorinated nitrobenzenes.

One criterion of a successful systemic fungicide, apart from the ability of the plant to take up the compound, either through root or shoot system, is that it should be non-toxic to the host.

The interest in, and development of systemic fungicides originates from the use of antibiotics for human diseases. A number of naturally-occurring antibiotics and synthetic substances, covering a wide range of chemical structure and complexity, have been examined for fungitoxicity. One group of compounds that has shown promising results are sulphonamides, and in particular *p*-aminobenzene sulphonamide:

$$H_2N - \langle \bigcirc \rangle - SO_2NH_2$$

Hassebrauk[135] showed that this compound reduced wheat rust when applied in solution to the roots of diseased plants. Another systemic fungicide which

has shown promise is 1-(*p*-sulphamyl-phenyl)-3,5-dimethyl-4-nitrosopyra-
zole:

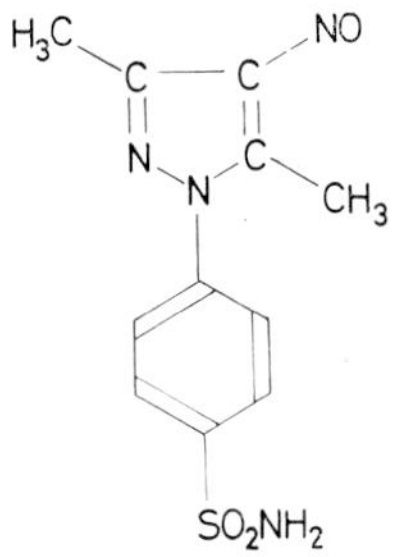

McNew and Sundholm[80] were the first to describe the fungicidal properties
of this compound which, though not markedly fungitoxic in *in vitro* spore
germination tests, is readily translocated within plants.

Several aspects of systemic fungicides, including translocation and detoxi-
fication within the plant, have been examined by Crowdy[136] and Crowdy
and Rudd-Jones[137]. In 1940 Woods[138] discovered that the antibacterial
action of *p*-aminobenzenesulphonamide could be reversed by *p*-aminobenzoic
acid:

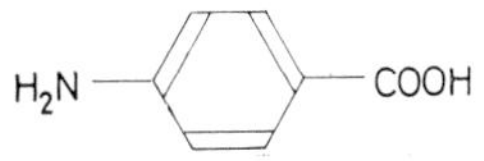

Almost immediately Dimond[139] showed that *p*-aminobenzoic acid reversed
the action of *p*-aminobenzenesulphonamide to *Trichophyton purpureum*.
Woods[138] considered that in bacteria, *p*-aminobenzenesulphonamide competed with *p*-aminobenzoic acid and if *p*-aminobenzoic acid was a metabolite,
i.e. an essential component of normal metabolism, then *p*-aminobenzene-
sulphonamide was an antimetabolite. Brian[140] later suggested that *p*-amino-
benzoic acid was similarly an essential metabolite for fungi.

The reputation of antibiotics was established in the field of medicine,
though in recent years they have been used as systemic fungicides. The
antibiotics are large complex molecules, but without exception they appear
to be translocated within plants. Certain antibiotics possess strong fungicidal
properties, but their instability and cost has limited their use as practical
fungicides. With regard to fungicidal activity, the most important antibiotics are those produced by actinomycetes. Whiffen[141] obtained Acti-dione

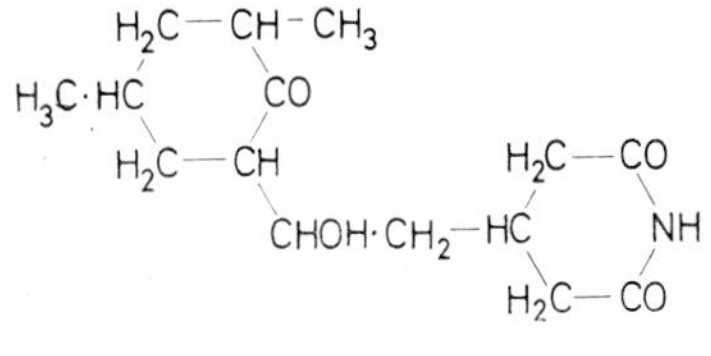

from cultures of *Streptomyces griseus*. Lemin and Magee[142], and Ford and
Leach[143] showed that this compound was readily taken up by tomato roots
and translocated to leaves. Wallen *et al.*[144] showed that it produced hyphal
monstrosities in *Alternaria*, and Berliner and Olive[145] found that it was a

75

fungal antimitotic. Other promising antibiotics have recently appeared and search is being made for compounds with specific fungicidal potential. Perhaps the most outstanding antibiotic with antifungal properties is griseofulvin:

Griseofulvin, which has been mentioned previously as an α,β-unsaturated ketone, was originally isolated by Oxford, Simonart, and Raistrick[146] from *Penicillium griseofulvum*. Brian, Curtis, and Hemming[147,148] studied the effect of griseofulvin on germination and mycelial growth of *Botrytis allii*, and showed that it caused severe morphological abnormalities. Under laboratory test conditions Brian[149] showed that when lettuce plants were grown in a solution containing griseofulvin, and subsequently inoculated with *B. cinerea* spores, the plants were markedly resistant to attack. Stubbs[150] showed a similar relationship of tomato plants to *Alternaria solani* attack. Brian[151] later found that under laboratory culture conditions *B. allii* became adapted to griseofulvin incorporated in liquid media, and also showed that griseofulvin progressively disappeared from the media when mycelial growth commenced. This loss was a consequence of fungal growth. These results are correlated with the findings of Abbott and Grove[152], who showed that loss of griseofulvin from media containing actively growing hyphae was due to enzymic breakdown at hyphal surfaces. In this context Brian[151] suggested that griseofulvin produced its effect by interfering with the synthesis of chitin in fungal cell walls.

The future of systemic and antibiotic fungicides is extremely promising. The introduction and use of these compounds and their ease of translocation within plants has also stimulated attempts to confer translocative properties on non-systemic fungicides.

FUTURE OF FUNGICIDES

In the last twenty years a vast number of inorganic and organic compounds of varying complexity have received attention as potential fungicides. This article has attempted to cover a representative sample from well formulated classes. Several miscellaneous compounds have been omitted, especially where little was known about their mode of action or where their application was restricted by economic or phytotoxic considerations.

Laboratory screening programmes have selected the brightest prospects from among thousands of compounds tested for specific or general fungicidal activity. These programmes, though desirable in many respects, have often produced fungicides with outstanding laboratory performance but which are disappointing in the field. Weathering of fungicides, degradation by micro-organisms, photolytic and hydrolytic breakdown, and physical properties associated with particle size are factors which exert their influence under field conditions. These interacting factors invariably reduce the field potential of a fungicide, though Byrde and Woodcock[89] noted an exception in the weakly toxic 1,4-diacetoxy-2,3-dichloronaphthalene, which is attacked by fungal esterases and converted to the more toxic hydroquinone, and subsequently to the highly toxic quinone. *In situ*, surface or systemic fungicides are essentially involved in a three component system; the host or material, the fungus, and the fungicide itself, all of which are affected by the micro-, and macro-environment. Though field testing is often precluded by reason of the expense entailed, a fuller understanding of host-pathogen-fungicide relationships would no doubt assist in the development and fruition of fungicide research.

One persistent but rational apprehension is the threat of fungi becoming resistant to fungicides. Though there has been little suggestion of this under field conditions there has been little search. A possible approach to the threat of development of resistant strains might involve the use of multiple fungicide treatments with fungicides possessing different modes of toxicity.

Derivatives of dithiocarbamic acid are at present the most efficient and economic fungicides in general use, and they may well retain their pre-eminence for many years to come. No doubt more potent protectant fungicides will be developed, but their introduction and economic application may have to await upon technical advances in bulk manufacture of organic chemicals. Nevertheless future prospects in the field of fungicides are encouraging and stimulating, and progress will continue on a broad front.

REFERENCES

1. Prévost, B. 'Mémoire sur la cause immédiate de la carie ou charbon des blés, et de plusieurs autres maladies des plantes, et sur les préservatifs de la carie'. *Phytopath. Class.* 1807, **6**, 1–94
2. Millardet, P. M. A. 'Traitement du mildiou par le melange de sulphate de cuivre et de chaux'. *J. Agric. prat., Paris* 1885, **2**, 707–710
3. Riehm, E. 'Prüfung eineger Mittel zur Bekämpfung des Steinbrandes'. *Mitt. Biol. Zentanst. Berl.* Abs. in *Zbl. Biochem. Biophys.* 1913, **40**, 424
4. Tisdale, W. H., and Williams, I. U.S. Patent 1,972,961. *Chem. Abstr.* 1934, **28**, 6948
5. Kittleson, A. R. 'A new class of organic fungicides'. *Science* 1952, **115**, 84–86
6. Bliss, C. I. 'The calculation of the dosage–mortality curve'. *Ann. appl. Biol.* 1935, **22**, 134–167
7. McCallan, S. E. A. and Wilcoxon, F. 'An analysis of factors causing variation in spore germination tests of fungicides'. *Contr. Boyce Thompson Inst.* 1939, **6**, 479–500
8. Litchfield, J. T. and Fertig, J. W. 'On a graphic solution of the dosage response curve'. *Johns Hopk. Hosp. Bull.* 1941, **69**, 276–286
9. Falck, R. 'Wachstumgesetze, Wachstumfaktoren und Temperaturwerte der holzerstörenden Mycelien'. 153–154 (Jena). Abs. in *Zbl. Bakt.* 1907, **20**, 348
10. Woolman, H. M. and Humphrey, H. B. 'Summary of literature on bunt, or stinking smut of wheat'. *Dep. Bull. U.S. Dep. Agric.* 1924, **1210**, 1–44
11. Horsfall, J. G. *Principles of Fungicidal Action* 1st edn: Chronica Botanica Co., Waltham, Mass, 1956,
12. Somers, E. 'The fungitoxicity of metal ions'. *Ann. appl. Biol.* 1961, **49**, 246–253

13. McCallan, S. E. A. and Wilcoxon, F. 'The action of fungus spores on Bordeaux mixture'. *Contr. Boyce Thompson Inst.* 1936, **8**, 151–165

14. Wain, R. L. and Wilkinson, E. H. 'Studies upon the copper fungicides. IX. Investigations with the exudate from fungus spores'. *Ann. appl. Biol.* 1946, **33**, 401–405

15. Martin, H., Wain, R. L. and Wilkinson, E. H. 'Studies upon the copper fungicides. V. A critical examination of the fungicidal value of copper compounds'. *Ann. appl. Biol.* 1942, **29**, 412–438

16. Tisdale, W. H. and Cannon, W. N. 'Ethyl mercury chloride as a seed grain disinfectant'. *Phytopathology* 1929, **19**, 80

17. Meyer, A. 'Recherches sur l'utilisation des matières colorantes organiques et de la 8-oxyquinoléine dans la lutte contre les maladies cryptogamiques de la vigne'. *Rev. Vitic., Paris* 1932, **77**, 117–120

18. Kahlenberg, L. and True, R. H. 'On the toxic action of dissolved salts and their electrolytic dissociation'. *Bot. Gaz.* 1896, **22**, 81–124

19. Goldsworthy, M. C. and Green, E. L. 'Availability of copper of Bordeaux mixture residues and its absorption by the conidia of *Sclerotinia fructicola*.' *J. agric. Res.* 1936, **52**, 517–533

20. Bodnar, J. and Terenyi, A. 'Biochemie der Brandkrankheiten der Getreide-arten. II. Mitteilung. Biophysikalische und biochemische Untersuchungen über die Kupferadsorption der Weizensteinbrandsporen'. *Hoppe-Seyl. Z.* 1930, **186**, 157–182

21. McCallan, S. E. A. 'Characteristic curve for the action of copper sulphate on the germination of spores of *Sclerotinia fructicola* and *Alternaria oleraceae*'. *Contr. Boyce Thompson Inst.* 1948, **15**, 77–90

22. Miller, L. P., McCallan, S. E. A. and Weed, R. M. 'Accumulation of 2-heptadecyl-2-imidazoline, silver and cerium by fungus spores in mixed and consecutive treatments'. *Contr. Boyce Thompson Inst.* 1953, **17**, 283–298

23. Janke, E., Beran, F. and Schmidt, G. 'Über die Einwirkung von Schwer-metallsalzen auf Pilze. II. Über die Einwirkung von Schwermetallsalzen auf Brandpilze'. *PflSchBer.* 1953, **10**, 5–6, 65–87

24. Macleod, R. A. and Snell, E. E. 'The relation of ion antagonism to the inorganic nutrition of lactic acid bacteria'. *J. Bact.* 1950, **59**, 783–792

25. Taylor, J. 'The effect of continual use of certain fungicides on *Physalospora obtusa*.' *Phytopathology* 1953, **43**, 268–270

26. Stakman, E. C., Stevenson, F. V. and Wilson, C. T. 'Adaption of mono-sporidial lines of *Ustilago zeae* to arsenic'. *Phytopathology* 1946, **36**, 411

27. Mader, E. O. and Schneider, C. L. 'Changes induced in *Sclerotinia fructicola* on copper sulphate media'. *Phytopathology* 1948, **38**, 17

28. Wilson, C. 'The development of increased tolerance to sodium arsenite by *Sclerotium rolfsii* and *Sclerotium delphinii*'. *Phytopathology* 1947, **37**, 24

29. Jurkowska, H. 'Investigations on the adaptability of *Aspergillus niger* to copper'. *Bull. int. Acad. Cracovie, Ser. B.* 4, 1952, 167–201

30. Greathouse, G. A., Block, S. S., Kovach, E. G., Barnes, D. E., Byron, C. W., Long, G. G., Gerber, D. and McClenny, J. 'Research on chemical compounds for the inhibition of growth of fungi'. Second Annual Report, 1953–1954, Contract DA-44-009-eng-1258, Project No. 8-91-02-001, Engng. Res. and Dev. Lab. Virginia

31. Arakatsu, Y., Yanagishima, N., Minagawa, T., Naika, N. and Ahida, J. 'Studies on the adaptation of yeast to copper. X. Effect on nutrients and inhibitors of the growth and pigmentation in the presence of copper'. *Mem. Coll. Sci. Engng. Kyoto, Ser B.* **21**, 1954, 97–106

32. Bartlett, G. W. 'Gain and loss of resistance in the fungus *Penicillium roqueforti*'. *Proc. roy. Soc.* 1959, **B, 150**, 120–130

33. Forsyth, W. *A treatise on the culture and management of fruit trees*. London
34. Robertson, J. 'On the mildew and some diseases incident to fruit trees'. *Trans. hort. Soc., London* **5**, 1824, 175–188
35. Mach, E. and Portele, K. *Weinlaube* 1884, **16**, 433
36. Marcille, N. 'Sur le mode d'action des soufres utilisés pour combattre l'oidium'. *Compt. Rend.* 1911, **152**, 780–783
37. Young, H. C. 'The toxic property of sulphur'. *Ann. mo. bot. Gdn.* 1922, **9**, 512–513
38. Doran, W. L. 'Laboratory studies of the toxicity of some sulphur fungicides'. *N.H. Agric. Exp. Sta. Tech. Bull.* 1922, **19**, 1–11
39. Roach, W. A. and Glynne, M. D. 'The toxicity of certain sulphur compounds to *Synchytrium endobioticum*, the fungus causing wart disease of potatoes'. *Ann. appl. Biol.* 1928, **15**, 168–190
40. Wilcoxon, F. and McCallan, S. E. A. 'The fungicidal action of sulphur. I. The alleged role of pentathionic acid'. *Phytopathology* 1930, **20**, 391–417
41. Pollacci, C. L. 'Della ragione per cui il solfo uccide l'oidio della vite, e sulla emissione d'idrogeno libero dalle piante'. *Gazz. chim. ital.* 1875, **5**, 451–460
42. Marsh, R. W. 'Investigations on the fungicidal action of sulphur. III. Studies on the toxicity of sulphuretted hydrogen and on the interaction of sulphur with fungi'. *J. Pomol.* 1929, **7**, 237–250
43. McCallan, S. E. A. and Wilcoxon, F. 'The fungicidal action of sulphur. II. The production of hydrogen sulphide by sulphured leaves and spores and its toxicity to spores'. *Contr. Boyce Thompson Inst.* 1931, **3**, 13–38
44. Sokoloff, D. V. 'The toxic action of hydrogen sulphide on certain moulds and tree pathogenic fungi'. *Mitt. forsttech. Akad. Kirov (U.S.S.R.)*, 1938, 70–77
45. Yarwood, C. E. 'Therapeutic treatments for rusts'. *Phytopathology* 1948, **38**, 542–551
46. Miller, L. P., McCallan, S. E. A. and Weed, R. M. 'Quantitative studies on the role of hydrogen sulphide formation in the toxic action of sulphur to fungus spores'. *Contr. Boyce Thompson Inst.* 1953, **17**, 151–171
47. Sempio, C. 'Sulla interpretazione del meccanismo intimo di azione dello zolfo come anticrittogamico'. *Mem. R. Accad. Ital.* 1932, **2**, 1–30
48. Eyre, J. V. and Salmon, E. S. 'The fungicidal properties of certain spray fluids'. *J. agric. Sci.* 1916, **7**, 473–507
49. Sempio, C. and Castori, M. 'Estrema sensibilita dei conididi di *Oidium moniloides* per tracce di vapori di zolfo'. *Riv. Biol.* 1949, **41**, 1–10
50. Yarwood, C. E. 'Effect of temperature on the fungicidal action of sulphur'. *Phytopathology* 1950, **40**, 173–180
51. Goldsworthy, M. C. 'The fungicidal action of liquid lime sulphur'. *Phytopathology* 1928, **18**, 355–360
52. Sciarini, L. J. and Nord, F. F. 'On the mechanisms of enzyme action. Part 22. Elementary sulphur as hydrogen acceptor in the dehydrogenations by living *Fusaria*'. *Arch. Biochem.* 1943, **3**, 261–267
53. Muskett, A. E. and Colhoun, J. 'Prevention of seedling blight in the flax crop'. *Nature, Lond.* 1940, **146**, 32
54. Goldsworthy, M. C., Green, E. L. and Smith, M. A. 'Fungicidal and phytocidal properties of some metal dialkyl dithiocarbamates'. *J. agric. Res.* 1943, **66**, 277–291
55. Dimond, A. E., Heuberger, J. W. and Horsfall, J. G. 'A water soluble protectant fungicide with tenacity'. *Phytopathology* 1943, **33**, 1095–1097
56. Klöpping, H. L. and van der Kerk, J. M. 'Investigations on organic fungicides. IV. Chemical constitution and fungistatic activity of dithiocarbamates, thiuram sulphides, and structurally related compounds'. *Rec. Trav. chim. Pays-Bas* 1951, **70**, 949–961

57. Davies, W. H. and Sexton, W. A. 'Chemical constitution and fungistatic action of organic sulphur compounds'. *Biochem. J.* 1946, **40**, 331–334

58. Dimond, A. E., Horsfall, J. G., Heiberger, J. W. and Stoddard, E. M. 'Role of the dosage-response curve in the evaluation of fungicides'. *Bull. Conn. agric. Exp. Sta.* 1941, **451**, 635–667

59. Parker-Rhodes, A. F. 'Studies on the mechanism of fungicidal action. V. Non-metallic and sodium dithiocarbamic acid derivatives'. *Ann. appl. Biol.* 1943, **30**, 170–179

60. van der Kerk, G. J. M. and Klöpping, H. L. 'Investigations on organic fungicides. VII. Further considerations regarding the relations between chemical structure and antifungal action of dithiocarbamate and bisdithio-carbamate derivatives'. *Rec. Trav. chim. Pays-Bas* 1952, **71**, 1179–1197

61. Sijpesteijn, A. K. and van der Kerk, J. G. M. 'Investigations on organic fungicides. VI. Histidine as an antagonist of tetramethylthiuram disulphide, (T.M.T.D.) and related compounds'. *Leeuwenhoek ned. Tijdscht.* 1952, **18**, 83–106

62. Sijpesteijn, A. K. and van der Kerk, J. G. M. 'Investigations on organic fungicides. VIII. The biochemical mode of action of bisdithiocarbamates. IX. The antagonistic action of certain imidazole derivatives and of α-keto acids on the fungitoxicity of dimethyldithiocarbamates, and diisothiocyanates'. *Biochem. biophys. Acta* 1954, **13**, 545–552

63. van Raalte, M. H. 'Het effect van metaal-ionen op de fungistatiche werking van natrium dimethyl dithiocarbamate'. *Meded. LandbHoogesch. Gent* 1952, **17**, 163–173

64. Goksøyr, J. 'The effect of some dithiocarbamyl compounds on the metabolism of fungi'. *Physiol. Plant.* 1955, **8**, 719–835

65. Owens, R. G. 'Studies on the nature of fungicidal action. I. Inhibition of sulphhydryl-, amino, iron and copper dependent enzymes *in vitro* by fungicides and related compounds'. *Contr. Boyce Thompson Inst.* 1953, **17**, 221–242

66. Barratt, R. W. and Horsfall, J. G. 'Fungicidal action of metallic alkyl bisdithiocarbamates'. *Bull. Conn. agric. Exp. Sta.* 1947, **508**, 1–51

67. Lopatecki, L. E. and Newton, W. 'The decomposition of dithiocarbamate fungicides, with special reference to the volatile products'. *Canad. J. Bot.* 1952, **30**, 131–138

68. Rich, S. and Horsfall, J. G. 'Gaseous toxicants from organic sulphur compounds'. *Amer. J. Bot.* 1950, **37**, 643–650

69. Klöpping, H. L. and van der Kerk, J. M. 'Investigations on organic fungicides. V. Chemical constitution and fungistatic activity of aliphatic bisdithio-carbamates and isothiocyanates'. *Rec. Trav. chim. Pays-Bas* 1951, **70**, 949–961

70 Ludwig, R. A. and Thorn, G. D. 'Studies on the breakdown of disodium ethylene bisdithiocarbamate'. *Plant Dis. Reptr.* 1953, **37**, 127–129

71. Ludwig, R. A., Thorn, G. D. and Unwin, C. H. 'Studies on the mechanism of fungicidal action of metallic ethylenebisdithiocarbamates'. *Canad. J. Bot.* 1955, **33**, 42–59

72. Horsfall, J. G. and Rich, S. 'Fungitoxicity of heterocyclic nitrogen compounds'. *Contr. Boyce Thompson Inst.* 1951, **16**, 313–347

73. Hochstein, E. P. and Cox, C. E. 'Studies on the fungicidal action of N-tri-chloromethylthio-4-cyclohexene-1,2-dicarboximide (Captan)'. *Amer. J. Bot.* 1956, **43**, 437–441

74. Rich, S. 'Reversal of captan fungitoxicity by L-histidine'. *Phytopathology* 1959, **49**, 321

75. Uhlenbroek, J. H. and Koopmans, M. J. 'Investigations on agricultural fungicides. II. Compounds structurally related to trichloromethylthiolsulph-onates'. *Rec. Trav. chim. Pays-Bas* 1957, **76**, 657–665

76. GATTANI, M. L. 'Adaption of fungi to fungicides and its significance in agriculture'. *Indian Phytopath.* 1951, **4**, 174–180

77. PARRY, K. E. and WOOD, R. K. S. 'The adaptation of fungi to fungicides; adaptation to captan; adaptation to thiram, ziram, ferbam, nabam, and zineb'. *Ann. appl. Biol.* 1959, **47**, 1–16

78. WELLMAN, R. H. and McCALLAN, S. E. A. 'Glyoxalidine derivatives of foliage fungicides. I. Laboratory studies'. *Contr. Boyce Thompson Inst.* 1946, **14**, 151–160

79. RADER, W. E., MONROE, C. M. and WHETSTONE, R. R. 'Tetrahydropyrimidine derivatives as potential foliage fungicides'. *Science* 1952, **115**, 124–125

80. McNEW, G. L. and SUNDHOLM, N. K. 'The fungicidal activity of substituted pyrazoles and related compounds'. *Phytopathology* 1949, **39**, 721–751

81. RICH, S. *Plant Pathology.* Vol. II. 1st edn: (Ed. Horsfall, J. G. and Dimond, A. E.) Academic Press, New York and London, 1960, 553–602

82. WEST, W. and WOLF, F. T. 'The mechanism of action of the fungicide 2-heptadecyl-2-imidazoline'. *J. gen. Microbiol.* 1955, **12**, 396–401

83. TER HORST, W. P. and FELIX, E. L. '2,3-Dichloro-1,4-naphthoquinone, a potent organic fungicide'. *Industr. Engng. Chem. (Industr.)* 1943, **35**, 1255–1259

84. CUNNINGHAM, H. S. and SHARVELLE, E. G. 'Organic seed protectants for lima beans'. *Phytopathology* 1940, **30**, 4

85. EDDINS, A. H. 'Downy mildew of cabbage'. *Florida agric. exp. Sta. Annu. Rep.* 1947, p. 111

86. OWENS, R. G. 'Studies on the nature of fungicidal action. II. Chemical constitution of benzenoid and quinonoid compounds in relation to fungitoxicity and inhibition of amino- and sulphhydryl-dependent enzymes'. *Contr. Boyce Thompson Inst.* 1957, **17**, 273–282

87. McNEW, G. L. and BURCHFIELD, H. P. 'Fungitoxicity and biological activity of quinones'. *Contr. Boyce Thompson Inst.* 1951, **16**, 357–374

88. TEHON, L. R. 'Fungistatic potencies of some fluorinated *p*-benzoquinones'. *Science* 1951, **114**, 663–664

89. BYRDE, R. J. and WOODCOCK, D. 'Fungicidal activity and chemical constitution. II. Compounds related to 2,3-dichloro-1,4-naphthaquinone'. *Ann. appl. Biol.* 1953, **40**, 675–687

90. WOOLEY, D. W. 'Observations on antimicrobial action of 2,3-dichloro-1,4-naphthaquinone, and its reversal by vitamin K'. *Proc. Soc. exp. Biol., N.Y.* 1945, **60**, 225

91. BRIAN, P. W. 'Studies on the biological activity of griseofulvin'. *Ann. Bot. N.S.* 1949, **13**, 60–77

92. FRON, G. 'La maladie de l'Orme'. *C. R. Acad. Agric. Fr.* 1936, **22**, 1081–1089

93. STODDARD, E. M. and DIMOND, A. E. 'The chemotherapeutic control of *Fusarium* wilt of carnations'. *Phytopathology* 1951, **41**, 337–340

94. DIMOND, A. E., PLUMB, G. H., STODDARD, E. M. and HORSFALL, J. G. 'An evaluation of chemotherapy and vector control by insecticides forcom bating Dutch elm disease'. *Bull. Conn. agric. Exp. Sta.* 1949, **531**, 1–69

95. ZENTMYER, G. A. 'Mechanism of action of 8-hydroxyquinoline'. *Phytopathology* 1943, **33**, 1121

96. MASON, C. L. 'A study of the fungicidal action of 8-quinolinol and some of its derivatives'. *Phytopathology* 1948, **38**, 740–751

97. ANDERSON, B. I. and SWABY, R. J. 'Factors influencing the fungistatic action of 8-hydroxyquinoline (oxine) and related compounds'. *Aust. J. sci. Res.* 1951, **B4**, 275–282

98. BLOCK, S. S. 'Fungitoxicity of the 8-quinolinols'. *J. agric. food. Chem.* 1955, **3**, 229–234

99. MANTEN, A. H., KLÖPPING, H. L. and VAN DER KERK, J. M. 'Investigations on organic fungicides. III. The influence of essential trace metals upon the

fungitoxicity of tetramethylthiuramdisulphide and 8-hydroxyquinoline'. *Leeuwenhoek ned. Tijdschr.* 1951, **17**, 58–68

100. ALBERT, A., GIBSON, M. I. and RUBBO, S. D. 'The influence of chemical constitution on antibacterial activity. Part VI. The bactericidal action of 8-hydroxyquinoline (oxine)'. *Brit. J. exp. Path.* 1953, **34**, 119–130

101. BLOCK, S. S. 'Examination of the activity of 8-quinolinol to fungi'. *Appl. Microbiol.* 1956, **4**, 183–186

102. ZENTMYER, G. A. and RICH, S. 'Reversal of fungitoxicity of 8-quinolinol and copper 8-quinolinate by other chelators'. *Phytopathology* 1956, **46**, 33

103. SEXTON, W. A. *Chemical Constitution and Biological Activity* 2nd edn: Spon, London

104. GALE, E. F. and FOLKES, J. P. 'The assimilation of amino acids by bacteria. 24. Inhibitors of incorporation of glycine in disrupted staphylococcal cells'. *Biochem. J.* 1957, **67**, 507–517

105. MARSH, P. B. and BUTLER, M. L. 'Fungicidal activity of bisphenols as mildew preventives on cotton fabrics'. *Industr. Engng. Chem.* 1946, **38**, 701–705

106. GOLDSWORTHY, M. C. and GERTLER, S. I. 'Fungicidal and phytotoxic properties of 506 synthetic organic compounds'. *Plant Dis. Reptr (Suppl.)* 1949, **182**, 89–109

107. HORSFALL, J. G. and RICH, S. 'Protective action of bis(2-hydroxy-5-chlorophenyl) sulphide'. *Phytopathology* 1950, **40**, 13

108. GRUENHAGEN, R. H., WOLF, P. A. and DUNN, E. E. 'Phenolic fungicides in agriculture and industry'. *Contr. Boyce Thompson Inst.* 1951, **16**, 349–356

109. BECHHOLD, H. and EHRLICH, P. 'Beziehungen zwischen chemischer Konstitution und Desinfektionswirkung. Ein Beitrag zum Studium der "innern Antisepsis" '. *Hoppe-Seyl. Z.* 1906, **47**, 173–179

110. SHIRK, H. G. 'Steric hindrance relationship of some phenols to fungistatic potency'. *Arch. Biochem. Biophys.* 1954, **51**, 258–265

111. WALKER, J. C. and LINK, K. P. 'Toxicity of phenolic compounds to certain onion bulb parasites'. *Bot. Gaz.* 1935, **XCIX**, 468–484

112. CADE, A. R. and GUMP, W. S. *Antiseptics, Disinfectants, Fungicides, and Chemical and Physical Sterilization.* 1st edn: Lea and Febiger, Philadelphia

113. WOLF, F. T. and WOLF, F. A. 'Morphological effects of thymol and related compounds upon the germination of fungus spores'. *Bull. Torrey bot. Cl.* 1950, **77**, 77–82

114. DOMAGK, G. 'Eine neue Klasse von Desinfektionsmitteln'. *Dtsch. med. Wschr.* 1935, **61**, 829–832

115. ROSELLA, E. and CHABERT, E. 'Efficacité comparée de différents sels d'ammonium quaternaire contre certains champignons phytopathogènes en viticulture en particulier'. *C. R. Acad. Agric. Fr.* 1955, **41**, 741–745

116. ANSON, M. L. 'The denaturation of proteins by synthetic detergents and bile salts'. *J. gen. Physiol.* 1939, **23**, 239–246

117. BROWN, W. 'On the *Botrytis* disease of lettuce with special reference to its control'. *J. Pomol.* 1935, **13**, 247–259

118. SMIETON, M. J. 'On the use of chlorinated nitrobenzenes for the control of club root disease of Brassicae'. *J. Pomol.* 1939, **17**, 195–217

119. BROWN, W. and SMIETON, M. J. '*Botrytis* disease of lettuce, its relation to damping off and mildew, and its control by pentachloronitrobenzene dust'. *Ann. appl. Biol.* 1940, **27**, 489

120. LAST, F. T. 'The use of tetra- and penta-chloronitrobenzenes in the control of *Botrytis* disease and *Rhizoctonia* attack of lettuce'. *Ann. appl. Biol.* 1952, **39**, 557–568

121. FOISTER, C. E. and WILSON, A. R. 'Dry rot of potatoes'. *J. Minist. Agric.* 1951, **57**, 229

3

ARTHROPODS AS PREDA[...]

JOHN S. EDWARDS

INTRODUCTION

IT is enunciated among the principles of insect phy[...] material of almost any kind in nature may serve as f[...] this live insects are no exception. Indeed we find [...] as a whole very many animals that live by means of p[...] of insects, other arthropods and, less frequently, grou[...] vertebrates.

Predation can mean 'simply the killing and eating[...] definitions, like good resolutions, are made to be [...] the purpose of this essay are animals that obtain thei[...] by capturing live animals one at a time, and which [...] feeds to complete the life-cycle. They are not the o[...] carnivore. Ectoparasites of vertebrates which do n[...] so only indirectly as vectors of pathogens or throu[...] grade with predators in some arthropod groups, n[...] The hymenopteran parasitoids, which develop at th[...] they eventually kill, are a special sort of predator an[...] but they will not receive the attention they deserv[...] characteristics and what is known of the mechan[...] recently been treated with great clarity by Salt[3,4]. [...] feeders which may also be predators within Milne's[...] we shall have in mind the sort of predation epitomiz[...] fly.

Predators are widespread through arthropod gr[...] phora to the Diptera. They predominate in the Arac[...] few in the Crustacea. There is a wide range of [...] general arthropods tend to prey on arthropods: it i[...] and many of the predatory adaptations, both mo[...] logical, are seemingly aimed at 'chinks' in the arthr[...] features are the presence of raptorial limbs, often[...] retain a firm hold on polished cuticle in some forms,[...] in others, piercing mouth-parts, paralysing secret[...] Many arthropod predators are not entirely carn[...] life-cycle or even within a developmental stage; pr[...] source of protein, while alternative foods such as ne[...] sap can provide a subsistence diet.

It is perhaps the dramatic element in the preda[...] has attracted the attention of a great many natur[...] literature has accumulated over the years treati[...] history, behaviour, and host range, as the well [...]

85

122. BROOK, M. 'Differences in the biological activity of 2,3,5,6-tetrachloronitro-benzene and its isomers'. *Nature, Lond.* 1952, **170**, 1022
123. FINGER, G. C., REED, F. H. and TEHON, L. R. 'Aromatic fluorine compounds as fungicides'. *Illinois State Geol. Survey Circ.* 1955, **199**, 1–13
124. SHIRK, H. G. and BYRNE, H. E. 'Effect of some nitrophenols on the respiration of *Myrothecium verrucaria* spores'. *J. biol. Chem.* 1951, **191**, 783–786
125. HEWLETT, M. A. 'Studies on the fungicidal activity of certain chlorinated nitrobenzene compounds'. Ph.D. Thesis, University of London, 1955
126. CAREY, M. A. and McDONOUGH, E. S. 'On the production of polyploidy in *Allium* with paradichlorobenzene'. *J. Hered.* 1943, **34**, 238–240
127. ROY, R. Y. 'A comparison of the mode of action of certain new chloronitro-benzene preparations with that of standard fungicides'. Ph.D. Thesis, University of London, 1947
128. REAVILL, M. J. 'The effect of certain chloronitrobenzenes on plant growth'. Ph.D. Thesis, University of London, 1950
129. BROOK, M. and CHESTERS, C. G. C. 'The growth of *Botrytis cinerea* Pers., *Fusarium caeruleum* (Lib.) Sacc. and *Phoma foveata* Foisters in the presence of tetrachloronitrobenzene isomers'. *Ann. appl. Biol.* 1957, **45**, 498–505
130. PARRY, K. 'A study of some factors affecting the susceptibility of fungi to fungicides'. Ph.D. Thesis, University of London, 1957
131. PRIEST, D. and WOOD, R. K. S. 'Strains of *Botrytis allii* resistant to chlorinated nitrobenzenes'. *Ann. appl. Biol.* 1961, **49**, 445–460
132. McKEE, R. K. 'Mutations appearing in *Fusarium caeruleum* cultures treated with tetrachloronitrobenzene'. *Nature, Lond.* 1951, **167**, 611
133. WAY, J. M. and KEYWORTH, W. G. 'Experiments on the control of *Botrytis* disease of lettuce'. *Ann. appl. Biol.* 1959, **47**, 685–697
134. BROWN, W. and REAVILL, M. J. 'Effect of tetrachloronitrobenzene on the sprouting and cropping of potato tubers'. *Ann. appl. Biol.* 1954, **41**, 435
135. HASSEBRAUK, K. 'Weitere Untersuchungen über Getreiderostbekampfung mit chemischen Mitteln'. *Phytopath. Z.* 1938, **11**, 14–16
136. CROWDY, S. H. 'The uptake and translocation of griseofulvin, streptomycin and chloramphenicol in plants'. *Ann. appl. Biol.* 1957, **45**, 208–215
137. CROWDY, S. H. and RUDD-JONES, D. J. 'The translocation of sulphonamides in higher plants. III. Acetylation and deacetylation of sulphanilamide in broad bean and wheat'. *J. exp. Bot.* 1958, **9**, 220–228
138. WOODS, D. D. 'The relation of *p*-amino benzoic acid to the mechanism of the action of sulphanilamide'. *Brit. J. exp. Path.* 1940, **21**, 74–90
139. DIMOND, N. S. '*p*-Amino benzoic acid prevents the growth-inhibitory action of sulphanilamide'. *Science* 1941, **94**, 420–421
140. BRIAN, P. W. 'Effect of *p*-amino-benzoic acid on the toxicity of *p*-amino-benzene-sulphonamide to higher plants and fungi'. *Nature, Lond.* 1944, **153**, 83–84
141. WHIFFEN, A. J. 'The production, assay and antibiotic activity of actidione, an antibiotic from *Streptomyces griseus*'. *J. Bact.* 1948, **56**, 283–291
142. LEMIN, A. J. and MAGEE, W. E. 'Degradation of cyclohexamide derivatives in plants'. *Plant Dis. Reptr* 1957, **41**, 447–448
143. FORD, J. H. and LEACH, B. E. 'Actidione, an antibiotic from *Streptomyces griseus*'. *J. Amer. chem. Soc.* 1948, **70**, 1223–1225
144. WALLEN, V. R., SUTTON, M. D. and SKOLKO, A. J. 'The effect of actidione on the growth of certain pathogenic fungi and on the germination of pea seed'. *Phytopathology* 1950, **40**, 156–160
145. BERLINER, M. D. and OLIVE, L. S. 'Meiosis in *Gymnosporangium* and the cyto-logical effects of certain antibiotic substances'. *Science* 1953, **117**, 652–654
146. OXFORD, A. E., RAISTRICK, H. and SIMONART, P. 'Studies in the biochemistry

83

of micro-organisms. 60. Griseofulvin, *griseofulvum* Dierckx'. *Biochem. J.* 1939, **33**

147. Brian, P. W., Curtis, P. J. and Hemmin normal development of fungal hyphae prod Biological assay, production and isolatio *mycol. Soc.* 1941, **20,** 173–187

148. Brian, P. W., Curtis, P. J. and Hemmin normal development of fungal hyphae prod Identity of "curling factor" with griseoful 30–33

149. Brian, P. W. 'Antibiotics as systemic fu *Biol.* 1952, **39,** 434–438

150. Stubbs, J. 'The evaluation of systemic f on tomato'. *Ann. appl. Biol.* 1952, **39,** 43!

151. Brian, P. W. 'Griseofulvin'. *Trans. Bri*

152. Abbott, M. T. J. and Grove, J. F. ' compounds by fungi. Part II. Griseoful

Wheeler[6], Brues[7], Bristowe[8], Clausen[9] and many others testify. In a diverting essay, Roeder[10] has recently reduced the drama to neurophysiological terms, as a contest of 'startle' and 'strike' mechanisms.

An important development of natural history studies has been the recognition of the potential value of predators and parasitoids in dealing with species that have taken advantage of the fruitful environment offered by man's crops and have thus become pests. The successes and failures of the biological control of insect pests are too widely known to need detailed mention here. It is only necessary to observe that planned introduction of parasitoids and, to a less extent, predators is now a widely accepted part of pest control measures, and with it the ecological study of predator–prey relationships has intensified. Indeed for some, 'the ultimate aim of studies on predation (and other population processes) is to provide a basis for the understanding of the dynamics of insect populations'[11] (parentheses mine). The study of predation as a population process which Hollings[11] has sought to systematize in his recent review is certainly an important aspect of animal ecology; it is, however, a study that depends on a background of knowledge of the behaviour and physiology of predators, and this will be my point of view in this review. But first it will be useful to survey briefly the distribution of predators in the Arthropoda, and to present a few examples of ecological studies of predation by arthropods, which will perhaps serve to illustrate the variety of predator–prey relationships.

DISTRIBUTION OF PREDATORS AMONG THE ARTHROPODA

Onychophora

Predation begins with the lowliest of the arthropods. *Peripatus* and the related genera are carnivorous, preying on invertebrates that share their habitat of decaying wood. An interesting feature of the group is their slime-throwing behaviour that has aroused some disagreement as to its precise function. The ejaculation of jets of a quickly hardening mucoprotein substance has been variously interpreted as a mechanism of defence or of offence but, as Alexander[12] suggests, it probably serves both functions. This mode of prey capture is not unique among the arthropods; it is also used in a rather more elaborate fashion by spiders such as *Scytodes*, which fixes its prey to the ground with zig-zag threads, and the Theridiidae which fling silk at their prey[8].

Crustacea

Crustaceans seem to have exploited the predatory habit least among the arthropods: their speciality is filter feeding. There are, nevertheless, a number of predators, particularly among the larger Crustacea, notably among the Brachyura, and the Decapoda Natantia. No crustacean predator is known to produce a venom. Their predatory specializations are mainly raptorial limbs, although there are also some intriguing mechanisms for killing prey, notably that of the pistol shrimps (*Alpheus* spp.) in which a trigger mechanism, using the dactyl of a greatly enlarged chela, stuns prey when released, and some Stomatopoda, squillids that have a razor-sharp dactyl on the second thoracic limb with which to slice their prey. A brief survey of the behaviour of predatory Crustacea is given by Marshall and Orr[13], and Schöne[14].

Myriapoda

The myriapods provide an interesting comparison of repugnatory and predatory mechanisms. The millipedes, which are vegetarians, possess variously developed segmental dermal glands that secrete quinones and are used as a defensive mechanism. There are, nevertheless, certain reduviid Heteroptera that are capable of penetrating the defence, and which are said to prey specifically on millipedes.

The carnivorous chilopods, in contrast to the millipedes, have poison glands in the forceps-like maxillipeds, which produce a paralysing secretion.

Arachnida

In this predominantly predatory group the Xiphosura, the Acarina, the Pycnogonida, Tardigrada, and probably the Opiliona cannot be reckoned as exclusively predatory. Only three of the arachnid classes, spiders, scorpions, and pseudo-scorpions are certainly known to use venoms to subdue their prey, although predatory mites may do so as well. The scorpions, solfugids, uropygids, and amblypygids, all of which have powerful grasping pedipalps, tear and kneed their prey after capture and introduce salivary secretions to effect external digestion, but they do not subdue their prey with venom. It need hardly be noted that some families of spiders carry web building behaviour to a high level of complexity, while others actively hunt.

Insecta

Sweetman's[15] great compilation of entomophagous insects lists 209 families in 15 orders with predatory members, and records biological data on a great many species of proved or potential value in biological control. Opportunism seems to be the guiding principle in matters of diet, for predators are found in such unlikely groups as the Lepidoptera in which larvae from no less than 13 families are predatory in habit, and even among drosophilids. Predation is not characteristic of the Orthoptera, the Thysanura or the Ephemeroptera, but certain species in these groups are exclusively predatory. The habit is dominant in the Neuroptera and Odonata; a quarter of the hymenopteran families are predatory; half those of the Heteroptera are characteristically so. The Coleoptera has 12 characteristically predatory families, while about a fifth of all families contain predatory members. The Diptera again has predators in at least a fifth of the families, in about 10 of which the adult or the larva is essentially predatory (data mainly calculated from Clausen[9]).

These bare figures may indicate a wide distribution and a wide variety of arthropod predation, but give no indication of its abundance nor of the variety and quantity of the prey, and the extent to which it affects the numbers of other arthropods. These are questions for the ecologist, questions which, despite their importance in agriculture and forestry, as well as in our understanding of natural communities, are only beginning to get quantitative answers.

THE ECOLOGY OF PREDATION

It has been said that there are as many varieties of economic theory as there are economists. The same might well be said of ecology when questions of population dynamics are being considered, although the causes seem to be opposite: superfluity of reliable data on one hand, and paucity on the other. The desire for generalization, for 'a set of principles which will explain the regulation of the numbers of all species'[16] has perhaps diverted attention from particulars, and has allowed too ready extrapolation from laboratory populations where the data are complete but the relevance to field conditions uncertain, and from field observations where the system is natural but the data are incomplete. While there is no shortage of views on how predation, and many other factors, may influence the numbers of animals in natural populations, we have as yet very few of the sort of data that will allow general statements about the place of predators in population dynamics.

A line of thought stemming from the mathematical models of Lotka, Volterra, and Nicholson sees predation as one of the so-called 'density-dependent' factors which tend to govern the numbers of animals within the limits allowed by climate and other factors which act independently of the density of animals. A different approach to the problem is expressed by Andrewartha and Birch[17] who see little purpose served by such concepts as density-dependent factors, and who consider that it is idle to attempt to generalize about the effects of particular factors on populations. While we have so few detailed and extended studies of whole populations and the agents of mortality acting on them, these two approaches might be looked on, at least from the distance, as complementary. It is clear that in some simple 'unbuffered' situations of the type found in the arthropod faunas of agricultural crops, where the number of species is few, the numbers of predators and their prey should be related, and this has been demonstrated in the field. Even the simplest of field situations is nevertheless a complex system, in which the precise relationships between a predator and its prey are difficult to determine. Attempts to resolve some of these complexities have led to experimental laboratory studies, but these necessarily suffer from simplifications which usually prevent the system from being self-perpetuating, and therefore from having much wider reference than the experimental conditions chosen. The use of increasingly elaborate 'experimental universes' may prolong the viability of the predator and prey populations, as Huffaker[18] has recently shown, but every new factor makes analysis more complex and the conclusions less general. It may seem obscurantist to suggest that a laboratory system of sufficient heterogeneity to ensure the perpetuation of predator and prey will have taken us back to Nature again.

Practical studies on arthropod predator–prey relationships have been stimulated by problems of biological control of pests, especially since it became evident in the early years of mass commercial use of new insecticides and fungicides that severe outbreaks of pests could arise when predators and parasites were destroyed while at the same time their prey were incompletely eradicated[19]. There are now sufficient reports to show that this is not an exceptional effect, but one that must be taken into account in planning control programmes. That the arthropod fauna of perennial crops such as orchards may be seriously altered as a result of destruction of predators, has been demonstrated very clearly in Nova Scotian orchards[20], and in studies at East Malling[21].

Phytophagous and predatory mites have risen to importance with the introduction of newer chemical control measures, and some attention has been paid to the powers and limitations of mite control by predators. Collyer and Kirby[21] found that the red spider mite, a pest of orchard trees, was controlled only when the ratio of predatory typhlodromid mites to prey was low. The predatory typhlodromids should exceed the red spider mite *Metatetranychus ulmi* until a considerable proportion of the winter eggs of *Metatetranychus* have hatched. If typhlodromids are reduced in number by the application of winter washes to the trees, they are unable to exert control. Collyer[22] showed that under insectary conditions and in the absence of other prey, *Typhlodromus tileae* was able to prevent the increase of *Metatetranychus* when 5, 25, or 50 prey were placed on seedlings of *Prunus* together with five female *Typhlodromus*. For the 3 months of the experiment, plants with predators on them had red spider mite populations of less than 50 per plant, while predator-free controls bore over 3,000 mites in up to 11 weeks. An example involving mites in which the experiments were conducted under greenhouse conditions and in the field is provided by Huffaker and Kennett's[23] work on predation by *Typhlodromus* spp. of the cyclamen mite *Tarsonemus pallidus* Banks, a pest of strawberry plants in California, for which there was no effective means of chemical control. A second mite, *Tetranychus telarius* and an aphid, *Capitophorus* sp., also feed on the plant and provide alternative prey for *Typhlodromus*. Predators of these species may also prey on *Tarsonemus* and *Typhlodromus cucumeris* which is in turn the main predator of *Tarsonemus* so that the predator–prey relationship of the strawberry mite and *Typhlodromus* can itself be modified by predators associated principally with other prey. Chemical control early in the season is effective against *Tetranychus* and aphids so that *Tarsonemus* presented the main problem in control.

The success of *Typhlodromus* in keeping *Tarsonemus* to harmless levels was due, in the view of Huffaker and Kennett, not so much to comparable reproductive capacities, both species laying about three eggs a day, as to 'well adapted capacities for searching, synchrony of seasonal activity and behaviour patterns'. At times of low prey density the predator is able to subsist on honeydew, white fly and plant exudates, while the prey persists in small numbers deep in the hairy crown of the plant. A 5-year study showed that an inherent oscillation in the density of *Tarsonemus* when free from predation, was damped by predation, and a directly related reciprocal oscillation in the numbers of predator and prey persisted at a prey density 20 times lower than in the absence of predators, when *Tarsonemus* was no longer economically important as a pest of the crop.

Turning now to insect predators, two examples will suffice to demonstrate that great differences in patterns of predation may arise from differences in the biology of the species concerned. Banks[24] examined the occurrence of coccinellids on a bean crop. They came from three sources: firstly, over-wintered adults which dispersed in spring from their hibernation sites, arriving on the beans after the bean aphid *Aphis fabae* which forms their principal prey; secondly, adults which had developed in spring on neigh-bouring nettles and which left the plants when they had depleted the nettle aphid *Microlophium*; and thirdly, adults which developed from eggs laid on bean by the spring arrivals. Although the latter had grown at the expense of *A. fabae*, they did not prevent the aphid from reaching damaging densities. The lag in the increase of numbers of predators, with their longer develop-ment time and lower fecundity, is known to all concerned with aphids on field crops, who find that predators such as aphidophagous syrphid larvae, coccinellids, and neuropterans usually reach effective levels of density after their aphid prey have reached damaging densities, and because of this their efficacy as a means of controlling pests is doubted. The importance of an adequate prey density early in the growing season has been noted earlier in Collyer and Kirby's work with orchard mites. Huffaker and Kennett even suggest that this may be achieved in strawberry plots by introductions of prey to facilitate the build-up of the predator. A large-scale attempt to overcome the lag in aphid–coccinellid ratios made in California with the ladybird *Hippodamia covergens* by collecting the ladybirds in vast numbers from their montane hibernation sites and liberating them in fields in spring failed because, it was eventually realized, a period of flight must precede the onset of predatory behaviour, and this disseminated them from the fields in which they were placed. It may be that a preliminary flight in large cages as Williams[25] suggests, or a simple wind tunnel that would simulate their 100-mile spring flight, would allow the ladybirds to settle and feed immediately. This is a good example of the need for knowledge of the be-haviour and physiology of an animal before its ecology may be fully under-stood.

The examples mentioned so far relate to agricultural situations in which monoculture provides conditions for relatively simple 'unbuffered' relation-ships, whose instability amplifies the effects that in more complex communities may defy analysis. A step in this direction has been taken by Richards and Waloff[26] in their 12-year study of a natural population of the beetle *Phytodecta olivacea* which lives and feeds on broom. In the years 1954–58 sampling techniques were used to estimate numbers of all stages of the beetle with the object of providing life-tables or 'budgets', as Richards and Waloff prefer to call them, and in doing so they found that predation was a very important agent of mortality during immature stages. The calculated total mortality of eggs and larvae lay, in different years, between 72 per cent and 99 per cent of all eggs laid: in 1957 and 1958 the figures were 78 per cent and 92 per cent of which 55 per cent and 81 per cent respectively could be ascribed to predation, the greatest single cause of mortality. The predators concerned were mainly Heteroptera belonging to the families Miridae, Anthocoridae, and Nabidae, while coccinellids, earwigs, harvestmen, spiders and mites were also present. These all differ in their habitat specificity, none were obligate predators of *Phytodecta* and alternative prey such as psyllids and aphids were also available on the broom plants. The course of events summarized in *Figure 3.1* based on field counts and estimates, gives a clear picture of the pattern of predation.

An interesting feature of the relationship is that the intensity of predation by mirids, the most abundant of *Phytodecta*'s enemies, is highest in early summer, and drops after mid-June, by which time the mirids have reached the adult stage. A disparity in numbers between immature and mature mirids may be due to parasitism, the over-all result being that the intensity of predation drops, and a greater number of *Phytodecta* reach maturity later in the summer.

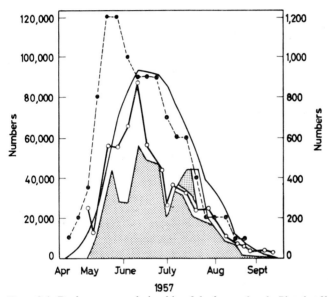

Figure 3.1. Predator–prey relationship of the broom beetle *Phytodecta*[26] Left-hand scale: total numbers other than *Phytodecta* females, to which the right-hand scale applies. Shaded area: actual numbers of eggs and larvae of *Phytodecta*. Area under broken line: estimated numbers of eggs and larvae in the absence of mortality. ◯, numbers of insect predators (instars I and II of Heteroptera omitted); ●, numbers of *Phytodecta* females on broom.

Quantitative estimates of the number of *Phytodecta* accounted for by predation were obtained independently by Dempster[27], using the serological 'precipitin' technique. The method, which involves testing extracts of predator against antisera produced by injecting rabbits with extracts of suspected prey, has been used in several studies of this type; Fox and McLellan[28], for example, used it to determine the food of certain pasture dwelling carabids, and despite certain limitations it can provide information not otherwise available. Dempster's estimates of the extent of predation of *Phytodecta* were in substantial agreement with those of Richards and Waloff made on circumstantial evidence, and Dempster was also able to demonstrate that carabid beetles were responsible, at least in part, for the known mortality of *Phytodecta* in the pupal stage, in the soil.

On two occasions in the course of the *Phytodecta* study, when a large decrease in the quantity of broom available to *Phytodecta* caused a concentration of predator and prey, the mortality of immature stages caused by predation increased. A density-dependent relationship between predator and prey arose here, not from an increase in prey numbers, which is the situation normally envisaged, but from an increase in density on the depleted host plant, a situation which the authors comment may be not uncommon in nature.

Studies of the scope of Richards and Waloff's provide a picture of the rôle of predators in a particular community. They require the evolution of appropriate sampling techniques, and must continue for a number of years in order to demonstrate the amplitude of variation in the various agents of mortality. It is only when we have many more of such studies that the degree to which we may usefully generalize about elements such as predation in population dynamics will become clear; and to appreciate the nature of these population processes we must know not only something of longevity, mortality, and fecundity, the life-tables of the species, but much of their behaviour and physiology as well. Let us look now at some aspects of the means by which predators locate, apprehend, and restrain their prey.

BEHAVIOUR AND PREDATION

We shall be concerned here mainly with the methods by which arthropod predators find their prey, because this aspect of their behaviour has been the most studied. There are, of course, other highly important facets such as the hunger mechanism whereby a previously satiated animal becomes once more alert to the presence of prey. The extent and the basis of prey specificity also present problems of great interest that have been little studied. Perhaps the most fascinating aspect of the behaviour of predators comes from the conflict of patterns of predation and mating. The often bizarre solutions to this situation, particularly among the spiders, have been a fertile field for natural historians, but we have very few detailed analyses as yet.

Turning now to modes of predation, we may distinguish two broad groups of predators: those that go forth and hunt their prey and those that sit and wait. In the first group all grades of refinement may be found from the seemingly random blundering into prey of predatory mites and some insect larvae, to the delicately controlled hunting flights of the dragon-fly. The sedentary predators also vary in their degree of sophistication: harpactocorine reduviids which take up positions on flower heads where they await the arrival of pollen and honey feeders are among the simplest; elaborations may be seen in the web of the spider and the pit of the ant lion.

Among both active and inactive predators vision is the principal, but by no means the universal, means of locating prey. Mechanical vibration, touch, and taste are also variously employed in different species. Detailed studies on predatory behaviour are not numerous but we do have information which is more than simply anecdotal on most modes of predation.

Considering first the minority group of predators not primarily dependent on vision for the location and capture of prey, the simplest examples are probably the predatory mites and larval insects such as syrphids, neuropterans, and coccinellids. We have detailed studies of two coccinellids[29],[30] and two neuropterans[29].

Fleschner's study[29] involved observations of the activity of predators in 'simplified artificial universes' that provided various combinations of light and topography. His three predators *Stethorus picipes* (Coccinellidae), *Chrysopa californica* (Chrysopidae), and *Conwentzia hagenii* (Coniopterygidae) all required contact with their prey before predation could take place. There

Table 3.1. Relative performances of three predators of the citrus red mite under identical conditions of uniform illumination and typography[29]

Species	Time for eclosion to death in absence of food and water h	Searching speed in./h	Total contacts with prey at a density of 1/in.²	Total captures	Min/max captures to complete development
Stenthorus	134	774	29	10	1/5
Conwentzia	139	1,300	50	11	
Chrysopa	702	2,675	149	149	1/10

was no evidence of distance perception of chemical stimuli in Y-tube olfactometer experiments. They moved about continuously until they made contact with prey, but after the first successful encounter their path became more tortuous for a time, a response which should have increased the likelihood of further contact with aggregated prey. The evidence that simple tropic responses might bring predator and prey into proximity differed for the three species. Under experimental conditions which, it must be remembered, were not intended to simulate the natural environment in which predation occurs, all species wandered at random over uniformly illuminated surfaces. The frequency of predator–prey encounters under these circumstances could be described in terms of modified gas law theory, and it was further possible to derive estimates of performance for some of the features of predatory behaviour, which, if they are difficult to interpret in terms of natural predation, at least provide interesting comparisons of performance (*Table 3.1*).

Banks[30] also studied a coccinellid larva, but his emphasis was on field observations, having demonstrated in the laboratory that his species behaved essentially as did Fleschner's, although he comments on the importance of the 'arc of searching' behaviour (*Figure 3.2*) which increases the area effectively searched for prey. On a bean plant the rate of movement was more or less uniform (although hairs and honeydew impeded them) but their direction was not random: they tended to follow the edges and veins of leaves. Walking continues until contact is first made with prey; after their first feed they make small turning movements in a restricted area (*Figure 3.3*).

The behaviour of these predators seems suited to more or less sedentary, locally abundant prey such as aphids or mites. Aphidophagous syrphid larvae would probably behave similarly. It would be of interest to compare the success of this type of predator with aphids that typically aggregate, such as *Aphis fabae*, and others that tend to disperse, for example *Myzus persicae*.

93

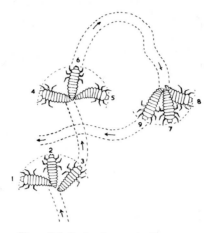

Figure 3.2. Path of a coccinellid larva
showing 'arc of searching' behaviour[30]

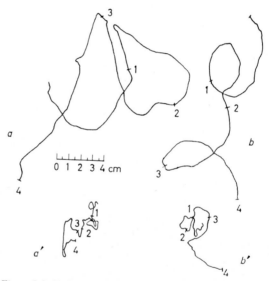

Figure 3.3. Paths of coccinellid larvae before (*a*, *b*) and
after (*a'*, *b'*) feeding showing change in pattern of
searching[30]

Sedentary predators not primarily dependent on sight make use of
mechanical vibration. Mechanoreceptors provide the first warning of the
presence of prey to the web-building spider, and dorsal mechanoreceptor
hairs evidently play a similar role for the ant lion, although vision also appears
to be involved[6].

For the great majority of predators vision plays the decisive part in
recognition and capture of prey. Observations by natural historians of the
large size of the eyes and the frequent presence of facets of differing size

within the eye was taken to indicate visual acuity, which might be expected where prey must be precisely located. Analysis of the visual powers of a number of predatory arthropods in the 1920's and 1930's brought to light simple optical mechanisms by which prey may be located and apprehended. The often quoted work of Baldus[31] on capture of prey by a dragon-fly larva (*Aeshna*) provides one example. He showed that the visual response to a moving object suffices to elicit predatory behaviour; the animal will snap at moving prey separated from it by a glass partition. As the distance between predator and prey diminishes the image of the prey moves over ommatidia of successively smaller diameter. In the region of the eye with ommatidia of smallest visual angle, namely $1°12'$, the axes intersect at a distance in front of the head equal to the strike distance of the extended mask. If the acuity of the compound eye is related to the arc subtended by individual ommatidia in a given area of the eye, as seems plausible, then the binocular image of the prey will be at its highest resolution at the distance at which the mask flies out to grasp it.

But visual stimuli are not of prime importance to all dragon-fly nymphs. Alverdes[32] described the use by *Agrion* nymphs of the antennae to locate prey, and more recently Richard[33], comparing the predatory behaviour of *Aeshna*, *Agrion*, and *Cordulia* species, notes the importance of mechanoreceptors on the antennae and the tarsi in the latter two. The early nymphs of all three are alike in their predation of protozoa which they detect by means of the antennae. In later instars vision becomes important to *Aeshna*, although the antennae may be used after loss of use of the eyes. Tactile stimuli provide the necessary information for *Agrion* in which the fore tarsi come to substitute for lost antennae, while *Cordulia* evidently relies more or less equally on the eyes and on mechanoreceptors situated on the antennae. The relative development of central nerve tracts in the three genera parallels these differences.

The tiger beetle (*Cicindela*) fixates prey at about 12 to 15 cm and seizes it as it comes between the pincer-like mandibles[34]. The sedentary cicindelid larva, which lacks compound eyes, is evidently able to locate moving prey with the six stemmata on each side of the head capsule, and to fixate prey at a distance of 3 to 6 cm. The eyes of the jumping spiders (Salticidae) which stalk and leap upon their prey also have overlapping areas of vision that allow binocular vision, particularly in the fields of the median eyes[35].

The stimuli releasing predatory behaviour in *Salticus scenicus* have been examined in detail by Drees[36] whose ethological study of the stimuli involved in predation and courtship provides most interesting data. Since three-dimensional models were more effective than flat ones in eliciting leaps, it seems that binocular vision plays a part in prey recognition as well as in location. While the spiders showed some discrimination as to over-all size of a moving flat shape, their powers of discrimination fell as hunger increased. Crane[37] notes the importance of movement in eliciting a predatory leap in Salticids, although she did observe predation of stationary prey. The backswimmer *Notonecta glauca*, a predatory heteropteran, has binocular vision over $94°$ in the horizontal plane, in a dorsal arc of $120°$ and a ventral arc of $80°$ (Ludtke[38]).

The possession of large compound eyes is nevertheless no proof that they alone are involved in finding prey. Moving prey do not necessarily elicit predatory responses in the water beetle *Dytiscus* which has well developed compound eyes[39]. It responds to chemical and tactile stimuli. *Notonecta* is also capable of locating prey trapped in the air–water interface from a distance of 15 cm by receptors sensitive to minute ripples which are associated with sensory hairs on the swimming legs[40].

The visual mechanisms described above appear to depend on simple fixation, supposedly by adjusting stance so that symmetrical images are received by the ommatidia of each side, thus ensuring that the prey is always faced and the information about the distance between the two animals is available. Mittelstaedt[41] has shown in his work with the mantid *Parastigmatophora unipunctata* that a mechanism involving simple symmetrical fixation is not necessarily the case in all predators that rely on vision to capture moving prey. His description of prey location by the mantid in terms of feed back, or control theory, is the first application to a predator of new developments in the study of behaviour, and suggests the direction that future work on prey capture may take. The results of his elegant experiments indicate that measurement of the deviation of the prey from optical symmetry is one factor in computing the direction of the stroke of the forelegs by which prey is caught. Since the stroke of the forelegs occupies only about 10 to 30 mseconds it is unlikely that its direction can be altered once it has been started: it must be preset in relation to the body position of the mantid. The way this is achieved was demonstrated by analysing the performance of free and tethered mantids under various conditions, in terms of percentage successful strikes, and of the angular deviation of unsuccessful strikes (*Figure 3.4*). A normal animal was successful in about 85 per cent of attempted captures, but when nerves from proprioceptive hairs of the neck were cut, the performance dropped to 20 to 30 per cent success. After bilateral section they were able to hit only those flies that were directly in front of them; flies that approached on the right of the mantid's head were missed to the left and vice versa, indicating that information about the position of the head with respect to the thorax must be involved in controlling the direction of stroke. The result of experiments in which the head was fixed with respect to the thorax, with and without the section of nerves from the neck proprioceptors, indicated that as far as orientation in the vertical plane is concerned, the direction of the capture stroke is controlled by a feedback mechanism utilizing information about the position of the head with respect to the neck, and of the deviation of the prey from the line of optical fixation. The 'optic centre message' depends on the angle between the prey and the fixation line. The 'proprioceptive centre message' is a function of the angle between the head and the body axis. In the mantid the fixation line evidently does not centre the prey, but deviates proportionally to the angle between the prey and the axis of the mantid's thorax. A notable feature of this system is that the head may be moved with respect to the body, so that in any stance the most acute part of the eye may be directed toward the prey. The approach to predatory behaviour used in this study might profitably be used to re-examine predation by dragon-fly nymphs and by salticid spiders in both of which the predatory stroke or leap must be 'preset'.

The examples chosen have shown the dominant role of vision in a number of predators, the frequent possession of binocular vision being associated with precise spatial location of prey. In comparison with vision, chemoreception is in general less important, although it may play a part in detection of prey in some predators, and has a qualifying role in others. *Dysticus* responds with hunting behaviour to the presence dilute of meat extract

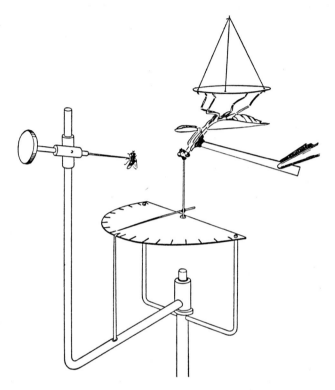

Figure 3.4. Mantid mounted in Mittelstaedt device for measuring the fixation deficit[41]. The animal is fixed by the prothorax, and the head is free to rotate about the vertical axis. The deviation of the head, and of the prey from the median plane of the thorax is measured on the dial.

in the water[39]. Certain dacetine ants which prey specifically on collembola are said to detect them by odour[42,43]. Bee odour is important in prey discrimination by the wasp *Philanthus*[44]. The prey of spiders may be rejected after being touched with forelegs and palps[45]. In groups where predatory and plant feeding species are closely related, as in the Heteroptera, we find chemoreception differing greatly in importance in discrimination of food: it appears to be of little or no value to the predators, but is critical for the plant feeders.

In the study of whole patterns of predation, the Hymenoptera, with their complex behaviour, have had the largest share of attention. Progressive provisioning by digger wasps has attracted the attention of a number of ethologists[46,47] and there are now a number of comparative studies of the provisioning of larval cells, but little is known about the actual capture of prey. Tinbergen's[44] work on the bee-hunting wasp *Philanthus triangulum* demonstrates the range of sensory modalities that may be involved in selective predation. Visual stimuli trigger the predatory sequence in the flying wasp: a bee-like object is approached while a localized source of bee odour elicits no response. At a distance of 10 to 15 cm *Philanthus* hovers and fixates the prospective prey. Olfactory stimuli now become critical if the object has the general form of a bee. A hover-fly is rejected unless it has been experimentally given a bee odour by contact with their bodies. *Philanthus* darts at the prey, and after it has been grasped, tactile stimuli appear to be important in releasing stinging behaviour, for a bee-scented hover-fly will be rejected after contact has been made with it; only a real bee is stung.

The selective predation by *Philanthus* raises the question of the extent of prey specificity among arthropod predators. There seems less reason for predators than for parasitoids, with their dependence on the physiology of their host, to develop prey specificity. Many predators nevertheless restrict their attack, as does *Philanthus*, to particular species of genera, indeed, Thomson[48] has suggested that there is little difference between parasitoids and predators in this respect. There is, however, such a wide variation from group to group among the predators, that a general comparison with the parasitoids has little meaning. In some groups specificity is certainly general: the Hymenoptera is a good example; *Philanthus* has been mentioned, and there are many similar examples. Pompilid wasps restrict their attention to certain spiders; some ants are highly specific in their choice of prey, others are less so[49]. Many predatory beetles, flies and bugs, on the other hand, seem to have broad tastes, although among these too there are examples of selective predators, for example the heteropteran bee assassins (Apiomerinae). The rigidity of prey selection can be lowered under stress: jumping spiders will attack larger models as starvation proceeds[36], and the digger wasp will take other species of spider when its usual prey, *Epeira*, is not available[5].

We should perhaps also distinguish between true prey specificity in which certain species are selected, while other seemingly suitable species in the environment are rejected (*Philanthus*, for example) and 'facultative' specificity when particular prey are taken simply because they are abundant in a particular habitat, for example coccinellids and aphids, and damsel flies with chironomids.

THE TOXICOLOGY OF PREDATION

The predator has located and made contact with its prey. Now comes the critical phase in the operation: the restraint of its struggling victim so that feeding may begin.

The problem is solved by the use of mechanical strength in such predators as the mantids, crustaceans, and many arachnids which tightly hold, tear, and knead their prey, often with the aid of powerful appendages, while digestive secretions pour from the mouth. Others make use of secretions that very rapidly immobilize their prey by killing or paralysing them, and many predators of this type are not markedly well equipped to hold their prey in prolonged restraint, relying rather on a quick 'knock down', to borrow a term from insecticide terminology.

The rapidity with which these predators subdue their prey has been cause for comment by many observers, some of whom have inferred the existence of highly potent venoms. De Geer[50], for example, in 1773 noted the ability of the assassin bug *Reduvius personatus* to paralyse flies very rapidly. Poisson[51] commented similarly on the backswimmer *Notonecta*, as did Melin[52], Whitfield[53], and others who worked with asilid flies, to give instance from the insects only. This rapid paralysis which is certainly a most striking feature of so many arthropod predator–prey encounters, may be due as much to the vulnerability of the organs within the haemocoele as to any special potency of the secretions used, for once it is within the body—and most predators have mechanisms for rapidly penetrating the integument—an injected secretion has access to the membranes surrounding nerve and muscle tissue, and the brief but convulsive struggling of the prey doubtless serves to speed its distribution through the haemocoele.

Many arthropod poisons with defensive or repugnatory functions are secreted by dermal glands, which produce a remarkable variety of noxious compounds in various arthropods[54] but we shall be concerned here only with the aboral and oral secretions that are used by hymenopterans and scorpions, and by other arthropods, respectively, to paralyse or to kill their prey. These we may refer to as venoms, no matter whether they arise from specific venom glands or from salivary or other glands of the body. The hymenopteran venoms are produced by accessory glands of the female reproductive tract. Oral venoms may originate in mandibular, maxillary, or labial glands, or in some cases combinations of these, in the insects; from cheliceral venom glands in the spiders; pedipalp glands in some pseudo-scorpions; from forceps glands in the centipedes. Since many arthropods digest their prey preorally, ingesting the fluid products of external digestion, it is not possible to distinguish clearly between the functions of killing and digesting except in their time-scale, but there can be no doubt that the predatory arthropods have evolved very rapidly acting poisons as part of their mode of nutrition.

Before surveying the source and composition of these venoms it should be observed that the number of venoms examined in detail is very small, and even the most studied are incompletely understood. In general, more interest has attached to the medical significance of the few that, because of their hazard to man, have been studied from the point of view of mammalian toxicology. The mechanism of their toxicity for their intended prey has seldom been a consideration. There have been obstacles to such study: small quantities and difficulties of purification have deterred work on substances of great biological interest, but the development and refinement of microtechniques for separating and characterizing biological materials is rapidly placing many more of the arthropod poisons within reach of serious study.

A further obstacle to progress in this field has been the lack of knowledge of the pharmacology of arthropods, and the lack of pharmacological preparations with which to compare their action.

Pharmacological studies stimulated by fundamental work on the action of chemical insecticides are now gaining momentum, and it is becoming increasingly clear that arthropods and vertebrates differ in the nature of many of the key substances serving bodily functions. For example, the transmitter substance at the insect myoneural junction is not acetylcholine, and has not yet been identified with certainty. Adrenalin does not have the functions it serves in the vertebrate, and histamine has no effect on insect tissues, to mention only three substances relevant in venom physiology. We may, therefore, reasonably expect arthropod venoms to differ in some respects from those intended for vertebrates.

The survey that follows will perhaps serve to show the widespread distribution, but most uneven state of knowledge, of the arthropod venoms.

Onychophora

Ejaculation of a rapidly hardening mucoprotein slime is not essential for successful predation by *Peripatus* as Manton and Heatley[55] have shown, although it may be so used[12]. Potential prey are briefly touched with the antennae, the mouth is pressed against the body and after slicing the prey with the blade-like mandibles copious saliva is poured from the large salivary glands. Heatley[56] detected amylase, glycogenase, protease, and carboxypeptidase activity in the saliva of *Peripatus*. Digested contents of the prey are sucked in and out during feeding, but externally digested material is not the only part of the prey that is consumed, for fragmented cuticle may also be found in the gut.

Chilopoda

The study of centipede venom extends back as far as the seventeenth century when van Leeuwenhoek showed that flies were killed by a secretion that issued from pores at the tips of the forceps. Plateau[57] removed flies from the forceps of *Scolopendra* at the moment of piercing and found that the first four or five flies were paralysed immediately, the next one or two were partially paralysed, and the centipede refused to cooperate further. The poison gland is located in the base of the forcep. It has a cuticular lining and each of the large gland cells is surrounded by delicate branch muscle fibres, the whole gland also having a muscle sheath. There is a growing literature on medical aspects of the bite of the centipede but as yet very little is known of the composition and action of the venom salivary glands. The presence of phospholipase[58], haemolysin[59], protease, and saccharase[60] and hyaluronidase[61] are reported.

Arachnida

Spiders (excepting the Uloboridae which lack venom glands), scorpions, some pseudo-scorpions, and possibly, some mites use venom to subdue their prey. Other arachnids simply grasp and tear their prey while it is firmly held. There are, of course, many other toxic secretions produced by various arachnids that are not used directly in predation. Harvestmen and whip-scorpions, for example, produce repugnatory substances. The saliva of ixodoid ticks such as *Dermacentor* cause tick paralysis inverte brates. This tick toxin evidently has the effect of blocking conduction in motor fibres[62].

Nothing is known of the venom of the pseudo-scorpion beyond observations that single or paired glands are found in the pedipalps of some species whose prey are paralysed before feeding begins. Preoral digestion is effected by salivary secretions which are poured from the mouth after the prey has been kneaded.

The composition and action of spider and scorpion venom have received perhaps as much attention as bee venom, all largely from a medical point of view, but it cannot be said that their composition or their mode of action is at all well understood. Kaiser and Michl[63] have recently reviewed the toxicology of arachnid venoms. There appears to be a wide range of toxicity in spider and scorpion venoms for vertebrates, and it is mainly the more venomous that have been examined.

Spider venom is secreted by the cheliceral glands. As long ago as 1885, Bertkau[64] demonstrated that the secretion of the pedipalp or salivary glands did not have a lytic action on insect tissues comparable with that of the cheliceral glands. Schlottke[65] found no evidence that the protease used for preoral digestion arises anterior to the stomach, the diverticula of which secrete a tryptic enzyme.

The need to distinguish between a venom obtained by simulated predation, e.g. by inducing the spider to bite an inert material, and that obtained by extracting the contents of particular glands is shown in recent electrophoretic studies on spider venoms. Four to six proteins have been isolated in different venoms under similar electrophoretic conditions. Muic et al.[66] separated six proteins by paper electrophoresis at pH 8·6 in the secretion of *Latrodectus tredecimguttatus* obtained by inducing the spider to bite a plug of cotton wool. Bettini and Toschi-Frontali[67] working with the same species, separated five proteins in the extracted contents of the venom gland, using similar electrophoretic conditions, a discrepancy which probably arose from the presence of protease in the secretion examined in the former study.

Bettini and Toschi-Frontali were able to isolate one protein fraction that was highly toxic when injected into *Periplaneta americana*, and which caused strong contraction of the isolated foregut of the beetle *Cybister*.

Lebez[68] reported the presence of a lipoprotein in the venom of *L. tredecimguttatus* which he regarded as the toxic component, but Cantori and Bettini[69] were unable to repeat his observations. Several enzymes have been detected in whole spider venom, although it is not always certain where they originated. Proteolytic activity is generally reported, but Cantori and Bettini did not detect protease in extracts of the venom glands of *L. tredecimguttatus*, using a gelatin substrate. Amino acid dehydrogenase activity is reported in the venom of *Phoneutria* and *Ctenus* species by Kaiser and Michl[63], and these species, together with *Araneus diadematus*[70], also show cholinesterase activity. Hyaluronidase is generally present, but was not detected in the venom of *A. diadematus*.

A number of recent studies on several species note the absence of haemolytic activity in whole spider venom, although there are early reports of haemolysis by *Latrodectus* venom.

Spider venoms are rich in free amino acids, of which glutamic acid and γ-aminobutyric acid are generally in highest concentration. The second of these is known to be pharmacologically active on the arthropod nervous system[71,72]. Fischer and Bohn[73] report the presence in the venoms of *Lycosa erythrocephala* and *Phoneutria fera* of strongly basic components (compounds of spermin or trimethyldiamine with *p*-hydroxyphenylpyruvic acid, and certain other tyrosine derivative. Almost all toxicological work has dealt with the action of the most potent of spider venoms on mammals and mammalian preparations. The composition and mode of action of less potently venomous species, that is the majority of spiders, on their invertebrate prey is quite unknown.

Work on scorpion venoms has again been largely from a medical point of view. It is reviewed by Kaiser and Michl[63]. Most scorpion venoms are strongly haemolytic. 5-Hydroxytryptamine is present in high concentration in the venom of some species, but the toxicity of the venom for mammals is not reduced after its removal[74]. The principal toxic components are neurotoxic proteins apparently resembling crotoxin from snake venom. They have been termed scorpamins by Miranda and Lissitzky[75], who isolated two low molecular weight protein fractions in the venoms of the North African scorpions *Androctonus australis* and *Buthus occitanus*. The mode of action of these neurotoxins is unknown. Weak ATPase activity was detected in the venom of *Euscorpius italicus*[59].

Insecta

Heteroptera

The piercing and sucking mouth-parts of the Heteroptera in which the mandible and maxillae take the form of long stylets enclosed by the labium are ideally suited to a predatory mode of life. The restriction to a liquid diet imposed by the narrow stylet canals is associated with preoral digestion and the elaboration of salivary glands. About half of the families in the order are to some extent predatory. Within the Reduviidae we find predators closely related to blood feeding parasites of vertebrates. Some may adopt both diets, although facultative blood feeders seem to be distinguished from obligate parasites such as *Rhodnius* by the pain of their bite. In other families, notably the Nabidae and Miridae, plant sap as well as prey may form part of the diet, but it is not clear whether reproduction can occur without predation.

The first experimental studies on predation by Heteroptera appear to be those of Poisson[51] who injected methylene blue into prey of backswimmers (*Notonecta* sp.) thus colouring the salivary gland contents of the bugs. When they subsequently preyed on chironomid larvae, coloured saliva was seen to be emitted from the tip of the stylets until the prey was immobilized. An extract of the labial or salivary glands of *Notonecta* injected into blattids, Diptera, and *Notonecta* caused paralysis and death. Poisson states that the contents of the maxillary glands are also toxic when injected into insects. His observation has not been re-examined and it is possible that his preparation was contaminated with salivary secretions. The maxillary glands of the carnivorous heteroptera are, nevertheless, larger than those of their plant feeding relatives[76], and they may have a purpose other than lubrication of the stylets, a function Linder ascribes to the mandibular glands only.

The salivary glands of the carnivorous heteroptera have muscular coats and large lumens compared with those of their non-predatory relatives[77].

Saliva is pumped into the prey by means of a large force pump in which muscles occupying a large proportion of the head capsule provide the inspiratory stroke while the elastic cuticle of the pump wall returns the plunger and ejects saliva through the stylet canal. The immediate effect of injection of saliva into a prey is convulsive struggling leading rapidly to tremors, and to flaccid paralysis.

The action and composition of the venomous saliva of a reduviid 'assassin bug' *Platymeris rhadamanthus* has been examined by Edwards[78] who collected

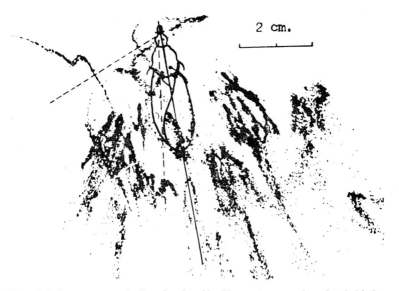

Figure 3.5. Spray pattern of saliva ejaculated by *Platymeris* on to a glass plate held above the animal[79]. Dotted lines indicate the 'arc of fire' achieved by deflecting the tip of the rostrum.

the secretion in quantity by exploiting the defensive spitting behaviour of the animal (*Figure 3.5*)[79]. The saliva is highly toxic when introduced into the insect haemocoele, while surface application and ingestion have no effect. At concentrations down to 10^{-6} in saline, saliva abolishes contractility in the cockroach heart; a 1 per cent solution stops conduction in central nervous connectives of *Schistocerca gregaria* in 120 seconds. The intact central nervous system is briefly stimulated to violent activity, volleys of repetitive discharges leading to electrical silence (*Figure 3.6*). The saliva is strongly haemolytic and rapidly breaks down tissue of insect prey. The salivary components having these effects are proteins, of which at least six were revealed by Tiselius electrophoresis at pH 6·5 and by starch gel electrophoresis at pH 8·5. None of the fractions was found to be toxic after separation and extraction from starch gel but it is probable that some denaturation had taken place, as the proteolytic component of the saliva proved to have its pH optimum near that used in the gel.

The whole saliva is strongly proteolytic, with a pH optimum about 8·2. Fibrin and elastin are attacked, but collagenase activity was not detected.

The affinity of the salivary endopeptidase for an azocasein substrate ($K_m = 0.07$ per cent) is closely similar to the figure obtained for the protease of *Calliphora* (blow-fly) larvae[80]. Whole saliva has hyaluronidase activity, which will reduce the viscosity of synovial fluid hyaluronate. Phospholipase activity was found to be weak compared with other paralysing venoms such as those of the bee and snakes, and lipase and esterase activity are negligible. Tests for ATPase and 5-hydroxytryptamine were negative.

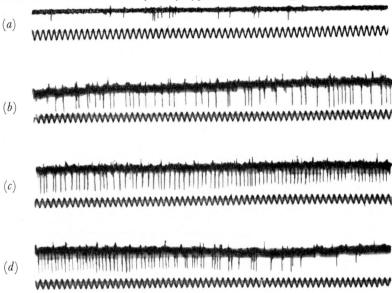

Figure 3.6. Extracts from oscillograph record of the action of *Platymeris* saliva on the abdominal nerve cord of *Periplaneta americana*[78].
(*a*) Records from last abdominal connective before application of saliva.
(*b*) and (*c*) Onset of repetitive discharge after application of 0·1 ml. 1 per cent saliva in the region of the last abdominal ganglion. (*d*) Decay of activity.
Time marker: 50 c/sec.

The observed effects of *Platymeris* saliva are consistent with the view that its paralysing activity is due to rapid penetration and lysis of nerve cell membranes. The presence of an alkaline endopeptidase and hyaluronidase is not sufficient to explain the action, and the level of phospholipase activity is not what would have been expected had it been the case of the observed rapid lysis, by analogy with certain other venoms. This point will be returned to later.

Neuroptera

The source and nature of the toxic secretion that passes down the mandibular furrow of the ant lion into a pierced prey remains to be demonstrated. Stäger[81] paralysed ants and other small arthropods by piercing them with needles bearing secretion from the tips of ant lion mandibles, and assumed the maxillary glands to be the source to the secretion, which he likened to the 'toxalbumen' of spider venom. Beard[82], on the other hand, refers to the 'progressive death in a larval victim of the ant lion due to a slow diffusion of secretion oozing from mandibular canals'.

Smith[83] found no evidence of the injection of fluids into the bodies of aphids that were prey of larval chrysopids.

Diptera

The biology of many dipteran predators has been described in detail, but there is as yet no information on the nature of the venoms which cause almost instantaneous paralysis in the prey of tabanid larvae and adult asilids. While many of the dipteran predators rapidly paralyse their prey, not all do; Haddow[84], in observations on a species of predatory culicid larva, comments that their prey continue to struggle while they are being consumed.

The venom of the adult asilid fly deserves special attention, for its paralytic effect is practically instantaneous. The flies' mouth-parts are almost invariably plunged into the head capsule of the prey, but mere mechanical damage to the brain is insufficient to immobilize an insect so promptly, as Le Conte showed more than a century ago in his studies on asilids. Without experimental evidence Whitfield[53] regarded the salivary glands as the source of a venom, while glands at the base of the labium were thought to produce a digestive secretion.

Some predatory mycetophilid larvae secrete droplets of oxalic acid at a concentration of 0·15 per cent, with a pH of 1·8, which are deposited on the silken threads of their traps, where they rapidly immobilize entangled prey[85].

Similar web traps with beads of unknown composition are produced by the larvae of another mycetophilid, *Arachnocampa luminosa*, in New Zealand, whose luminescent organ is said to attract prey to the dangling adhesive lines[86].

Hymenoptera

We come now to the most interesting of all arthropod venoms. Not all of the parasitoid Hymenoptera (Parasitica) paralyse their prey: ichneumons insert their eggs with little evident disturbance to the prey. Others induce temporary paralysis, while the chalcidoids permanently paralyse their prey. They are in general minute animals and their secretions are available in exceedingly small quantities. Beard[87] has examined the toxicology of *Habrobracon* venom which induces a permanent flaccid paralysis very shortly after the prey is stung. The venom is selective in its action, for the heart and gut continue rhythmic activity for several months while the body wall musculature is paralysed. The electrical activity of the central nervous system seems to be little altered. Beard likened the venom to curare in that it appears to inactivate the myoneural junctions of skeletal muscle, but the data available at that time did not suggest the presence in the venom of any pharmacological agent known from insects. Studies on the nature of the myoneural transmitter substance in insects have so far failed to identify any compound with certainty, although it seems certain that acetylcholine is not involved[88]. Following their recognition in vertebrates, attention has turned recently to active amines such as 5-hydroxytryptamine and tryptamine analogues, which at high concentrations block neuromuscular transmission

105

in insect skeletal muscle[89], and it has been suggested that a tryptamine derivative may act as the neuromuscular transmitter substance in the insect peripheral nervous system[90]. It may be that an inhibitor, perhaps of related structure, able to block receptor sites at the junction is injected in the paralysing venom; or that some such substance is released from the tissues of the prey by a component of the venom of some aculeates (see below). However, *Habrobracon* venom paralysed *Ephestia kuhniella* and *Galleria melonella*, while larvae of *Pyrausta nubilalis* and *Popillia japonica* were unaffected. Such prey specificity is an obstacle to simple explanation.

Aculeate venoms, secreted by the female accessory glands, serve predatory and defensive functions and may paralyse or kill immediately. Nielsen[91] found no significant modification of respiratory rate of the prey paralysed by several species of wasp. Histological examination of the prey of *Ammophila* revealed degeneration of the ganglia, and Hartzell[92] describes lesions in the ganglia of a cicada caused by the venom of the killer wasp *Sphecius*. It has yet to be shown that these effects arise from a venom component specific in its lysis of nerve cells, or whether the sting is invariably inserted into a ganglion so that the venom is more or less restricted to the central nervous system. The application of bee venom to the surface of a cockroach abdominal ganglion briefly stimulates volleys of repetitive discharge leading to inactivity, so this venom can pass inward through the neural lamella; but we have as yet no data to gauge the similarity of these venoms.

In the venom of Hymenoptera of medical importance, histamine and histidine, 5-hydroxytryptamine, acetylcholine, enzymes such as hyaluronidase, phospholipase and ATPase as well as other pharmacologically active proteins have been reported[93].

Histamine, which has been reported in bee and wasp venoms, does not seem to have any significance in the predatory function of aculeate venoms as it is without effect on insects. 5-Hydroxytryptamine is present in the venom of several wasps, but has not been detected in bee venom. Hornet venom is rich in acetylcholine, while another vespid venom, that of *Vespula vulgaris*, is said to contain a cholinesterase. Neumann and Habermann[93] separated three protein fractions in bee venom, of which one, their fraction 0, is considered to be inert. Fraction I, a basic protein, is strongly haemolytic, lowers the membrane potential of striated frog muscle, and excites, then blocks, the perfused ganglion cervicale superius of the cat. A similar neurotoxic activity was also observed when cockroach ganglia were treated with whole bee venom[79]. Fraction I also inhibits plasma cholinesterase. Fraction II has little or none of these effects. It shows phospholipase and hyaluronidase activity but was not lethal to mice at a dose of 5 mg/kg. Their results suggest that toxicity and phospholipase activity do not necessarily run parallel, and that lysis may be brought about by proteins that split neither phospholipids nor proteins.

The ants, like other aculeates, seem to make use of sting venoms variously for predation and for defence. Of the primitive and more exclusively carnivorous subfamilies, the Ponerinae and the Dorylinae, we have no information about the use of venom. Formicine ants' venom is well known for its high content of formic acid. Much attention has been paid to the dolichoderine and myrmecine ants, whose secretions have attracted the attention of chemists more than physiologists, with the result that much is known of their chemical composition but little of their mode of action. Pavan[94] has summarized work on these substances. The myrmecine ant *Solenopsis saevissima* paralyses its prey with a venom that is strongly haemolytic. Its source and chemistry is discussed by Blum and Callahan[95].

Coleoptera

Very little is known about the way in which carnivorous beetles subdue their prey, although the many observations that death rapidly follows capture shows that some at least may secrete venomous substances. Gut secretions are poured on to the prey, beetles in general lacking salivary glands, but paralysis may be caused by a secretion from the maxillary glands. Portier[96] observed that the prey of dytiscids rapidly succumb and darken as the result of a secretion which passes from the gut down furrows in the mandibles and into the prey, and suggested that this material contains a toxin. Wigglesworth[97] made similar observations on cicindelid larvae, and considered that the protease activity he found in the fluid that is poured over the prey was insufficient to account for the rapidity of paralysis. After the prey is crushed between the mandibles, a fluid is ejected from the mouth, and the dissolved tissues are ingested. Not uncommonly, immature Coleoptera ingest only fluid products of external digestion, while the adults chew and devour the entire prey.

Mode of Action of Venoms

These pages have brought together observations of very unequal detail on a number of arthropod venoms. The inadequacies are obvious, but is a pattern evident? Lytic factors, not necessarily phospholipases, which might be expected by analogy with snake venoms, are very widely distributed. Hyaluronidase and protease, also of frequent occurrence, attack components of the intercellular matrix and thus facilitate the spread of toxic substances in insects, as in vertebrates. Rapid penetration and direct lysis of axons may be the most general mode of action in oral venoms but many of the hymenopteran venoms act more subtly on the metabolic machinery. Their paralysing venoms may act by blocking myoneural transmission, perhaps with tryptamine derivatives, variously causing temporary or permanent paralysis. It is not clear whether the breakdown of ganglion cells observed with some wasp venoms is caused by the sting actually penetrating the ganglion: this possibility deserves further investigation, bearing in mind the observation of Peckham and Peckham[98] that the larval prey of *Ammophila* vary greatly in their degree of paralysis and site of stinging, but that other wasps, for example, the pompilids, show great regularity in the site of stinging.

Preoral digestion follows paralysis by oral venoms. In some groups, for example the Heteroptera, the salivary secretions serve both functions; in others, for example the spiders, separate venom glands are involved, and digestive enzymes such as protease are poured into the prey from salivary or digestive glands. Where hyaluronidase and protease are present they will facilitate the penetration of active components of venoms, but they are not in themselves sufficient to account for the rapid paralysis that is such a notable feature of the arthropod venoms. Proteases will cause contraction and depolarization of frog sartorius muscle[99] and rapidly bring the cockroach heart to systolic standstill, but Tobias showed that papain, chymotrypsin and collagenase, as well as hyaluronidase have no effect on conduction and trans-surface potentials of isolated lobster axons. If cell lysis is the reason for rapid paralysis we must look to other venom components.

Cell membranes contain lipoprotein layers in which phospholipids appear to play an important part. It might be expected that an enzyme capable of gaining access to, and disrupting, the cell wall phospholipids would seriously damage the functioning cell. The configuration of the phospholipid–protein layers probably varies in different cells[100], and their susceptibility to structural damage may also therefore vary. Phospholipases are among the most widespread components of animal venoms[58] but have only been demonstrated in a few arthropod venoms to date. Phospholipases cause depolarization of lobster axons, observations which led Tobias to the view that the integrity of the phospholid layer of the nerve cell is essential for normal functioning. It was earlier thought that lysis was brought about by lysolecithin, which is produced when phospholipase A acts on lecithin, and which is capable of disrupting orientated layers of the strongly polar phospholipid molecules, but phospholipases attacking the molecule at various points are also able to depolarize lobster axons. While Richards and Cutkomp[101] reported that 'injection of maximal doses of lysolecithin into the haemocoel of cockroaches was without effect,' Tobias found lysolecithin to be active on lobster axons, and noted that the ionic environment influences its activity. It will be remembered that Neumann and Habermann's[93] active Fraction I of bee venom was haemolytic and blocked nerve transmission, while their fraction II, in which they detected phospholipase A, had none of these effects. Again, *Platymeris* venom is strongly haemolytic, and causes rapid general lysis of insect tissues, but *in vitro* tests for phospholipases revealed only very weak activity, in comparison with snake venoms, for example. While *in vitro* tests for such enzymes may not be entirely conclusive, since the behaviour of lipids and phospholipids in tissues as enzyme substrates are likely to be different because of their orientation, and ionic environment, it may be that the widespread lytic activity of arthropod venoms is caused by proteins other than lipases or phospholipases.

The rapidity of paralysis of arthropod prey poses further problems. At least some of the well recognized effects of snake venoms on vertebrates, namely haemolytic and histamine shock reactions, can play no part in the arthropod, although mechanisms involving the release of bound active substances from the prey tissues may be important. The liberation of adrenalin from perfused cat adrenal glands by bee and cobra venoms[102] and of acetylcholine from brain tissue by viper venom phospholipase[103] are examples of mechanisms in vertebrates that may operate with different active substances in the arthropod.

It seems very probable that some hymenopteran venoms, and many other insect venoms, act by destroying the excitability of nerve and muscle by lysis of cell membranes. The penetration and inactivation of the central nervous system of the cockroach by assassin bug saliva is achieved within a matter of seconds. Now the insect nerve cord is ensheathed by a non-cellular layer, the neural lamella, which overlies a layer of perineurial cells. The neural lamella is composed of collagen fibres embedded in a matrix of mucopolysaccharide[104,105]. This sheath is readily permeable to small molecules[106], but it is improbable that protein molecules could enter the nerve cord sufficiently rapidly to account for the observed effects, unless the neural lamella is altered or destroyed. A fragile cylinder which remains after pieces of nerve cord have been subjected to prolonged immersion in *Platymeris* saliva, differs in histological appearance from the fresh material, and is probably the collagenous part of the structure (collagenase could not be detected in the saliva of *Platymeris*) from which the mucopolysaccharide matrix had been removed. It may be that the hyaluronidase in the saliva is able to break down a component, the matrix thus allowing entry of toxic components of the venomous saliva.

If these observations hold for other arthropod venoms, it is unlikely that the venoms are species specific in their action, and this would suggest that prey specificity is not to be explained on a toxicological basis. The paralysing venoms of the Hymenoptera on the other hand may be more specific in their action, but more work is required on this aspect of toxicology.

CONCLUSION

I have ranged widely in this essay in an attempt to present topics that contribute to a picture of arthropods as predators. Even so I have been able to deal with only a few aspects; my choice has inevitably been a subjective one, and the picture is rather sketchy and uneven for we have so little information on many aspects. If there is little room for theory where facts are in short supply, the greatest need is for more quantitative population studies on predator–prey relationships. They are accumulating slowly but there are many gaps: we know virtually nothing about spiders in this respect. There is no substitute for field studies where populations are concerned, laboratory studies may show how many prey a predator can consume, only field studies will show how many they do consume, and when.

Modern chemical insecticides have made the ecological problems raised by predation more urgent. So far it has often been possible to evolve by trial and error a programme where biological and chemical control exist in peaceful coexistence, even in co-operation, but much more must be known about predators and parasites before control programmes can be worked out by prediction.

Quite apart from field applications, the behaviour of predator and prey, the mechanisms of prey detection and capture, and the alarm reactions of prey present problems of great interest, even if most predator–prey encounters are weighted too heavily in the predator's favour to qualify as contests in neurophysiology, as Roeder[10] has viewed them. The complex behaviour of some hymenopteran predators, their prey specificity, and provisioning behaviour have proved fertile studies for ethologists, and many more problems along these lines await attention. The extent and means of intraganglion stinging, as suggested of the pompilid wasps, for example, deserves study; the sensory mechanisms may be similar but simpler than for host location by hyperparasites.

The Hymenoptera undoubtedly present the most fascinating questions in the toxicology of arthropod venoms. The requisite background knowledge is now accumulating that will enable serious attacks on the composition and action of these substances. While it may be doubted whether their study will yield anything of direct value in the insecticide field, comparative studies on their composition will certainly contribute to an understanding of arthropod pharmacology.

Auto-immunity has been demonstrated in several venom producing arthropods. We can as yet only guess at its basis.

These few topics, that come immediately to mind, leave one in agreement with Brues[7] that: 'so far predatory insects have not received the attention that they deserve at the hands of the biologist': his comment is true, in general, of arthropods as predators.

Addendum—Since this manuscript was submitted, Rathmeyer[107,108] has published an extensive account of stinging by the bee hunting wasp *Philanthus*, in which ganglionic stinging is shown to be exceptional. Further evidence is also provided that the site of action of wasp venoms is peripheral.

REFERENCES

1. WIGGLESWORTH, V. B. *The Principles of Insect Physiology*, 5th edn: Methuen, London, 1953
2. MILNE, A. 'Definition of competition among animals'. *Symp. Soc. exp. Biol.* 1961, **XV**, 40–61
3. SALT, G. 'Competition among insect parasitoids'. *Symp. Soc. exp. Biol.* 1961, **XV**, 96–119
4. SALT, G. 'The haemocytic reaction of insects to foreign bodies'. *The Cell and the Organism* (Ed. J. A. Ramsay and V. B. Wigglesworth): Cambridge University Press, Cambridge, 1961, 175–192
5. FABRE, J. H. *Souvenirs Entomologiques* Delgrave, Paris, 1879
6. WHEELER, W. M. *Demons of the Dust. A Study in Insect Behaviour:* Norton, New York, 1930
7. BRUES, C. T. *Insect Dietary:* Harvard University Press, Cambridge, Mass., 1946
8. BRISTOWE, W. S. *The Comity of Spiders*, Vol. II: Royal Society, London, 1941
9. CLAUSEN, C. P. *Entomophagous Insects:* McGraw-Hill, New York, 1941
10. ROEDER, K. D. 'A physiological approach to the relation between predator and prey'. *Smithson misc. Coll.* 1959, **137**, 287–306
11. HOLLINGS, C. S. 'Principles of insect predation'. *Annu. Rev. Ent.* 1961, **6**, 163–182
12. ALEXANDER, A. J. 'Notes on onychophoran behaviour'. *Ann. Natal Mus.* 1957, **14**, 35–43
13. MARSHALL, S. M. and ORR, A. P. 'Feeding and nutrition'. *The Physiology of Crustacea* (Ed. T. H. Waterman) Vol. 1: Academic Press, New York, 1960, 227–258
14. SCHÖNE, H. 'Complex behaviour'. *The Physiology of Crustacea* (Ed. T. H. Waterman) Vol. 2: Academic Press, New York, 1961, 465–520
15. SWEETMAN, H. L. *The Principles of Biological Control:* Wm. C. Brown Company, Dubuque, 1958
16. BURNETT, T. 'Experimental host parasite populations'. *Annu. Rev. Ent.* 1959, **4**, 235–250

17. ANDREWARTHA, H. G. and BIRCH, L. C. *The Distribution and Abundance of Animals:* Chicago University Press, Chicago, 1954

18. HUFFAKER, C. B. 'Experimental studies on predation'. *Hilgardia* 1958, **27,** 343–382

19. RIPPER, W. E. 'Effect of pesticides on balance of arthropod populations'. *Annu. Rev. Ent.* 1956, **1,** 403–438

20. PICKETT, A. D. and PATTERSON, N. A. 'The influence of spray programs on the fauna of apple orchards in Nova Scotia. IV. A review'. *Canad. Ent.* 1953, 472–478

21. COLLYER, E. and KIRBY, A. H. M. 'Some factors affecting the balance of phytophagous and predacious mites on apples in South East England'. *J. hort. Sci.* 1955, **30,** 97–108

22. COLLYER, E. 'Some insectary experiments with predacious mites to determine their effect on the development of *Metatetranychus ulmi* (Koch) populations.' *Ent. exp. appl.* 1958, **1,** 138–146

23. HUFFAKER, C. B. and KENNETT, C. E. 'Experimental studies on predation. Predation and the cyclamen mite population on strawberries in California'. *Hilgardia* 1956, **26,** 191–222

24. BANKS, C. J. 'An ecological study of Coccinellidae associated with *Aphis fabae* Scop. on *Vicia faba*'. *Bull. ent. Res.* 1958, **46,** 561–587

25. WILLIAMS, C. B. *Insect Migration:* Collins, London, 1958

26. RICHARDS, O. W. and WALOFF, N. 'A study of a natural population of *Phytodecta olivacea* (Forster) (Coleoptera, Chrysomeloidea)'. *Phil. Trans.* 1961, **244,** 205–257

27. DEMPSTER, J. P. 'A quantitative study of the predators on the eggs and larvae of the broom beetle *Phytodecta olivacea* (Forster), using the precipitin test'. *J. Anim. Ecol.* 1960, **29,** 149–167

28. FOX, C. J. S. and McLELLAN, C. R. 'Some Carabidae and Staphylinidae shown to feed on a wireworm, *Agriotes sputator* (L.), by the precipitin test'. *Canad. Ent.* 1956, **88,** 228–231

29. FLESCHNER, C. A. 'Studies on searching capacity of the larvae of three predators of the citrus red mite'. *Hilgardia* 1950, **20,** 233–265

30. BANKS, C. J. 'The behaviour of individual coccinellid larvae on plants'. *Brit. J. Anim. Behav.* 1957, **5,** 12–24

31. BALDUS, K. 'Experimentelle Untersuchungen über die Fernlokalisation der Libellen ((*Aeschna cyanea*)'. *Z. vergl. Physiol.* 1926, **3,** 475–505

32. ALVERDES, F. 'Beobachtungen an Ephemerida und Libellenlarven'. *Biol. Zbl.* 1924, **43,** 577–605

33. RICHARD, G. 'Contribution à l'étude éthologique des Odonates'. *Proc. XI int. Congr. Ent.* 1960, **1,** 604–607

34. FRIEDERICHS, H. F. 'Beiträge zur Morphologie und Physiologie der Sehorgane der Cicindeliden (Col.)'. *Z. Morph. Ökol. Tiere* 1931, **21,** 1–172

35. HOMANN, H. 'Beiträge zur Physiologie des Spinnenauges'. *Z. vergl. Physiol.* 1928, **7,** 201–268

36. DRESS, O. 'Untersuchungen über die angeborenen Verhaltensweisen bei Springspinnen'. *Z. Tierpsychol.* 1952, **9,** 169–207

37. CRANE, J. 'Comparative biology of salticid spiders at Rancho Grande, Venezuela'. *Zoologica* 1949, **34,** 159–214

38. LUDTKE, H. 'Die Funktion waagerecht liegender Augenteile der Rückenschwimmer'. *Z. vergl. Physiol.* 1935, **22,** 67–118

39. TINBERGEN, N. *The study of Instinct:* Oxford University Press, London, 1951

40. RABE, W. 'Beiträge zum Orientierungsproblem der Wasserwanzen'. *Z. vergl. Physiol.* 1953, **35,** 300–325

41. MITTELSTAEDT, H. 'Prey capture in mantids'. *Recent Advances in Invertebrate Physiology*: University of Oregon Publication, Eugene, 1957, 51–71

42. WILSON, E. O. 'The ecology of some North American dacetine ants'. *Ann. ent. Soc. Amer.* 1953, **46,** 479

43. BROWN, W. R. 'A preliminary report on dacetine ant studies in Australia'. *Ann. ent. Soc. Amer.* 1953, **46,** 465

44. TINBERGEN, N. 'Über die Orientierung des Bienenwolfes. II. Die Bienenjagd'. *Z. vergl. Physiol.* 1935, **21,** 699–716

45. PETERS, H. 'Die Jadghandlung der Kreuzspinne (*Epeira diademata*)'. *Z. vergl. Physiol.* 1931, **15,** 693–748

46. BAERENDS, G. P. 'Fortpflanzungsverhalten und Orientierung der Grabwespe, *Ammophila campestris* Jur'. *Tijdschr. Ent.* 1941, **84,** 68–275

47. EVANS, H. E. *Studies on the Comparative Ethology of Digger Wasps of the Genus Bembix*: Comstock, Ithaca, 1957

48. THOMPSON, W. R. 'On the relative value of parasites and predators in the biological control of insect pests'. *Bull. ent. Res.* 1929, **19,** 343–350

49. VOWLES, O. N. 'The foraging of ants'. *Brit. J. Anim. Behav.* 1955, **3,** 1–13

50. DE GEER, G. *Memoirs pour servir a l'histoire des Insects*, Tome III: Pierre Hesselberg, Stockholm, 1773

51. POISSON, R. 'Etude des hemiptères aquatiques'. *Bull. biol.* 1924, **58,** 49–305

52. MELIN, D. 'Contributions to the knowledge of the Swedish Asilids'. *Zool. Bidr. Uppsala* 1923, **8,** 1–317

53. WHITFIELD, F. G. S. 'The relation between the feeding habits and the structure of the mouth parts in the Asilidae'. *Proc. zool. Soc. Lond.* 1925, 299–638

54. EISNER, T. 'The effectiveness of arthropod defensive secretions'. *Proc. XI int. Congr. Ent.* 1961, **3,** 264–268

55. MANTON, S. and HEATLEY, N. G. 'Studies on Onychophora. II. The feeding, digestion, excretion and food storage of *Peripatopsis*'. *Phil. Trans.* 1937, **227B,** 411

56. HEATLEY, N. G. 'The digestive enzymes of the Onychophora'. *J. exp. Biol.* 1936, **13,** 329–343

57. PLATEAU, F. 'Recherches sur les phenomènes de l'appareil digestif chez les Myriapoda'. *Mem. Acad. R. Belg.* 1878, **42,** 1–91

58. ZELLER, E. A. 'Enzymes as essential components of bacterial and animal toxins'. *The Enzymes* (Ed. J. B. Sumner and K. Myrback) Vol. 1, part 2: Academic Press, New York, 1951, 968–1012

59. HASE, A. 'Beiträge zur experimentellen Parasitologie'. *Z. angew. Ent.* 1927, **12,** 243–297

60. CORNWALL, J. W. 'Some centipedes and their venom'. *Indian J. med. Res.* 1916, **3,** 541–577

61. FAVILLI, G. 'Occurrence of spreading factors and some properties of hyaluronidase in animal parasites and venoms'. *Venoms* (Ed. E. E. Buckley and N. Porges) Vol. 2: A.A.A.S. Publication, Washington 1956, 81–89

62. MURNHAGAN, M. 'Site and mechanism of tick paralysis'. *Science* 1960, **131,** 418–419

63. KAISER, E. and MICHL, H. *Die Biochemie der tierischen Gifte*: Deuticke, Vienna, 1958

64. BERTKAU, P. 'Über den Verdauungsapparat der Spinnen'. *Archiv. mikr. Anat.* 1885, **24,** 398–451

65. SCHLOTTKE, E. 'Über die Verdauungsfermente der Vogelspinnen'. *S.B. naturf. Ges. Rostock* 1936, **6,** 89–106

66. MUIC, N., STANIC, M. and MENIGA, A. 'Beiträge zur Kenntnis des Spinnengiftes von *Latrodectus tredecimguttatus*'. *Z. physiol. Chem.* 1956, **305,** 70

67. BETTINI, S. and TOSCHI-FRONTALI, N. 'Biochemical and toxicological aspects of *Latrodectus tredecimguttatus* venom'. *Proc. XI int. Congr. Ent.* 1960, **3,** 115–121

68. LEBEZ, D. 'Beiträge zum Studium des Giftes von *Lactrodectus tredecimguttatus* Rossi'. *Z. physiol. Chem.* 1954, **298,** 73

69. CANTORE, G. P. and BETTINI, S. 'Contribution to the study of the pharma-cological effect of the venom of *Latrodectus tredecimguttatus*'. *Riv. Parassit.* 1958, **19,** 297–306

70. JAQUES, R. 'Hyaluronidase content of animal venoms'. *Venoms* (Ed. E. E. Buckley and N. Porges) : A.A.A.S. Publication, Washington, 1956, 291–293

71. EDWARDS, C. and KUFFLER, S. W. 'The blocking effect of gamma-aminobutyric acid and the action of related compounds on single nerve cells'. *J. Neurochem.* 1959, **4,** 19–30

72. SUGA, N. and KABUKI, Y. 'Pharmacological studies on the auditory synapses in a grasshopper'. *J. exp. Biol.* 1961, **38,** 759–770

73. FISCHER, F. G. and BOHN, H. 'Die Giftsekrete der brasilianischen Tarantel *Lycosa erythrognatha* und der Wanderspinne *Phoneutria fera*'. *Z. physiol. Chem.* 1957, **306,** 265–269

74. ADAM, K. R. and WEISS, C. '5-Hydroxytryptamine in scorpion venom'. *Nature, Lond.* 1956, **178,** 421–422

75. MIRANDA, F. and LISSITZKY, S. 'Scorpamins: the toxic proteins of scorpion venoms'. *Nature, Lond.* 1961, **190,** 443–444

76. LINDER, H. J. 'Structure and histochemistry of the maxillary glands in the milkweed bug'. *J. Morph.* 1956, **99,** 575–612

77. BAPTIST, B. A. 'Morphology of the salivary glands of Hemiptera–Heteroptera'. *Quart. J. micr. Sci.* 1941, **83,** 91–139

78. EDWARDS, J. S. 'The action and composition of the saliva of an assassin bug, *Platymeris rhadamanthus*. Gerst. (Hem. Red.)'. *J. exp. Biol.* 1961, **38,** 61–77

79. EDWARDS, J. S. 'Spitting as a defensive mechanism in a predatory reduviid'. *Proc. XI int. Congr. Ent.* 1961, **3,** 259–263

80. EVANS, W. A. L. 'Studies on the digestive enzymes of the blowfly *Calliphora erythrocephala*. II. Kinetic constants of the larval gut proteinase'. *Exp. Parasitol.* 1958, **7,** 69–81

81. STÄGER, R. 'Studien am Ameisenlöwen'. *Biol. Z.* 1925, **45,** 65–93

82. BEARD, R. L. 'The nature of certain arthropod venoms and their effects on insect physiology'. *Proc. XI int. Congr. Ent.* 1960, **3,** 44–47

83. SMITH, R. C. 'The biology of the Chrysopidae'. *Mem. Cornell agric. exp. Sta.* 1922, **58,** 1287–1372

84. HADDOW, M. B. 'Note on the predatory larva of the mosquito *Culex tigripes*'. *Proc. R. ent. Soc. Lond.* 1942, **17A,** 73–74

85. MANSBRIDGE, G. H. and BUSTON, H. W. 'On the biology of some Ceroplatinae and Macrocerinae'. *Trans. R. ent. Soc. Lond.* **81,** 75–132

86. RICHARDS, A. M. 'Observations on the New Zealand glow-worm, *Arachno-campa luminosa* Skuse 1890'. *Trans. roy. Soc. N.Z.* 1960, **88,** 559–574

87. BEARD, R. L. 'The toxicology of *Habrobracon* venom; a study of a natural insecticide'. *Bull. Conn. agric. exp. Sta.* 1952, 562

88. HARLOW, P. A. 'The action of drugs on the central nervous system of the locust (*Locusta migratoria*)'. *Ann. appl. Biol.* 1958, **46,** 55–72

89. HILL, R. B. and USHERWOOD, P. N. R. 'The action of 5-hydroxytryptamine and related compounds on neuromuscular transmission in the locust *Schistocerca gregaria*'. *J. Physiol.* 1961, **157,** 393–401

90. DAVEY, K. G. 'A pharmacologically active agent in the reproductive system of insects'. *Canad. J. Zool.* 1961, **38,** 39–45

91. NIELSEN, E. T. 'Über den Stoffwechsel der von Grabwespen paralysierten Tiere'. *Vidensk. Medd. dansk. naturk. Foren. Kbh.* 1935, **99,** 149–231

92. HARTZELL, A. 'Histopathology of nerve lesions of a cicada after paralysis by the killer wasp'. *Contr. Boyce Thompson Inst.* 1935, **7,** 421–425

93. NEUMANN, W. and HABERMANN, E. 'Paper electrophoresis separation of pharmacologically and biochemically active components of bee and snake venoms'. *Venoms.* (Ed. E. E. Buckley and N. Porges) A.A.A.S. Publication, Washington, 171–174

94. PAVAN, M. 'Biochemical aspects of insect poisons'. *Proc. int. Congr. Biochem.* 1958, **12,** 15–36

95. BLUM, M. S. and CALLAHAN, P. S. 'Chemical and biological properties of the venom of the fire ant *Solenopsis saevissima*'. *Proc. XI int. Congr. Ent.* 1960, **3,** 290–293

96. PORTIER, A. 'Recherches physiologiques sur les insectes aquatiques'. *C. R. Soc. Biol., Paris* 1909, **56,** 379–382

97. WIGGLESWORTH, V. B. 'Observations on the Furau (Cicindelidae) of Northern Nigeria'. *Bull. ent. Res.* 1930, **20,** 403–406

98. PECKHAM, G. W. and PECKHAM, E. G. *Wasps, Social and Solitary:* Houghton Mifflin, New York, 1905

99. TOBIAS, J. M. 'The effects of phospholipase, collagenase and chymotrypsin on impulse conduction and resting potential in the lobster axon with parallel experiments on frog muscle'. *J. cell. comp. Physiol.* 1955, **46,** 183–207

100. PICKEN, L. E. R. *The Organisation of Cells:* Oxford University Press, London, 1961

101. RICHARDS, A. G. and CUTKOMP, L. K. 'Neuropathology in insects'. *J.N.Y. ent. Soc.* 1945, **53,** 313–355

102. FELDBERG, W. 'The action of bee venom, cobra venom, and lysolecithin on the adrenal medulla'. *J. Physiol.* 1940, **99,** 104–118

103. GAUTRELET, J. and CORTEGGIANI, E. 'Étude comparative de la libération de l'acétylcholine in tissue cérébral *in vitro*'. *C.R. Soc. Biol., Paris* 1939, **131,** 951–954

104. WIGGLESWORTH, V. B. 'The nutrition of the central nervous system in the cockroach *Periplaneta americana* L.'. *J. exp. Biol.* 1960, **37,** 500–512

105. ASHURST, D. E. and CHAPMAN, J. A. 'The connective tissue sheath of the nervous system of *Locusta migratoria*'. *Quart. J. micr. Sci.* 1961, **102,** 463–468

106. TREHERNE, J. E. 'The distribution and exchange of ions and molecules in the central nervous system of *Periplaneta americana*'. *J. exp. Biol.* 1962, **39,** 729–746

107. RATHMEYER, W. 'Paralysis caused by the digger wasp *Philanthus*'. *Nature, Lond.* 1962, **196,** 1148–1151

108. RATHMEYER, W. 'Das Paralysierungsproblem beim Beinenwolf, *Philanthus triangulum* F. (Hym. Sphec.)'. *Z. vergl. Physiol.* 1962, **45,** 413–462

4

ANATOMICAL AND PHYSIOLOGICAL ADAPTATIONS IN DIVING MAMMALS

R. J. Harrison and J. D. W. Tomlinson

"To grope down into the bottom of the sea after them; to have one's hand among the unspeakable foundations, ribs, and very pelvis of the world; this is a fearful thing."
                                                                    Herman Melville

INTRODUCTION

Marine mammals have fascinated biologists for over two thousand years and man has been quick to appreciate the commercial uses of their products[1]. Their swimming and diving abilities, their intelligence and circus tricks, their aggression or friendliness to man, even their mating habits have been the subjects of reports that have entered the realms of fantasy and mythology. Certain anatomical and physiological modifications have been evolved in most mammals which spend a major part of their time in water; in general the greater the modification the better the performance. As with submarines or Olympic swimmers, those that dive longest and deepest, swim fastest and farthest with expenditure of least energy may earn success. Aquatic existence is by no means without special dangers, however, and success in the environment is not just a matter of construction, shape and power. The very medium that is so buoyant to a whale can drown it, can fatally affect a seal if imbibed too liberally and can, under certain circumstances, be the cause of acute pain and even death if submersion is too deep. Constant exposure to water has a deleterious action on mammalian skin, even more so when the water is disturbed by waves, tides and currents and is liable to become frozen. All marine mammals have to accommodate to changes in temperature in the environment and if the animal habitually migrates, the alteration in temperature may be considerable.

All mammals can live for a short time when submerged in water, longer if they are able, or can learn, to swim; but only if they can dive with facility can they really be considered 'at home' in their environment. The first questions to be answered are, therefore: how long can diving mammals remain submerged, and how deep can they dive? We shall then consider some of the adaptations present in their anatomy, and discuss, where there is any evidence, the functional significance of these adaptations. It must be emphasized that this review is not exhaustive and is mainly concerned with topics that have interested the authors, particularly with reference to whales and seals. General descriptions of the anatomy of aquatic mammals have been given by Howell[2] and many others[3,4].

DURATION AND DEPTH OF DIVES

It is obviously difficult to give precise figures for the maximum duration of a dive for any species. Many factors, such as the fitness of the animal, length of previous dives, age and so on, can influence performance. Diving the animal to death is not necessarily an accurate way of assessing a record dive: it is not certain at what point short of death recovery would have followed. *Table 4.1* gives the longest recorded dives for those animals for which

Table 4.1. Record dives by animals

Animal	Duration of dive	Authority
Pigeon	1 min	Bohr (1897)[5]
Hen	3 min	Bohr (1897)[5]
Penguin	7 min	Scholander (1940)[6]
Duck	17 min	Richet (1899)[7]
Platypus	5–10 min	Burrell (1927)[8]
White rat	2 min 6 sec	Bert (1870)[9]
Water rat	2 min 17 sec	Bert (1870)[9]
Musk rat	12 min	Irving (1939)[10]
Coypu rat	7 min	Authors' observations
Beaver	7 min	Scholander (1940)[6]
	15 min	Irving (1939)[10]
Rabbit	3 min	Bert (1870)[9]
Cat	2 min 55 sec	Bert (1870)[9]
Dog	4 min 25 sec	Bert (1870)[9]
Common seal	28 min	Harrison (1960)[11]
Grey seal	20 min	Matthews (1952)[12]
Ringed seal	20 min	Freuchen (1935)[13]
Elephant seal	More than 30 min	Matthews (1952)[12]
	12·5 min	Paulian (1957)[14]
Manatee	7–16 min	Parker (1922)[15]
Porpoise	12 min	Scholander (1940)[6]
Blue whale	50 min	Irving (1939)[10]
Finback whale	30 min	Irving (1939)[10]
Sperm whale	75 min	Irving (1939)[10]
Bottlenosed whale	120 min	Irving (1939)[10]
Man (pearl and sponge divers)	2 min 30 sec	Irving (1939)[10]

observations are available: some were in fact obtained from dives to extinction. It will be seen that many marine mammals can stay submerged for periods of time well in excess of those for other mammals or even diving birds. During everyday life, however, dives are obviously of much shorter duration.

The maximum depth reached by a diving mammal is as difficult to determine as the duration of a dive. The literature is full of anecdotes of the fouling of nets, hooks and cables by whales and seals at immense depths, but there is little accurate information as to how deep they habitually dive or could dive if necessary. However deep the cable or line were thought to be, there is no certain evidence that the animal was not dead or dying before fouling it, nor that the animal could have returned safely to the surface from such a depth. Matthews[12] has argued that there are no theoretical reasons why a whale should not go to almost any depth. Some of the arguments he uses will be discussed later, but it does appear that seals, at least under experimental conditions, have limits to the depths at which they can survive for more than very short periods.

Table 4.2 lists some of the deepest dives that have been quoted in the literature, but it must be emphasized that the evidence is not always supported by recordings with proper instruments and is in some instances second-hand.

Table 4.2. Record depths of dives

Animal	Depth of dive	Authority
Penguin	At least 12 m	Experimental diving. Scholander (1940)[6]
Common seal (2 years old)	91·4 m	Experimental diving. Harrison and Tomlinson (1960)[16]
Grey seal (young)	128–146 m	Caught on a hook. Collett (1881)[17]
Grey seal (4 months old)	22 m	Line attached. Scholander (1940)[6]
Weddell seal	91·4 m	Diving below ice. Bertram (1940)[18]
Hooded seal (6 months old)	75 m	Line attached. Scholander (1940)[6]
Harp seal	182 m	Caught in a net. Nansen (1925)[19]
Harp seal	273 m	Caught on a hook. Collett (1881)[17]
Steller sea lion	110–146 m	Fishermen's observations. Kenyon (1952)[20]
Porpoise	20 m	Line attached. Scholander (1940)[6]
Fin whale	275 m	Neck broken by impact with sea bottom. Howell (1930)[2]
Fin whale	355 m	Line attached. Scholander (1940)[6]
Sperm whale	900 m	Entangled in a cable. Laurie (1933)[21]
Man	165 m	In flexible suit with special breathing mixture. Davis (1955)[22]

DIVES BY COMMON SEALS

The diving performance of newborn common seals (*Phoca vitulina*) pups up to several months old and adolescents up to 3 years old, was ascertained by attaching them to boards after the manner described by Scholander[6] and immersing them in the sea, in water in a shallow tank, and under water in a pressure-chamber. The chamber was capable of simulating rapidly pressures of up to 100 m of water. Seals were also secured in a specially designed lace-up 'Terylene' corset to enable free swimming to take place at the end of ropes either in a tank or at sea (*Figures 4.1* and *4.2*). Recordings from axillary electrodes were obtained on an Elmquist portable electro-cardiogram during all dives. Respiration rate was assessed by counting the nostril opening that accompanies every breath. When necessary, seals were anaesthetized with 3 to 10 ml of a 1 in 40 solution of thiopentone injected into the extradural vertebral vein (p. 135), as if performing a lumbar puncture. Anaesthesia was maintained either by further injection of thiopentone or by introduction of an endotracheal tube and administration of nitrous oxide and oxygen.

Seals of different ages were dived in several ways for varying lengths of time. The animals were never submerged until they died, as the heart rate recordings indicated when they were becoming embarrassed from oxygen exhaustion. Young seals could not tolerate diving for as long as adolescents and adults. The pups are able to dive for remarkable periods even at birth: pups from a day to a week old can dive for up to 8 minutes. Seals 2 to 3 years old are able to tolerate shallow dives for 25 to 30 minutes. It is more than likely that adult seals can stay submerged for even longer if forced to.

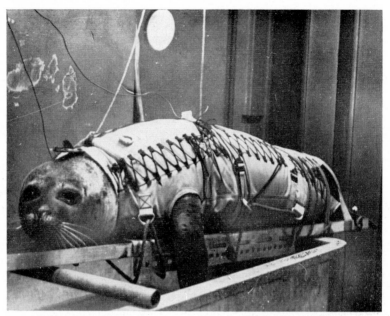

Figure 4.1. Photograph of a 2-year-old common seal restrained in its harness, with axillary electrodes in place and about to be dived in a shallow tank.

Figure 4.2. Photograph of a 2-year-old seal in its harness towing a frogman at sea.

We have considerable evidence, however, that common seals in their natural environment do not habitually dive for longer than 5 to 10 minutes.

Investigations of heart and respiratory rate were made on seals out of water and the heart rate was recorded during all experimental dives and other procedures. The animals were secured on boards or in harness as loosely as possible and were not anaesthetized during the dives unless specifically stated. No animal was dived again unless the heart rate and behaviour had returned to conditions prevailing at the beginning of the first dive.

Heart and Respiratory Rate in Resting Surfaced Seals

The heart rate displays considerable variation, and even irregularity, in all animals whatever their age and whether or not they have recently dived[23]. Young pups have a resting heart rate of from 90 to 180 beats/minute; in 2- to 3-year-old adolescents it varies from 75 to 180 beats/minute. Proximity to the investigator, or indication to the seal that it is about to dive (by submerging it a number of times for a few seconds), does not unduly influence the heart rate. Any tachycardia that resulted from a struggle to secure the seal to a board, or in its harness, soon subsided and seals often went peacefully to sleep during a pause in a diving programme.

Respiratory rate out of water is comparatively regular at 18 to 20/minute in both pups and adults. It is less regular when the seal is immersed in a harness with only its nostrils above water. The heart rate increased rapidly from 112 to 144 when a seal was immersed suddenly to its neck, head still above water, and fell to 120 after 5 minutes. It occasionally slowed from 120 to 60 for a few seconds following a voluntary respiratory pause longer than normal. Tweaking the vibrissae caused episodic slowing of the heart rate to 75 beats/minute for a few seconds; smacking the face raised the rate to 165 beats/minute. Throwing cold water over the face had little effect on the heart rate.

Prevention of respiration by forcible closure of the nostrils and mouth of a seal out of water caused a fall in heart rate from 130 to 80 after 5 seconds, to 48 after 22 seconds, to 15 after 48 seconds, and was followed by violent struggling that prevented further recordings. One yearling common seal was anaesthetized, and an attempt was made to determine the effect that variations in respiratory rate would have on heart rate. Increasing the respiratory rate artificially to 40 for a period of 2 minutes had no appreciable effect on the heart rate. The respiratory rate was then lowered to 5; after 1·25 minutes, when the heart rate had dropped to 17, the animal collapsed, but was later resuscitated.

Shallow Dives just below the Surface

Young 2- to 3-year-old common seals were, for example, dived, secured on a board, for periods of up to a maximum of 28 minutes (see *Figure 4.3*). In longer dives intermittent struggling started at 15 minutes and became extreme during the last few minutes, so the animals were brought to the surface. The diving bradycardia did not develop as rapidly as in the grey seal *Halichoerus*[6]; the slowest heart rate (4 beats/minute) occurred between

1 and 3 minutes after diving. Thereafter the heart rate usually increased gradually as time passed. The degree of bradycardia and the rate at which it developed were not significantly affected by the rate at which the heart

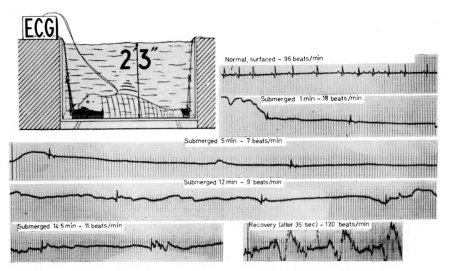

Figure 4.3. Electrocardiographic recordings taken during a 15 minute dive by a 2-year-old common seal in a shallow tank.

was beating before the dive commenced. Repeated diving of the same animal (after short recovery periods of a few minutes) did not influence the rate of onset, degree of bradycardia, or recovery behaviour. There was always a

Table 4.3. Heart rates of 6 1-month-old common seal pups before, during and after a 5 minutes shallow dive (beats/minute)

Seal pup	Surfaced	30 seconds	1 minute	3 minutes	5 minutes	Surfaced after dive
1	120	—	6	15	10	—
2	132	—	12	13	13	216
3	144	—	—	10	15	—
4	140	8	8	10	8	150
5	140	9	10	10	13	240
6	120	—	9	12	15	150

recovery tachycardia lasting for 5 to 10 minutes after a dive of more than a few minutes. The slowest and longest lasting bradycardia was observed in older seals: the bradycardia also developed more rapidly.

The heart rates of six pups, all about a month old, which were dived under identical conditions for 5 minutes, are given in *Table 4.3.* It shows the degree of variation exhibited by the heart rate during dives of this length. The heart rates on recovery were recorded 20 to 30 seconds after surfacing. Several pups of similar age were dived for longer periods. After 8 minutes the heart rate had risen from 24 to 30 (*Figure 4.4*), except in one pup in which it stayed fairly low at 14: prolongation of the dive beyond this time embarrassed the animals so they were surfaced. The behaviour of the heart rate in older seals is given in *Figure 4.4* which shows that the release of the bradycardia as time passes during a dive is more marked in longer dives. The heart rate never rose above about 40, even when the animal was struggling to reach the surface after a long dive.

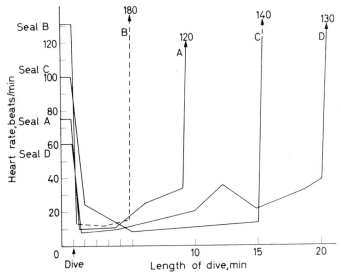

Figure 4.4. Diagram to show characteristics of heart rates during dives by four common seals. The resting heart rates in the animals surfaced are shown on the left, with the recovery rates a few seconds after surfacing and removal from water indicated at the top of the diagram. Seal A was a week-old pup: Seal B was a 3-month-old pup: Seal C and Seal D were both 1 year old. The diagram indicates that as the dives progressed there was a varying degree of release of bradycardia.

A 2-year-old seal was secured in a harness that left its head, four flippers and tail free; guide ropes and electrocardiograph leads were attached. The animal swam freely in a shallow tank and dived for periods of several minutes. The heart rate showed changes similar to those recorded when the seal was secured to a board. It was noticed that the seal exhaled when it broke the surface after a dive; this observation has been frequently confirmed by us and is also mentioned by Matthews[12]. Another young seal behaved similarly in a harness when allowed to swim in the sea. It towed a small dinghy containing two men with ease at about walking speed and subsequently towed a skin-diver for a short distance under water.

A seal secured to a board was prepared for diving in a shallow tank; before diving and throughout the dive it was forcibly prevented from exhaling by closing its nostrils or mouth. The heart rate was 144 beats/minute on the surface (nose and mouth closed) and fell to 24 beats/minute after 30 seconds. It remained at that rate for 75 seconds after which the seal struggled so violently to exhale that no further recording was possible. We

121

have noted repeatedly that seals exhale under water several times during a dive. The first occasion is usually 1 to 1½ minutes after the dive starts, and subsequently at irregular intervals. The amount of air exhaled each time is difficult to assess but appears to be of the order of 10 to 20 ml. It seems that it is necessary for the animal to deflate its lungs slightly as a dive progresses.

These experiments indicate that common seal pups can dive in shallow water for periods of up to 8 minutes before becoming embarrassed, that 2- to 3-year-old seals can stay submerged for periods up to about 30 minutes, and that it is probable that adults can dive for even longer.

Deep Dives

Three types of experimental deep diving were carried out: (*a*) one-week-old pups were lowered into the sea on a board to depths of up to 6 m; (*b*) two-year-old seals were placed in a tank filled with water inside a pressure-chamber and the air pressure increased by stages to depths equivalent to up

Table 4.4. Heart rates of young common seals during dives of varying length at different depths

Seal	Surfaced	30 seconds	1 minute	3 minutes	5 minutes	8 minutes	Surfaced after dive
1	75	10 (7 m)	5 (7 m)	5 (7 m)	5 (7 m)	8 (7 m)	175
2	90	5 (10 m)	5 (10 m)	6 (10 m)			120
3	108	9 (10 m)	5 (10 m)	5 (10 m)	7 (10 m)		150
4	130	13 (10 m)	6 (30 m)	6 (30 m)	8 (30 m)		160
5	120	22 (1 m)	14 (18 m)	17 (91 m)	7 (91 m)		156
6	60	—	— (91 m)	4 (91 m)	9 (91 m)	13 (91 m)	Died

to 30 m, and (*c*) two-year-old seals similarly secured were taken rapidly to 90 m and kept there for periods up to 5 minutes. *Table 4.4* indicates the variations in heart rate that occurred during some of these experimental dives.

The pups showed an immediate bradycardia to between 10 and 16 beats/minute, but within a few minutes under water the rate began to rise to 30 beats/minute. The older animals, when submerged in the pressure-chamber, displayed an immediate bradycardia of 4 to 15 beats/minute which was maintained for up to 5 minutes at depths equivalent to 70 m. There was no indication in the older animals of a gradual decrease in the bradycardia as the dive progressed at a constant depth. There was, however, an increase in heart rate as the animal returned to shallower depths. The pups often showed a marked decrease in bradycardia after quite a short period (1 to 3 minutes) at only 20 feet. There was no noticeable change in the bradycardia of adolescent seals in dives of short duration down to 70 m. One young seal, having been taken down to the equivalent of 30 metres in the pressure tank, managed to raise its nostrils above the water when the pressure, being reduced, was at the equivalent of 15 m. It appeared healthy immediately after the dive, and carried out shallow diving during the ensuing weeks without ill effect. Three months later the seal became anorexic, lost weight and was killed. Extensive surgical emphysema was seen in the lungs, thoracic wall and vertebral venous system at post-mortem examination. It was concluded that the animal had inhaled air under pressure and ruptured a lung during the return to the surface.

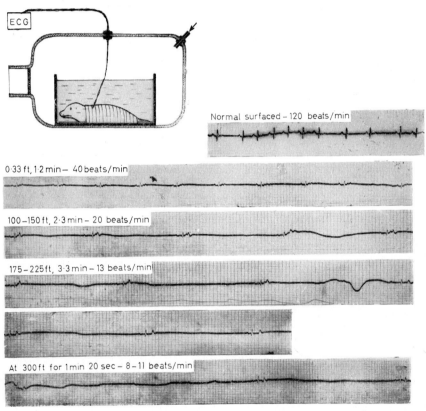

Figure 4.5. Reproduction of electrocardiographic recordings of a 2-year-old common seal dived in a pressure tank (see sketch at top left) to a depth equivalent to 300 feet of water. The heart rate slowed to 8 during the 1 minute 20 seconds the seal was kept at this depth. The animal 'returned' safely to the surface and appeared quite fit.

A 2-year-old seal was taken rapidly to a depth of 91 m in 4 minutes (*Figure 4.5*). It remained at this depth for 1 minute 20 seconds, and returned to the surface by stages, being held for 30 seconds at every 20 m to make ECG recordings. On return to the surface the respiratory rate was 30/minute; the animal appeared fit and active, and displayed no signs of 'bends'. The same animal was dived to 91 m the next day and kept there for 5 minutes. Towards the end of this period the cardiac complex on the electrocardiographic recordings indicated some degree of physiological 'defeat'. The animal was returned to the surface and its heart was beating slowly on removal from water. Its pupils were dilated and muscular movements were weak. The heart stopped a few seconds later and the animal could not be resuscitated. A post-mortem examination showed no evidence of air embolism, lung damage or haemorrhage. It is possible that the animal suffered a 'squeeze' at this depth such that the heart could not contract fully and cerebral anoxia followed.

Every seal was observed to exhale air soon after it was immersed in water, and again later as the pressure increased in the chamber.

These experiments suggest that, with the methods used, common seals, 2 to 3 years old can dive with ease to depths down to 70 m and even deeper for short periods. Young pups cannot tolerate such deep dives and after a few minutes begin to exhibit a decrease in bradycardia. It also appears that there is a limit to the depths young common seals can dive and that this limit is about 100 m.

Exposure of Seals to Increased Air Pressure

It was considered to be of interest to investigate the effect on a seal of exposing it simply to a steady increase of air pressure simulating depths equivalent to those it had 'dived' when under water. Two-year-old seals were placed in a pressure-chamber and allowed to breath naturally as the air pressure was increased. The respiratory rate was assessed by counting the nostril openings over periods of half a minute. Increased air pressure equivalent to a depth below water of 70 m caused a bradycardia from 120 to 30. It was not sustained, however, and the heart rate rose to 150 for periods lasting up to 5 seconds. The increase in air pressure caused the respiratory rate to slow from 24 to 8, and it was noticed that this was correlated with the periods of most marked bradycardia. Increase in air pressure to depths equivalent to 10 and to 30 m caused no disturbance of respiration and little slowing of the heart rate. The seals were in no way embarrassed by exposure to increased air pressure but did seem puzzled by the experience. It appeared that only when the seal held its breath was there any heart slowing, again indicating that the bradycardia is linked with interruption of regular respiration.

STIMULATION AND SECTION OF THE VAGUS NERVES IN SEALS

Stimulation of the intact right vagus of an anaesthetized seal pup out of water resulted in slowing of the heart rate from 120 to 22 beats/minute, with immediate recovery to 120 on cessation of stimulation. Stimulation of the intact left vagus resulted in disappearance of the ventricular complex on the recordings: P waves continued to occur at 120 a minute. Stimulation of either vagus in an adult seal completely abolished the heart beat for the period it was applied.

Section of the right vagus in the neck in an anaesthetized pup caused no change in the heart rate (180) and a fall to only 100 on diving, although the beats were irregular. Section of both vagi in pups caused no change in the heart rate when surfaced: in an adult the rate increased from 60 to 90. In short dives, other anaesthetized pups with bilateral vagal section showed no slowing of the heart. Another pup was anaesthetized and both vagi were exposed: it was then dived and after the heart rate had fallen to 24, both vagi were sectioned with the seal under water. There was an immediate rise in heart rate to 156 which persisted for the remainder of the dive and after surfacing.

Intact vagus nerves are, therefore, essential for the production of the marked bradycardia which occurs when seals are submerged, and section of one vagus does not materially affect the slowing of the heart under the conditions of our experiments. Section of the right vagus in an anaesthetized seal pup, with subsequent stimulation of the peripheral end of the cut nerve, produced a complete cessation of heart beat. This continued for the 1·5 minutes duration of the stimulation. Recordings made by means of a cannula tied into a carotid artery, showed that there was an abrupt fall of the blood pressure with no recovery while vagal stimulation was applied. There was, therefore, no 'vagal escape'* mechanism in these animals, and electrocardiographic recordings taken at the time showed no evidence of any normal heart beat, although it is possible that a typical beat might have occurred once or twice during the 1·5 minutes stimulation.

If the diving bradycardia is entirely vagus controlled, it may well be that, during the duration of a dive, it is of great importance to the animal that there should be nothing to disturb the vagal discharge responsible for the slow heart rate. We have dived a seal pup with both vagi sectioned: no bradycardia occurred, and the animal was brought to the surface after a dive of 1 minute. We do not yet know what the effect on such an animal would be if the dive were prolonged, but we suspect that it would be unlikely to be able to dive for much longer than a terrestrial mammal.

In normal yearling and older seals, shallow experimental dives of up to 28 minutes duration have been carried out. An interesting finding in these dives is that after a varying interval the heart rate increases from its lowest level, in some cases in quite a marked manner. In 2- to 3-year-old animals the maximal slowing occurred 2·5 minutes after the dive commenced, when the heart rate was 8 beats/minute. After 12 minutes diving the heart rate in one animal was 32 beats/minute, and 38 beats/minute in another. It is noteworthy that the older seals have in any case a much slower resting heart rate on the surface than the young pups—the former averaging 150 beats/minute, and the latter 65. In the animal taken down rapidly to the equivalent of 300 feet in a pressure-chamber, the slowest heart rate was 4 beats/minute after 3 minutes (depth 200 feet), and then increased to 15 beats/minute after 9 minutes (300 feet).

Other experimental dives show that there is usually a rise in heart rate as the dive proceeds. The rise is not a gradual or inexorable one, but shows considerable variation in both magnitude and onset in different animals. Often a slower rate can occur for a time during the period of increase in heart rate. The rise, such as it is, indicates that either the vagus comes to have less control over the intrinsic heart rate, that its discharge is toned down in response to other afferents reaching the vagal centre, or that other nerves, perhaps sympathetic, act antagonistically to boost the rate. We were

* The phenomenon of increase in heart rate and rise of blood pressure in spite of continued vagal stimulation which causes at first a reduction of these.

impressed with the fact that the 'vagal escape' phenomenon appears to be absent in seals, but in any case its true mechanism (in other animals) seems not yet clearly understood, although its effects are well-described and occur quite shortly after vagal stimulation is commenced.

The possibility that there might be some unusual distribution of the autonomic supply to the seal's heart led us to dissect the vagus and sympathetic trunks. Although little was expected from such dissection, as the exact nerve distribution to the heart itself might probably be of great importance and yet impossible to discover accurately, one or two interesting facts emerged.

Vagus and Sympathetic Trunks in the Seal

The sympathetic trunk in the cervical region of common seals is of small calibre and intimately connected to the larger vagal trunk by fibrous tissue. Indeed, at first sight there appears to be only a single nerve, but once the two are separated at one point it is quite easy to strip them apart throughout their length. There is usually a communicating branch or branches between the anterior cervical sympathetic ganglion and the vagal trunk just caudal to the vagal ganglion.

At the rostral extremity of both right and left thoracic sympathetic trunks there is a large ganglion, corresponding to the stellate ganglion. From this, a large nerve passes in a dorso-cranial direction accompanying the vertebral artery. A much smaller branch passes ventro-cranially and it is this which constitutes the single thin sympathetic trunk in the cervical region.

There is also a third branch from the ganglion, intermediate in size to those mentioned above, which manifests a small swelling, connected on the right side to the phrenic and recurrent laryngeal nerves by thin strands. Sections taken of this swelling show it to be a definite ganglion containing numerous autonomic neurons. On the left side a similar ganglion, situated on a branch from the stellate, communicates with a small plexus which has connections with the vagus and phrenic nerves. So far as could be verified, this ganglion had no communication with the recurrent laryngeal nerve, unlike the right, but it is possible that some slender connections may exist.

From the left vagus, where it lies on the aortic arch, a number of fine branches are given off which form a plexus with branches of the sympathetic coming from the left stellate ganglion. A similar mixed sympathetic and vagal plexus exists on the right side, formed by a branch from the vagus, given off just distal to the recurrent laryngeal nerve, and one from the stellate ganglion of the same side. The distribution of the nerves from these mixed plexuses could not be determined accurately, but it is considered that they terminate in the heart, great vessels and lungs.

The above short description shows that there is a close relationship between the sympathetic trunk and vagus nerve. They intercommunicate freely at many points, and innervate the heart from mixed plexuses, as well as by direct branches. There would appear to be a considerable sympathetic component. The two small ganglia, packed with cells, would appear to be unique to seals, and their connections with the phrenic nerve are perhaps not without significance in view of the role that the latter plays in innervation of the caval sphincter (p. 138).

Effect of Drugs on the Seal Heart

In view of the effects of vagal stimulation on the seal heart, we endeavoured to find out how the heart reacted to certain drugs, both in the intact animal, and in an isolated heart perfusion apparatus, and also what was the effect of stimulation of the cut vagus in the isolated perfused heart. The right carotid artery was exposed in anaesthetized seal pups, the vagus was dissected free and the artery was cannulated and connected with a manometer attached to a recording drum. The heart rate was 140/minute. 5 mg of adrenaline were injected and there was an immediate increase in amplitude of the heart beat with a slight rise in blood pressure, but the heart rate appeared to slow. Injection of 25 and 100 μg of acetylcholine produced no demonstrable effect either on the rate and amplitude of the heart beat or on the blood pressure, but 400 μg produced a marked slowing of heart rate and slight fall in blood pressure. 50 μg of noradrenaline produced a slight rise in blood pressure. An injection of 2 mg of acetylcholine produced a marked fall in blood pressure lasting 30 seconds but the heart rate was only little affected. After 1 mg neostigmine there was a marked fall in blood pressure, the heart slowed, stopped for 45 seconds, and then recovered; the blood pressure rose, but over a further period of 2 minutes the heart slowed again, the blood pressure fell and eventually cardiac arrest set in.

Seal hearts were removed from several young animals and perfused through the coronary vessels with McEwen's solution. When first set up the ventricles were usually fibrillating, which could be stopped by lowering the temperature of the perfusion fluid to below 20°C for a short time, or, sometimes, by injecting isotonic potassium chloride.

Noradrenaline (0·5 to 5 μg), adrenaline (0·1 μg), isoprenaline (0 05 μg) and nicotine (3 mg) all produced a marked increase in heart rate and amplitude of contraction. Acetylcholine (2 to 5 μg) produced transient arrest of heart action, but doses of from 2 to 10 μg produced no effect after 10 mg atropine had been added to the 15 l. perfusion bath (i.e. 0·66 μg/ml). Histamine (10 to 100 μg) evoked no response from the heart. A 10 per cent solution of potassium chloride (0·6 ml) stopped the heart completely: the ventricles recommenced beating before the atria. 1 ml of isotonic calcium chloride produced a moderate increase in amplitude, but no change in heart rate. In these experiments which lasted some 6 hours, the temperature of the perfusing fluid was 37°C, and the coronary flow approximately 110 ml/minute. Cooling the heart to 26°C stopped the atria but the ventricles continued to beat at 20°C.

Electrocardiographic leads were taken directly from the muscle in another perfused seal heart. The heart rate was 96/minute at the start of the experiment. Stimulation of the left vagus abolished the ventricular beat, but the atria continued at the previous rate for some 15 seconds. The stimulus was continued for 75 seconds and during this time several isolated ventricular beats were seen, which became more frequent after 1 minute's stimulation, e.g. 13 in an 8-second period. The atrial rate varied from 30 to 120/minute.

On cessation of stimulation the atria and ventricles returned to a rate of 96/minute. After a few minutes' rest the heart rate had fallen to 84, and 1 μg of adrenaline was injected. This raised the rate to 132/minute after 20 seconds and also increased the amplitude of the heart beat. The heart rate regained its original level after 3 minutes. Atropine (250 μg) was added to the perfusion fluid close to the heart and 3 minutes later stimulation of the vagus produced no effect on either the amplitude of contraction or the heart rate.

From these results we have no reason to believe that the innervation of the seal's heart, or its response to certain drugs, in any way differs from those obtaining in other mammals.

The authors are indebted to Dr A. Stafford for carrying out the experiments on the isolated heart.

HEART RATE OF CETACEANS AND OTHER DIVING MAMMALS

Little accurate information exists about the heart rate of whales, whether surfaced or submerged. Scholander[6] took electrocardiograms of porpoises kept at the surface and also diving freely. Figure 56 of his paper suggests that the heart rate was between 160 and 180 beats and that no diving bradycardia occurred. Forced submersion also was not accompanied by any slowing of the heart. *The Handbook of Biological Data* (1956)[24] gives the following heart rates: dolphin, 150; porpoise, 150; whale (*Beluga* spp.), 12 to 13. It also gives that for the manatee as 50 to 60.

Both the muskrat[25] and the beaver[6,26] display a diving bradycardia. There is some difference of opinion as to how long beavers can dive (between 3 and 15 minutes, *Table 4.1*) but there is no doubt that during the dive a bradycardia gradually develops to as low as 6/minute.

DIVES BY COYPU RATS

The large aquatic hystricomorph rodent *Myocastor coypu* was introduced into the British Isles from South America at the end of the 1920's. Numbers of coypus are now at large in East Anglia; they have an appetite for root crops and the lower parts of reeds. A recent article[27] stated that the coypu was capable of staying submerged for 20 minutes but this has not been authenticated.

Several adult specimens were dived experimentally by us. The heart rate of the animals on the surface varied between 168 and 216 beats/minute; as soon as they were immersed a marked diving bradycardia occurred similar to that observed in seals. One animal had been kept in captivity for over a year and had been allowed to dive in a shallow tank. It was dived experimentally for periods of up to 6 minutes (*Table 4.5*, dives 1 to 4) at the end of which period below water (depth 2 feet) it was exhausted and ground its teeth repeatedly. The heart rate fell abruptly to as low as 4 beats/minute and the bradycardia developed as soon as the rat was immersed. There was some evidence of an increase in the heart rate as the dive progressed and there was a recovery tachycardia on surfacing that reached a rate of 210.

All coypus showed a diving bradycardia, but it was noticed that animals brought straight from the wild into captivity did not develop such a marked bradycardia (*Table 4.5*, dives 5 to 10) on diving as those that had been in captivity for several months. One animal showed a marked dislike of being submerged more than 3 minutes, another returned to the surface dead after 6·5 minutes (*Table 4.5*). The animals brought from the wild were less easy to handle than those kept in captivity for some time and their diving performance may have been a reflection of their apprehensive and nervous

Table 4.5. Table to show heart rates of coypu rats during experimental dives

Duration of dive	Dive number									
	1	2	3	4	5	6	7	8	9	10
Surfaced	216	192	168	180	182	180	180	184	172	168
30 sec	11	9	4	12	11	12	18	33	15	17
1 min	32	32	5	8	11	18	20	25	20	15
1·5 min			7	4	15	20		27	15	12
2 min				6	19	24		30S	?	14
3 min				6	20S	12S			?	15
4 min				7					?S	20
5 min				8						30
6 min				9						50D

S indicates that the animal struggled violently.
D indicates that the animal died at the end of the dive.

state. It may well be that under the conditions of an experimental dive they were unable to exhibit their best performance. It is therefore possible that if coypus were to dive voluntarily for a specific purpose they might well be able to exceed a dive of 6 minutes total length. It seems unlikely, however, that they could dive for much longer than this time and it is suggested that the long periods of diving ascribed to these animals may, in reality, be punctuated by the animal taking a quick breath with only its nostrils above water. This act is definitely performed by seals (personal observations) and can easily be hidden from the observer by a small wavelet.

The venous system of coypus displays some interesting features (see pp. 131 to 143 for variations in the venous system of other diving mammals). The posterior vena cava is single, lying on the right of the aorta, and measures 8·0 mm in diameter caudal to the renal veins but 15·0 mm at its point of entry into the liver substance, which closely surrounds it. There is no hepatic sinus and no enlargement of the hepatic veins. There is no caval sphincter where the posterior vena cava penetrates the diaphragm and the vessel has a long intrathoracic course (2·5 cm) before entering the heart. Two anterior venae cavae sweep round the heart and unite to form a single sinus that enters the right atrium a short distance dorsal to the posterior vena cava. The azygos system is well developed and provides a direct communication between the anterior and posterior cavae. Only the rostral four or five intercostal veins drain into the left azygos vein, which drains into the left anterior vena cava and is smaller than the right azygos. The intravertebral veins display the common mammalian pattern—two ventro-lateral channels with segmental cross-anastomoses. They are largest in the lumbar region (3·5 mm) and become smaller and flattened cranially. There are no direct communications with the anterior vena cava. There is an extensive, retial-like plexus amidst the dorsal cervical musculature, reminiscent of the marked venous plexus in this region in seals.

LOCOMOTION THROUGH WATER

Scheffer[28] reviews observations of the speed of pinnipeds in water. Top swimming speed of a frightened northern fur seal is 17 miles/hour but cannot be sustained. A Californian sea lion has swum underwater at 10·6 miles/hour. We have no accurate observations on the speed of common seals, but adults have easily escaped underwater from motor boats pursuing them at 10 miles/hour. Neither rapid nor slow swimming affected the bradycardia displayed by a 2-year-old free-swimming seal in a tank at the end of ropes. We agree with Scholander[6] that brief periods of struggling during forced experimental dives or during free-swimming dives did not appear to influence the bradycardia, but prolonged struggling often made it impossible to take electrocardiographic recordings. Scholander also states that struggling during a dive did not appear to increase oxygen elimination from the blood, nor did it markedly increase the lactic acid content of arterial blood. He supports Irving's conclusions[10] that there is a strongly reduced muscular blood flow during diving, presumably irrespective of the speed of swimming or degree of struggling, and that this is mediated through the sympathetic nervous system. There is also evidence that active swimming below water alters the oxygen requirements. The length of time a seal can remain submerged, whether active or not, would appear to depend ultimately on how long it can keep its brain and heart supplied with adequate oxygen: other organs apparently can survive with a much reduced oxygen supply for at least the period of the dive.

The maximum sustained speed of blue and fin whales has been estimated by Kermack[29] to be approximately 15 knots. McCarthy (quoted by Kermack) used asdic to show that the blue whale has a maximum speed of 20 knots that could be maintained for little more than 10 minutes. The ability of dolphins and porpoises to ride bow waves of ships travelling sometimes in excess of 20 knots or at slower speeds on surf or wind-generated waves has been the subject of much discussion. Space prohibits a review of all the theoretical interpretations of shape, drag, and flow involved[30] or of recent experiments with models[31] but at least no author has yet shown that these animals possess any unique anatomical or physiological specialization, other than those of cetaceans generally, to perform this trick. Fejer and Backus[30] even suggest that large cetaceans could easily use wave-riding techniques for migratory travel. Backhouse and Smart[32] emphasize that insufficient attention has been paid to the breaking character of the bow wave and illustrate their point with a striking photograph.

BODY TEMPERATURE

Heat loss to the water is a vital problem for any aquatic mammal. It is increased by the possibility that migration may well expose an animal to a temperature change of as much as 25°C. Unfortunately there are few statistically significant samples of the body temperatures of marine mammals, and it is obvious that few recordings will have been made under natural conditions.

Laurie[21] and Parry[33] give figures for the deep body temperature of recently dead specimens of *Balaenoptera musculus* of 35·1°C and 35·5°C. Parry also gives an estimate of the thermal conductivity of whale blubber as 0 0005 g-cal/cm²/°C/cm. He concludes that: 'In temperate and polar waters most whales lose heat at a greater rate than the basal metabolic rate of land homotherms, even when the blood flow through the blubber is negligible.' The arrangement of blood vessels in the blubber (see p. 148) may well provide a mechanism for regulating heat loss, but it appears that whales must keep swimming in order to keep warm.

Pinnipeds definitely display considerable lability in body temperature: it may rise or fall within a range of 4°C during ordinary activities[28]. Adult northern fur seals have a mean body temperature at rest of 37·7°C: pups have a mean rectal temperature of 38·2°C[34]. Sustained terrestrial activity causes a rise in body temperature to as high as 43·9°C, although temperatures above 41·5°C are found only in seals incapacitated by heat exhaustion. It seems that some pinnipeds can be driven on land to a state of heat exhaustion or distress that can even kill them. Most pinnipeds lose heat on land by panting, though common seals gasp rather than pant like a dog. Sweating is a negligible method of heat loss (except perhaps in some otariids, such as the northern fur seal which waves its naked flippers, said to be profusely supplied with sweat glands). Pinnipeds may also weep copious tears on hot days, but this can hardly cool them much.

Young common seals kept in captivity by us had a mean rectal temperature of 37·0°C: in pups it was 38·0°C. All disliked being kept indoors, stopped eating and lay inert and gasping. The seals kept in the open chose to lie all day in shallow water-filled baths rather than lie on boards in warm weather. The strongest, and oldest, always selected a position beneath a pipe that delivered a stream of cold water into the bath and only left it to eat, to repel visitors or on the coldest days. Scholander, Irving, and Grinnell[35] demonstrated a fall in body temperature of 2·5°C during experimental dives with young common seals.

MODIFICATIONS IN THE VENOUS SYSTEM OF DIVING MAMMALS

The venous systems of many aquatic mammals display a number of striking adaptations that it is tempting to associate with their powers of diving. It is known, however, that no single feature is alone a hallmark of the ability to remain submerged for remarkable periods of time. Several of these adaptations are found in land mammals that are not known to take naturally to water or to have had aquatic ancestors. They will be described below under appropriate headings: for further details see Slijper[3] and Barnett *et al*[36].

The Posterior Vena Cava

Duplication of the posterior vena cava seems to be the rule in all species of Pinnipedia, and examination of numerous specimens of *Phoca vitulani* (*Figure 4.7*) and *Halichoerus grypus* shows the details of the pattern to be remarkably constant. Murie[37], however, illustrates a single posterior vena cava in the Patagonian sea lion, *Otaria jubata*.

The two limbs of the duplicated posterior vena cava are particularly large, elastic and thin-walled: the right limb is frequently the larger vessel[16].

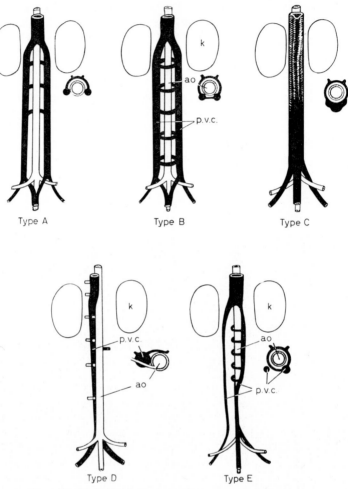

Figure 4.6. Variations in the posterior vena cava in Cetacea[36]. ao, aorta; k, kidney; p.v.c., posterior vena cava.

The two limbs receive the numerous renal veins from the stellate renal plexus (p. 135) and many tributaries from the plexuses of veins draining the hind flippers, pelvis, and lateral abdominal wall. There is free communication via these tributaries with the internal vertebral veins (p. 135). The vessels are larger in seals, relative to the size of the animal, than in any other mammal. The fact that the blood volume of the seal, per kilogram of body weight, is some 70 per cent greater than that of man is probably relevant in this respect[16].

The posterior vena cava is also duplicated in the manatee (*Trichechus*)[33]. The two limbs arise from the converging venules that accompany the radiating fan of arteries formed in the pelvis by the termination of the hypogastric branches of the aorta. The posterior vena cava is double in the adult dugong, and in a 20-cm foetus examined by us.

There is considerable inter- and intraspecies variation in the arrangement of the posterior vena cava in the Cetacea: Slijper[3] described five main types. These are shown diagrammatically in *Figure 4.6*; it will be seen that in Types A, B and E the abdominal posterior vena cava is duplicated as far rostral as the level of the renal arteries and that it is by the anatomy of the tributaries passing around the aorta that the three types may be differentiated. Type A is found in the common porpoise *Phocaena* and has been regarded as the more or less typical arrangement for the Cetacea, but Slijper has not found it at all common: he gives a list of many recorded variations. Type B has been observed in the sperm whale *Physeter* and the fin whale *Balaenoptera*, and Type E only in *Phocaena*. In Type C the posterior vena cava is in the form of a single vessel, but showing evidence of being formed by fusion of three trunks covering the ventral aspect of the aorta; it has been found in *Phocaena*, the killer whale *Orca* and the bottle-nosed whale *Hyperoodon*. In Type D the vessel lies to the right of the aorta and is pierced by the lumbar arteries; this rare arrangement in Cetacea has only been described in *Hyperoodon*. Slijper[3], and Harrison and Tomlinson[16] comment on the plentiful anastomoses between one or both limbs of the posterior vena cava and the internal vertebral venous system (see p. 135). Slijper also examines the possible embryological explanations of the various patterns encountered in the abdominal venae cavae of Cetacea, and discusses whether any of the patterns may represent persistence of foetal characteristics into adult life.

There is in all phocids that we have examined a remarkable enlargement of the posterior vena cava immediately caudal to the diaphragm and cranial to the liver[16,36,80]. This dilation of the vessel forms a capacious hepatic sinus in adult common seals: it is overlaid by the lobes of the liver and the dilated hepatic veins open into its caudal aspect (*Figures 4.7* and *4.8*). It contains little blood in anaesthetized seals out of water, but as it is caudal to the caval sphincter (see p. 138) it can be assumed that the hepatic sinus could under certain circumstances become distended with blood, up to a litre in adults, and thus act as a reservoir. There may be some dilatation of the suprahepatic portion of the vena cava in the beaver and the hippopotamus and possibly other aquatic mammals[36], but in none does it appear to be as marked as in phocids. We have been unable to find a caval reservoir in Cetacea.

Renal Veins and Subcapsular Renal Plexuses

In Cetacea the main renal venous drainage is by a large renal vein, which emerges from the mesial slit: it is frequently duplicated at its commencement, but usually drains as a single vessel into the ipsilateral limb of the duplicated posterior vena cava. In addition to this main method of drainage there is also a poorly developed superficial subcapsular plexus over the ventri-medial surface of the kidney, which drains into the main renal vein at the mesial slit. Cave and Aumonier[40] state that the rare and primitive

Cetacean *Caperea marginata* lacks a superficial network of renal veins and that only a single renal vein is present. The renal veins in certain Cetacea are described by Gervais[41] and many others[42,43]. Beauregard and Boulart[44] considered that there were no communications between the superficial and internal veins, and that the former acted as a 'Pfortaderzirculation' between the renal vein and the vena cava. Ommanney[43] denied such anastomosis.

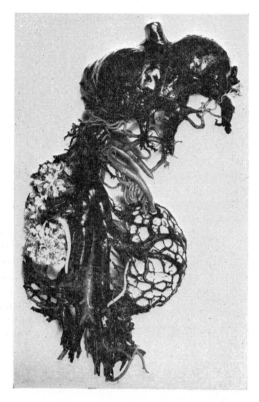

Figure 4.7. Photograph of a cast of the abdominal vessels of a young common seal showing the renal stellate plexuses, reniculi, the duplicated posterior vena cava and the hepatic sinus (top)[16]

The kidney in the Pinnipedia is a multi-lobular organ consisting of up to eight main lobes, each containing about a hundred reniculi with their own arterial supply and venous drainage (*Figure 4.7*). Fine venules drain blood from the lobules into veins lying between the lobules, the interlobular veins. These pass by communicating veins to the surface of the organ, where there is a very well marked stellate venous plexus, lying in the gutters formed by the projection from the surface of the superficial lobules. The communicating veins from the interlobular veins to this plexus enter it at points about the circumference of each lobule, and if the plexus is removed the points of emergence can be seen as small pits.

134

The superficial plexus drains into the homolateral limb of the posterior vena cava, usually by three main veins, from the two poles and the midpoint of the medial border; occasionally there are other subsidiary renal veins which help to drain the plexus. The vein draining the anterior pole receives the adrenal veins.

The pattern of drainage of the pinniped kidney is quite different from that in the majority of mammals, in that all the blood drains first centrifugally to a large stellate plexus on the surface of the organ, and thence to the posterior vena cava, there being no renal veins accompanying the artery of supply and emerging at a hilum. The stellate plexus has other important communications besides the vena cava. It communicates with the large extradural intravertebral vein present in these animals by one or two large channels passing through the lower lumber intervertebral foramina; with the lateral abdominal wall veins; with the commencement of the azygos vein, and also the pelvic plexus of veins[16].

In connection with the renal veins the existence of a vein draining into them from the perirenal fat should be noted. The vein was first noted in man by Eustachius (1564) and it anastomoses with the gonadal veins below and the renal capsular veins, the suprarenal veins and the azygos system above. It is present in the slow loris *Nycticebus*[45], and Harris[46] considers it to be in man the remnant of the primitive post-cardinal vein. In Pinnipedia all those vessels usually connected by the perirenal vein are in extensive communication, and it is possible that this indicates the embryological origin of part, at least, of the complex of veins in this region in this group. The position of the ureter ventral to the plexuses round the kidney, however, also suggests that the supracardinal vein and its anastomoses are also involved.

Internal Vertebral Venous Systems

The Pinnipedia, Cetacea, and Sirenia all exhibit pronounced modifications in the so-called internal vertebral venous system. This system includes all those veins found inside the spinal canal and having intimate relations to the dura[36]. The basic plan, exhibited by the majority of mammals and man, consists of two thin-walled longitudinal channels, ventral to the spinal cord and lying on the dorsal surfaces of the vertebral bodies. Numerous cross-anastomoses are present: they are usually segmentally arranged and receive the basivertebral veins draining the vertebral bodies. Plentiful communications exist between the internal vertebral system, dural veins, intercostal, lumbar and sacral veins and also the cranial sinuses.

The extradural venous system in *Phoca*, *Halichoerus*, the elephant seal, *Mirounga leonnia*, and the sea lion *Zalophus californianus* is represented by a large, single vein (*Figure 4.8*) lying *dorsal* to the spinal cord for the greater part of the extent of the spinal canal[16]. This vein, in the caudal part of the spinal canal, receives at least three large communications from the renal and pelvic plexuses of veins present in these mammals. It also receives communications from the lateral segmental veins in the sacral, thoracic, and lumbar regions, and from veins in the dorsal musculature. The dorsal communications in the cervical region are particularly large, and drain a well marked venous plexus situated in the dorsal musculature. They pierce the ligamenta flava to enter the large extradural vein. The extradural vein divides in the cervical part of the spinal canal and comes to lie on either side of the cord. The two limbs join anterior to the dorsal arch of the atlas to form a sinus, and from this two veins pass through the hypocondylar canals to enter the transverse sinuses. The importance of the vein is indicated by the fact that in a young common seal it is 3 cm in transverse diameter and 1 cm dorso-ventrally, and also has communications with every other component of the venous system, including the large azygos vein. This system is devoid of valves, and after radio-opaque material is injected into the vein, it can be shown in the cranial sinuses and the abdominal veins in a very short time[16].

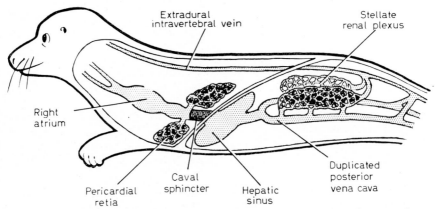

Figure 4.8. Diagram to show the principal venous adaptations in seals: note the obliquity of the diaphragm.

The jugular system and also the external vertebral system of veins in the Pinnipedia are remarkably undeveloped, and thus one is forced to conclude that the only large venous pathway from the brain in these animals is by the extradural vertebral system. It is also tempting to correlate the marked enlargement of this system, and its numerous communications, with the presence of a strong sphincter of striated muscle on the intrathoracic posterior vena cava.

A limited number of observations have been made on the venous system in Cetacea[3,16,43,47], but all agree that there is a prominent internal vertebral system, although there are variations in the details of the arrangement. In foetuses of *Balaenoptera*, and the common dolphin *Delphinus*, the pattern and appearance of the vertebral venous system conforms to that which is common in the majority of mammals, but in the anterior thoracic region the two ventrally placed longitudinal veins leave the spinal canal through the first dorsal intervertebral foramina to join a dorsal (posterior) thoracic vein which drains into the anterior vena cava. Anterior to this point the vertebral canal is packed with retial tissue with no well developed longitudinal channels visible in it. In the adult porpoise (*Phocaena*) there is a large vein that lies ventral to the cord and which is grooved by this structure. That part of the vertebral canal not occupied by the spinal cord and this large vein is packed with retial tissue in which are embedded two large arteries lying dorsal to the cord. The large vein leaves the canal through the first right thoracic intervertebral foramen, which is greatly enlarged: the vein then joins the anterior vena cava. There are similar veins which emerge through the next three cranially placed foramina. Anterior to this the vertebral canal, as in *Balaenoptera*, is filled with retial tissue, which communicates with the basi-cranial rete.

Fawcett[38] describes two spinal veins lying ventral to the cord in the Florida manatee, which he states receives venous drainage from the intercostal vascular bundles. He also remarks that these veins are smaller in calibre than the corresponding vessels in porpoises and whales. A similar pair of intravertebral venous channels were found in a 20-cm foetal dugong, but they were of considerable size and, although lying ventral to the cord for most of their course, in the cervical region the channels pass dorsal to the cord to enter the skull. A section through the low cervical region of an adult dugong examined by us shows a large extradural vein on the dorsal aspect of the cord, with two smaller channels lying ventrolaterally. More anteriorly in the cervical region the veins are absent and the cord is surrounded by retial tissue.

It should be emphasized that an internal vertebral system is of considerable functional importance in all mammals including man[36,48]. Besides draining the vertebral bodies of their haemopoietic products and taking part in the venous drainage of the spinal cord, the system also plays a significant role in stabilizing venous pressure during respiratory exertion. The extradural veins in seals undoubtedly provide alternative pathways for venous drainage, particularly from the nervous system. Blood from the brain and spinal cord of seals passes almost entirely into the extradural system, as there is no drainage of cerebral blood by an internal jugular vein. The major portion of this venous blood would appear to drain into the stellate renal plexus and thence to the posterior vena cava. A smaller portion could, however, undoubtedly reach the right heart via 'para-caval' channels if the caval sphincter is closed.

The Azygos System

There is considerable doubt as to whether there is an azygos system in the Cetacea. Hunter[49] remarked that it was absent in whales, its functions being taken over by veins in the spinal canal, which were protected from the raised pressure obtaining on diving. Ommanney[43] described two small veins in an 86 cm foetal fin whale which he considered represented the azygos system, but Walmsley[44] could find no trace of these in a 143 cm foetus. In a 92 cm *Balaenoptera* foetus we could find no evidence of an azygos system, nor could we demonstrate it in two adult and one foetal *Phocaena*. It may be that the large vein issuing through the right first thoracic intervertebral foramen and passing to join the anterior vena cava represents the arch of the azygos vein. There is a small vein, joining this arch, lying on the right side in the gutter between the oesophagus and the vertebral bodies, but this drains only a very small part of the first two or three intercostal spaces. The main drainage of these passes to the extradural intravertebral vein, as does the rest of the intercostal veins.

Burow[50] stated that in *Phoca* there were two azygos veins which united together in the thorax and entered into the anterior vena cava by a single trunk. Resin casts made by us[16] in a number of seals show that the azygos system commences in the anterior part of the abdominal cavity by the continuation ventrally of the lateral tributaries of the extradural intravertebral vein, two of which are enlarged and communicate with the anterolateral portion of the renal plexus of veins. In the abdomen there is a pair of azygos veins of equal size, but in the thorax, where the lateral tributaries are enlarged to become the intercostal veins, the system becomes dominantly right-sided, the left azygos being reduced to a slender longitudinal anastomosis between contiguous intercostal veins. The right azygos is of considerable size, 10 by 6 mm in a newborn common seal pup, and drains virtually all the blood collected by the intercostal veins of both sides. There are communications in each segment between the intercostal veins and the extradural vein, and thus the latter is brought into very free communication with the azygos vein.

In so far as the azygos system might be considered to be a normal mammalian finding, it could be argued that the large veins present in the spinal canal in these two animals have taken over its functions[51]. Yet in seals there is both a very large extradural vein and a well developed azygos system. If the azygos is a functional part of the vertebral system of veins, then one might perhaps expect mammals with an enlarged vertebral vein or veins to possess a large azygos vein, the better to enable the blood in the vertebral veins to drain into the anterior vena cava.

The absence of an azygos system in *Phocaena*, which possesses a large intravertebral vein, would appear to refute this. There is, however, a large vein connecting the intravertebral vein to the anterior vena cava, which could take over the suggested drainage function of a normal azygos system. Further comments on the azygos system in mammals and its development can be found in Barnett *et al*[36]. It seems undeniable that Franklin[52] was correct in stating that the azygos system is particularly important because of its extensive connections. In man, blood may pass back from the superior vena cava into the azygos vein when the right heart begins to fail. There may well be conditions during diving, particularly if prolonged and at depth and with the heart rate slowed considerably, when the azygos acts as a secondary venous pathway equalizing pressures on each side of the diaphragm and relieving a tendency to overload the right heart.

The Caval Sphincter

The presence in seals of a muscular sphincter, surrounding the posterior vena cava rostral to the diaphragm, was first described by Burow in 1838[50]. Gratiolet[53] recorded one in the hippopotamus, but this was ill-defined and Cave[54] found no sphincter in any way comparable to that of seals in the animals he examined. Burne[55] found a sphincter in the walrus *Odobaenus rosmarus*. We[16] have confirmed the presence of a well marked sphincter in *Phoca*, *Halichoerus*, the Weddell seal *Leptonychotes*, the crab-eating seal *Lobodon* and also in *Mirounga*, in which it is particularly well developed. An incomplete sphincter is present in the Hawaiian monk seal *Monachus*, and a 'sphincter' made up of slips of diaphragmatic muscle is found in *Zalophus* and *Phocaena*, but was notably absent in the dolphin *Tursiops*. In foetal Sei

138

and fin whales we have found a band of diaphragmatic fibres passing transversely behind the posterior cava, but these bear little resemblance, either from the morphological or functional points of view, to the sphincter in Pinnipedia. In *Phoca* the structure consists of a sheet of coarsely striated muscle fibres arranged around the cava immediately rostral to the diaphragm (*Figure 4.9*) in the form of a funnel, 5 cm in length and 0·5 to 1·5 mm thick[16].

The sphincteric muscle is separated from the diaphragm by a narrow tendinous ring, and is supplied by some 300 nerve fibres from the phrenic

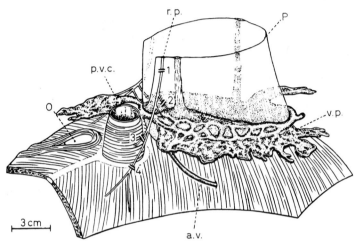

Figure 4.9. Drawing to show the caval sphincter about the posterior vena cava (p.v.c.), branches of the right phrenic nerve (r.p.) and the arrangement of the pericardial venous plexus (v.p.) in *Phoca*[16].

O, oesophageal opening in diaphragm; P, pericardium. The figures indicate points at which the right phrenic nerve was cut for estimating the number of fibres in each branch.

nerves, predominantly the right. We could find no evidence of a discrete bundle of these fibres in the phrenic nerve trunk. The sphincter appears not to contract during normal breathing in an anaesthetized seal, but contracts strongly when either the right phrenic nerve or its branches to the sphincter are stimulated. This contraction is sufficiently strong completely to occlude the caval blood flow, at least in an anaesthetized seal on land. Injection of radio-opaque solution into an abdominal vein, during stimulation of the right phrenic nerve, results in the radio-opaque material being dammed back in the hepatic sinus[16].

No sphincter has been found by us in beavers, otters, sloths, coypu rats or any other mammal. The sloth *Choloepus* has a marked kink at the diaphragmatic orifice of the posterior cava, and contraction of the diaphragm could therefore affect the flow of blood through it. Franklin[56] noted a band of diaphragmatic muscle passing over the thoracic part of the posterior cava in dogs, and considered this might exert a constricting effect on the vessel. Various dispositions of valves at the termination of the posterior cava have been described in certain mammals, but neither these, nor diaphragmatic muscle 'slings' or bands could, in our opinion, have a function comparable to a well developed caval sphincter separated from the diaphragm and possessing its own nervous innervation. We have shown that such a sphincter can control the flow of blood through the cava from the abdominal veins to the right atrium, and that it can contract independently of the diaphragm. To ascertain the possible effect on the heart rate of closure of the sphincter, the posterior vena cava was clamped just rostral to the liver in an anaesthetized seal pup. This procedure had no effect on the heart rate, nor did stimulation of the nerve to the sphincter, and this in spite of the fact that the venous return to the heart must have been, at least temporarily, much reduced.

STIMULATION AND SECTION OF THE PHRENIC NERVE

The right phrenic nerve was sectioned in the cervical region in several anaesthetized seals, which were subsequently allowed to recover. Stimulation, under anaesthesia, of the peripheral part of the nerve produced no effect on the heart rate, nor did stimulation of the intact left phrenic.

When the animals had recovered from the operation they were dived in a shallow tank. In all there was an eventual bradycardia similar to that arising in normal seals, but its onset was delayed. In one animal after 12 seconds the heart rate was 150 as opposed to 60 at the same time in the same animal before operation. After 30 seconds it was 75 as opposed to 35, but at the end of 1 minute the heart rate in the operated animal was 30; the same rate as obtained after a 1 minute dive in the unoperated state. The animals were killed 10 and 12 days after section of the nerve, and the spinal cord examined for degenerative lesions to determine the segmental origin of the nerve and the presence or absence of a phrenic nucleus, such as has been described in the rhesus monkey[57].

The degeneration present showed the right phrenic nerve in the common seal to arise predominantly from the neurons in the fifth cervical segment of the cord, with additions from C4 and C6. The material was too sparse for us to identify with certainty a definite phrenic nucleus, or a separate nucleus for the nerve supplying the sphincter, but the neurons do form a striking group in the anterior horn, particularly on the right side.

RETIA MIRABILIA

Closely packed networks of arteries and veins in varying proportion, and possibly including lymphatics[52] are found in most if not all marine mammals. Galen (c. 180) had remarked on such networks in other mammals and the expression *plexus retiformes—maximum miraculum* originated in his time. Tyson[58] was the first to see in porpoises and large cetaceans the masses of thoracic vascular tissue lying on each intercostal muscle outside the parietal pleura, but Owen[59] gave the tissue the name 'retia mirabilia'. Barnett, et al.[36] have divided all retia, whether in network or bundle form into four types:

Type 1—Diffuse plexiform anastomoses of arteries and veins in the limbs of certain mammals, especially edentates and primates

Type 2—A vascular bundle of small arteries, intermingled with veins, enclosed within a common fibrous sheath

Type 3—The thoracic retia of Cetacea

Type 4—An arterial plexus or convolution unassociated with any comparable modification of the adjacent veins

Vascular networks and bundles found in marine mammals are mainly of types 2, 3 and 4. Vascular bundles of type 2 are found in the caudal rete of manatees[38]. The main artery and its vena comites break up into nearly parallel small arteries and venules, sometimes intermingling freely. In the bundle, vessels are separated by loose connective tissue and the whole is encased in a strong fibrous sheath. The main artery may divide proximally, one branch dividing into the bundle, the other running alongside it as in the femoral rete of some sloths[60] or, as in the manatee, running within it. Vascular bundles are also found in the limbs, spinal canal and other sites in Cetacea. Walmsley[47] describes and reviews the literature on the voluminous bilateral vascular masses of the thoracic retia (type 3) of whales which lie along the dorsal wall of the thorax and have variable extensions into the neck, vertebral canal and skull[3]. These retia are true arterio-venous plexuses with many anastomoses among the arteries themselves and also the veins, but with no arterio-venous anastomoses. The plexus is embedded in loose areolar tissue and there is no restricting fibrous sheath. Fawcett[38] has described the thoracic retia of *Tursiops* and pigmy sperm whale *Kogia* in which arteries predominate. All veins in these retia are very thin walled.

The retia of Pinnipedia correspond to those of type 3 more than any other, but are composed mainly of veins. Most Pinnipedia and some Cetacea (*Figure 4.10*) have a circum-pericardial fringe of retial tissue that is capable of considerable enlargement. It communicates with the posterior vena cava by quite large veins that enter it just above the caval sphincter. Branches of the pericardiaco-phrenic artery enter the retia, as well as numbers of myelinated nerve bundles.

De Kock[61] has recently investigated the arteries in the neck in pilot whales (*Globicephala*) and porpoises. The common carotid is virtually non-existent and the single trunk of the innominate divides into the two carotids and the subclavian. Other authors[3,62] have stated that the cetacean internal carotid does not supply the brain, and that the entire cerebral arterial supply is from the vertebral arteries. The internal carotid appears to taper and to become reduced in the adult to a fibrous strand, after entry into the tympanic cavity. De Kock found, however, in the forms he examined, that there is no evidence of permanent occlusion but significant localized variation of the internal carotid. The vessel wall at its origin contains many elastic laminae (25 times the number in the corresponding vessel in a mouse). Above the carotid sinus the wall contains a disproportionately large amount of muscle as far cranial as the tympanic cavity. In the dead state the vessel is strongly contracted, giving it a tapered appearance, but it possesses a lumen containing red blood corpuscles. He suggests that this evidence of elasticity and muscularity, together with an abundant innervation of the external coats, indicates 'a local mechanism of control of blood flow over this part of the circulation, possibly of intermittent function'. It is perhaps also relevant that we have found marked bundles of circularly arranged muscle

141

fibres blending with the outside of the adventitial coat above the sinus on the internal carotid of seals, though by no means developed sufficiently to occlude the vessel.

De Kock also finds in pilot whales a sheath of connective tissue containing retia mirabilia that is firmly adherent to the walls of both carotids, but which is not found on other great arteries. He suggests that these retia may in some way be concerned in maintaining a steady blood supply to the brain. It would appear that they bear a strong resemblance to the retia type 4.

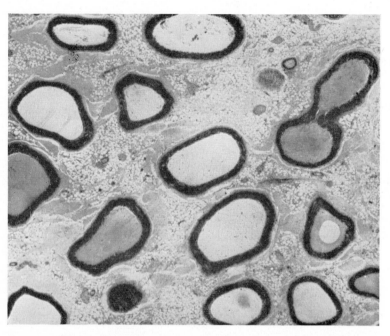

Figure 4.10. Photomicrograph of a section of a pericardial rete from *Lagenorhynchus cruciger*. The retial mass drains into the posterior vena cava above the diaphragm. Marked amounts of elastic tissue are present in the vessel walls

Daniel *et al.*[63] describe carotid retia in a number of non-diving mammals and consider that they have a haemodynamic significance affecting the cerebral blood supply. We have not found carotid retia of any type in pinnipeds.

Various hypotheses have been advanced to account for the presence of retia mirabilia, and many suggestions have been made as to their function both in marine mammals and in the other, often quite unrelated, forms in which they occur. It is of course quite possible that they may on occasions and in particular sites subserve all the functions ascribed to them. Unfortunately, it is only possible to make experimental observations on few of the mammals possessing them.

Retia have been associated with slow limb and body movement or sustained habitual posture. Carlisle[64] first propounded this hypothesis as a result of his observations on sloths. It enjoyed great popularity until the behaviour of sloths and their types of retia were critically studied by Wislocki and Straus[60], although Davies[45] comments that frequent anatomoses would be expected in the muscular arteries of slow-moving animals. Certain marine mammals, such as Sirenia, are indeed sluggish and others can remain asleep or dozing while kept floating just on or below the surface by slow, almost imperceptible muscular movements. Fawcett[38] has, however, remarked that porpoises are among the fastest swimmers in the entire animal kingdom. All Cetacea and Pinnipedia are capable of rapid limb and body movement.

Retia have also been ascribed the function of blood reservoirs from which stored oxygenated blood can re-enter the circulation on diving[55,65]. Certainly the retial vessels contain much elastic tissue which may indicate that their contained blood could vary in volume. Much increase in total volume of some retia could, however, be an embarrassment in that nervous tissue would be compressed. Laurie[21,66] has calculated that the retia in Cetacea are not large enough to store a quantity of blood significant to be of use during a dive of any length.

It is probable that vascular bundles (retia type 2) can assist venous return both passively and actively. Hyrtl[67] first suggested this and Barnett et al.[36] review the anatomical and experimental evidence in support of these contentions. Small veins in the bundle are not easily occluded by external pressure as they receive support from the thicker-walled arteries about them. They also have some intrinsic rigidity due to their narrow calibre. Steady flow will be maintained through the rete even when muscles about them are in sustained contraction. Vascular bundles may also improve the venous return by intermittent pressure from pulsating arteries acting on neighbouring thin-walled veins—a form of 'peripheral heart'. Many retia may, therefore, act as devices overcoming interruptions of blood flow that muscular or other pressures are capable of effecting.

It has been suggested that the venous plexuses around the arteries supplying the fins of whales remove heat from arterial blood and thus prevent the heat loss that would occur in cold water[68]. The walls of the veins in the plexus are thinner than those of more superficial veins and so facilitate heat absorption by venous blood. Should activity increase arterial flow, then swelling of the artery would compress the circum-arterial veins and increase heat loss from the superficial limb veins.

The thoracic retia of Cetacea have been suggested to be adaptations to pressure differences experienced during diving[36,47]. They probably prevent rupture of alveolar capillaries that might result from initial differences between external and intrathoracic pressures as dives become deeper. Blood will engorge the retia and they will expand to occupy more space in the thorax until the pressure within the lung equals that on the body wall. It is not impossible that the pericardial retial masses found in Pinnipedia and some Cetacea also act as intrathoracic 'space-fillers' during a dive. The authors find these retia to contain little blood in seals on the surface, but they are experimentally capable of considerable distension[16]. The forcible dilatation of the retia with saline had no effect on the heart rate in anaesthetized seals. It appears unlikely, therefore, that they have any function as baroreceptors.

THE LUNGS

As might be expected, the lungs of aquatic animals exhibit certain interesting variations from the normal mammalian pattern. There are many observations on cetacean lungs, although the significance of most features is obscure[69-76]. In smaller species, such as *Tursiops*, Wislocki[75] described certain adjustments of bronchial morphology in adaptation to an aquatic existence. Their lungs show, in comparison to other mammals, a greater rigidity (due to increase in cartilage, fibrous tissue and muscle), a greater elasticity, an increased vital capacity due partly to a larger amount of lung tissue, a larger alveolar surface area and the extension of the respiratory epithelium far into the bronchioles. They also show an increased resistance to outside compression, firstly due to their rigidity and secondly to the presence of circular muscle sphincters associated with valves (myo-elastic valves) in the smallest bronchioles. Similar valves have been described in the common dolphin *Delphinus*[75], in the spotted dolphin *Prodelphinus*[77] and in the small white whale *Delphinapterus*[74].

There is an interesting difference between the lungs of the smaller and larger cetaceans. The latter, *i.e.* blue, fin, hump-backed, sperm and bottle-nose whales, have no myo-elastic valves in the bronchioles which appear to be found only in frequently-breathing toothed whales[78], but have well developed myo-elastic structures situated in the septa projecting into the central portion of the air sacs. These structures are represented in the lungs of the smaller cetacea but are very much less marked. The muscular parts of these structures could act to close air sacs, whilst the elastic part could

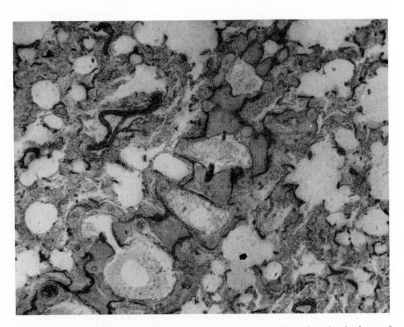

Figure 4.11. Photomicrograph of the bronchiolar myo-elastic valves in the lung of
Lagenorhynchus cruciger.

144

facilitate rapid evacuation of air during expiration[76]. The common porpoise also possesses myo-elastic valves in the small bronchioles, although some authors have denied this. They are, however, less marked than in *Tursiops, Delphinus, Delphinapterus*[75] or *Lagenorhynchus*[79]. These valves divide the smaller bronchiolar passages into segments and also can presumably influence the flow of inspired or expired air (*Figure 4.11*). They may also act as a series of dead air spaces in which air could, as it were, be isolated and compressed during a dive without danger of increased solution in the pulmonary circulation[74,76].

Other aquatic mammals possess similar bronchiolar valves, but they are not so marked as in *Tursiops*. Their presence in the common seal has been confirmed by us and they are also present in the elephant seal, Weddell seal, grey seal and in the Hawaiian monk seal *Monachus schauinslandi*[80].

Resin casts of common and grey seal lungs show complete symmetry of the bronchial tree[81]. Those of the porpoise lungs show an asymmetry with a tracheal bronchus on the right side and with the respiratory area condensed at the periphery like a 'pie-crust', while *Zalophus* retains a typical terrestrial carnivore pattern.

The morphology of the sirenian lung has been described in the Florida manatee[82] and in the dugong[74,83]. There are giant air sacs, corresponding to the alveolar ducts and saccules of terrestrial mammals, from which the alveolae branch out with widely opened mouths. The respiratory sacs are 10 times the size of those in man.

THE KIDNEY

It is well known that both the cetacean and pinniped kidney exhibit a distinct lobulation into reniculi[36,40,43,47]. Descriptions have also been given of the vascular arrangements (p. 133) associated with this lobulation, and there is by no means any constancy of pattern among aquatic mammals. Our knowledge of renal function in marine mammals, however, is very scanty and what there is hardly helps to explain the anatomical characteristics. Kellogg[4] supposes that the reniculi may provide a more effective mechanism for the elimination of excess salts ingested with food. Slijper[84] suggests that the fact that a fresh water dolphin *Platanista gangetica* had kidneys with only 80 reniculi and that they were smaller than those of a porpoise of nearly half the size but which had 250 reniculi is evidence that Kellogg's supposition is true. Lobulation may also result in an increase in the number of glomeruli in the total kidney substance. It may even indicate the existence of segmental units that function either singly, or in groups, or all at once depending on some intrinsic neuro-vascular control. Cave and Aumonier[40] doubt whether these speculations have much substance and are inclined to think that the renicular arrangement is more directly concerned with increased efficiency of urine discharge from the medullary papillae. They describe the presence of a perimedullary muscular basket (*sporta*) in *Capera, Physeter, Phocaena* and *Lagenorhynchus* (*Figure 4.12*). They consider that the muscle is sufficient to compress and thus milk the ducts of Bellini, expediting discharge of urine, but neither sufficient nor appropriately arranged to effect total temporary obstruction. Such a sporta is not seen in the kidneys of other wholly or occasionally aquatic mammals. It is apparently not determined solely by an aquatic existence, and is found so far in the cetacean kidney only. There are unfortunately no accurate estimations of a chemical nature to throw any light on the functions of the cetacean kidney.

Some observations are, however, available on renal function in seals[81–84]. The urinary concentrating mechanism is highly developed. Feeding can raise the glomerular filtration rate markedly. Diving, or simulated diving

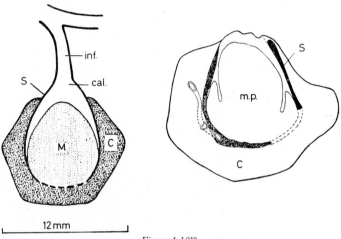

Figure 4.12[40]

Left: Diagram showing the construction of a reniculus of *Caperea* sectioned to show continuity of calyx wall with the perimedullary basket. C, cortex; M, medulla; S, *sporta*; inf., infundibulum; cal, calyx
Right: Diagram to show a *sporta* of a *Caperea* reniculus pierced by a blood vessel. m.p., medullary pyramid.

by holding a cone over the seal's nostrils, reduces the filtration rate and the renal plasma flow to about one fifth of the resting values. The ability of seals to concentrate urea is rather poor and it is possible that active transport of urea is not pronounced in seal renal tissue. Struggling also affects renal function; the proportion of urea in the urine with respect to that in the plasma is decreased. It is still not possible to make exact statements about the effect of diving on glomerular filtration rate. Schmidt-Nielsen and colleagues[88] return to the supposition that it is possible that the reniculi show intermittency of function.

The arrangement of the pyramids in the kidneys of the dugong appears to be unique[89]. In coronal sections the pyramids look as if they are arranged in pairs facing the renal pelvis with single polar ones. The supposed pairs are actually joined by raised bars of renal tissue across the ventral wall of the renal sinus so that each pyramid girdles the cavity. The elongated kidneys thus do suggest a retained segmental structure.

FEATURES OF THE INTEGUMENT

That whales possess fatty blubber and lack hairs, and that seals have a luxurious pelage as well as blubber is well known. What is not well understood is the precise implication of these and other features found in the skin of aquatic mammals. Blubber not only acts as a protection against cold—a subcuticular insulating blanket—but also controls loss of heat. Rate of heat loss is important to an animal that migrates through oceans of varying temperature at continually altering speeds and states of muscular activity, that lacks epicrine sweat glands and cannot rest for long or take shelter. Cetaceans, too, must avoid excessive exposure to sunlight, for they can become sunburned. Blubber varies in thickness with the seasons of the year and may act as an energy reserve, besides being a source of fat during lactation in females. Its thickness also varies in different parts of the body in both seals and whales. This may be associated with development of stresses in different parts of the integument as the animal progresses through water. It is also related to movement of limbs, flippers and flukes, and it may play a critical part in adapting the shape of the animal by streamlining it. Furthermore the semi-fluid nature of blubber means that it could be in motion beneath the epidermis during swimming, thus constantly causing slight alterations in the shape of the animal, and in the resistance of the skin against the flow of water. The skin of seals also possesses attributes similar to those of whales, but the pelage as well has become waterproofed. Glandular secretions, special arrangements of hair structure, and a device to close the pilary canal of resting hairs, prevent water-logging of the skin. The integument of whales lacks hairs and glands and is said to be devoid of sense organs[33]; certainly one can whack a living dolphin with a stick without causing it any apparent discomfort, but the evidence for complete lack of sensory nerve endings would seem to be inconclusive.

Blubber consists of the epidermis, dermis and the thick and fatty hypodermal tissues of whales. The epidermis in *Phocaena* and *Balaenoptera* is composed of a superficial stratum corneum and a deeper stratum germinativum[33]. A flattening of cells parallel to the surface, a thickening of the intercellular substance and reduction of nuclei and cytoplasm marks the transition between the two layers. The deeper part of the epidermis is penetrated by dermal ridges lying parallel to the animal's long axis. Dermal papillae arise from the summits of the ridges with a density of about $25/mm^2$. Cylindrical cells with large nuclei line the ridges and papillae. Prickle cells with many intercellular fibrils lie superficial to the papillae. In pigmented whale skin, pigment granules occur most densely in the cylindrical cells. The dermis consists of masses of connective tissue fibres, compactly arranged at the base of the epidermis but less dense and with included fat cells where it merges into the hypodermis. This thick layer is composed of fat cells interlaced with bundles of connective tissue fibres: it corresponds to the panniculus adiposus.

Parry[33] has studied the blood supply of blubber; it is far more vascular than is generally supposed. Arterioles run up to the base of the epidermis and give rise to twigs which extend up the dermal ridges to supply capillaries in the papillae (*Figure 4.13*). Venules collect twigs from the ridges and extend down through the dermis and hypodermis after connecting with a venous plexus in the dermis on their way. Blood from the papillae may run directly down through the dermis and hypodermis in these large venules, or it may flow through the narrower vessels of the dermal plexus. Pressure differences between one part of the blubber and another may well influence the type of flow. Parry also illustrates dilatations of the large venules at the base of the epidermis not unlike, but not as large as, those present in seal skin. Smaller venules are also found accompanying the arterioles in the superficial layer of the epidermis.

Slijper[90] has made an analysis of the thickness of blubber in blue and fin whales. Great differences in thickness occur over the body and depend on

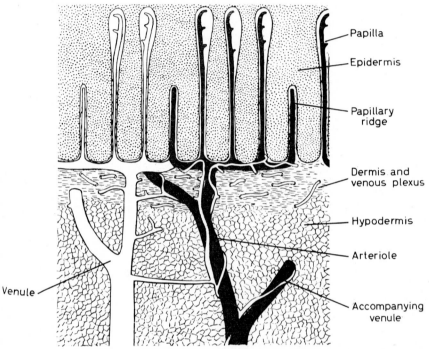

Figure 4.13. A reconstruction of the blood circulation in the superficial regions of the blubber of *Phocaena.* To avoid confusion, arterial and venous vessels are not both shown in the same dermal ridge[33].

demands made by the general body outline. He finds that measurements made either in the dorso-median line just cranial to the dorsal fin or in the ventro-median line cranial to the anus give the best indication of over-all blubber thickness. The relative thickness of blubber increases with increasing body size and can be related to metabolic changes. Blubber is thickest in pregnancy and thinnest towards the end of lactation. There are marked seasonal variations in blubber thickness, probably connected with feeding conditions, but as Slijper emphasizes conclusions may be vitiated by the length of the whales and the proportion pregnant in any seasonal sample. The amount of blubber present will presumably affect the displacement and thus the buoyancy of an animal. The effect of blubber on swimming and diving performance is not known, but presumably there is an optimum thickness (even if only theoretical) for performance under any biological or environmental condition. Slijper suggests that blubber thickness may provide valuable information on migration habits of whales.   Lack of space prohibits a discussion of the composition and physical properties of blubber, but some references are given on page 151.   It would seem, however, that investigation of the effects on the performance of frogmen, divers, submarines and underwater projectiles of an outer casing of a blubber-like substance or foam may well give fruitful and even startling results.

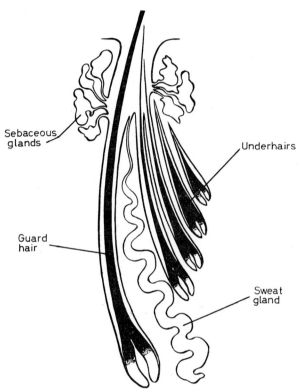

Sebaceous glands

Underhairs

Guard hair

Sweat gland

Figure 4.14. Schematic representation of a hair group in the skin of a common seal showing all the elements present. All of the hairs emerge in one pilary canal, into which also open the single, coiled sweat gland and the sebaceous glands[93].

Seals possess numerous adaptations in their skin[91–93], but it is not known for sure whether they are all associated with aquatic life: indeed, some are not understood at all.   The epidermis is very thick, is heavily pigmented and lacks a stratum granulosum.   The stratum corneum possesses nuclei even in its surface layers, as in the oesophageal lining of most animals, and appears to be a relatively permanent layer judging from the lack of mitoses in the epidermis.   These features would certainly seem excellent adaptations to marine life since a surface layer of scaly keratin might easily become water-logged and flake off, as, for example, does the stratum corneum of sunburned human skin in the bath some days after exposure.   The abundant pigment and its distribution external to the nucleus in each epidermal cell suggests that the melanin is shielding the cells from sunlight.   It may also play a part in heat absorption. Cetacean skin may also be heavily pigmented, sometimes in characteristic patterns that could camouflage the animal against a background of dark waves and spray.

Hair follicles grow in groups composed of a large overhair and four or more underhairs, all of which share one pilary canal (*Figure 4.14*). The overhair, or guard hair, is flattened and fits over the base of other guard hairs like a scale. The small underhairs pack the space between the guard hairs and among them innumerable small air bubbles are trapped and remain present during dives of short duration. We have noticed that if a large area of skin has been shaved for some operative procedure the seal often shivers when immersed in cold water. An interesting adaptation is found in resting hair follicles that may well protect the skin against erosion. A thickened, partially keratinized collar grips tightly around the hair above the club and blocks the seepage of either water or sebum into the lower part of the follicle. The hair follicles are particularly rich in pigments and are profusely vascularized.

Numerous, large and active sebaceous glands encircle each pilary canal and open into it by long narrow ducts. Their secretion covers the skin and hair with a waterproof, oily film that is readily appreciated by anyone handling a seal. Sebum of most mammals is miscible with water[94], but sebum of seals appears to lack hydrophilic substances[93]. If it really has become adapted for waterproofing, for making the animal 'slippery', and perhaps for aiding in heat conservation by helping to trap numerous air bubbles in the underhair, then the sebum of seals would show particularly significant specializations.

One moderately coiled apocrine gland lies parallel to each follicle of overhairs and opens into the pilary canal (*Figure 4.14*). These sweat glands are numerous, but small and their function is somewhat paradoxical. The amount of PAS-positive secretion stored in the lumen of the glands is out of proportion to the number of similarly reactive granules in the gland cells. It appears that the viscous and condensed secretion is manufactured slowly; all that is known so far of its properties suggests that it is of a mucoid, non-fatty nature. It is not readily miscible with sebum. Some mammals have a characteristic odour which is traceable to skin glands[95]. Seals certainly have a strong odour which is difficult to remove from hands or clothing that have been in contact with seals, but it is not known whether the sweat glands are the source of such an odour-producing substance. It is not impossible that these glands are excreting a waste product.

A marked feature of the dermis is its vascularity. Enlarged venules in the papillary layer form spaces that resemble cavernous sinuses and that may act as a blood reservoir. The skin could play an important part in accommodating venous blood during the period of diving bradycardia. The heat-retaining property of the skin and pelage would then become essential. It is possible that the persistence of a thick pelage in Pinnipedia has allowed the diving bradycardia to evolve without the seal suffering excessive heat loss under water. It is not definitely known whether a diving bradycardia is present in Cetacea (see earlier); what evidence there is suggests that it does not occur. Some Cetacea at least appear to combat heat loss by counter-current vascular heat exchange in the fins[68,96].

The blubber of seals is not perhaps always as striking as that of whales, but it can account for as much or more than a quarter of the body weight[28]. Analyses of the properties of the blubber of grey seals have been made by Hilditch and Pathak[97] and of other seals by Winter and Nunn[98], who should be consulted for other references.

THE PLACENTA

The observation by us that a prematurely born common seal pup exhibited a diving bradycardia similar to that of young pups, caused us to investigate whether there were any features in the placenta that might be associated with prevention of foetal anoxia. No observations on diving by pregnant seals have been made, except that pregnancy does not appear to inhibit performance as judged by the ability of pregnant cows to swim under water out of rifle range. A cow one week after parturition certainly displayed an experimental diving bradycardia, and it can be assumed that cows and their foetuses in late pregnancy have the ability to slow their heart rates. It would be fascinating to find out the behaviour of the foetal seal heart, although the marked apprehension and nervous disposition of pregnant cows might vitiate any observations.

Early writers stated that the chorio-allantoic placental band was zonary, labyrinthine and had an irregular lobulated margin. The relationship of maternal to foetal tissues was thought to be endotheliochorial. Harrison and Young[99] have recently investigated the near-term placenta of *Phoca* and *Halichoerus* with the electron microscope. The maternal sinusoids are strikingly dilated and lined by an irregularly thickened endothelium lacking the lace-like appearance described in the cat[100]. They are surrounded by a thick, dense membrane, containing reticulum, against which the trophoblastic cell membranes are frequently folded. This membrane contains vacuoles and many irregular dense bodies. The endothelium of the numerous foetal capillaries closely adjacent to each maternal sinusoid is markedly thinned and the perivascular membrane is thinner than the maternal layer, and appears laminated. The placental barrier is reduced in many places to less than $1·0 \mu$ in total thickness, half of which may consist of non-cellular perivascular substance (*Figure 4.15*).

This perivascular substance about maternal vessels is present in some form or other in most carnivore placentae, and it has been debated as to whether it is a remnant of maternal tissue which has undergone attrition by erosive trophoblast, or whether it represents an active secretory or 'protective' product of the maternal endothelium. Electron micrographs strongly suggest that in pinniped placentae it is no inert layer and that it may well play an important part in placental transfer. It is tempting to suggest that the thin placental barrier aids in gaseous exchange and that it is an adaptation to an aquatic existence. It is also possible that the thin barrier allows maternal hormones an easier passage across to the foetal circulation than in other mammals and may thus be a cause of the production of the precocious enlargement and activity of the reproductive organs of near-term foetal seals[101,102].

The lobulated, marginal region of the pinniped placental band is easily identified because of its yellowish-brown to dark red-brown colour. Often

11

151

referred to as 'marginal haematomata', regions of similar construction are also found with a more central distribution in the band. These haematomata are encountered in other carnivore placentae as well. In seals these regions consist of blood and debris-filled spaces lined by tall columnar trophoblast cells. The blood is of maternal origin: in places actual rupture of maternal

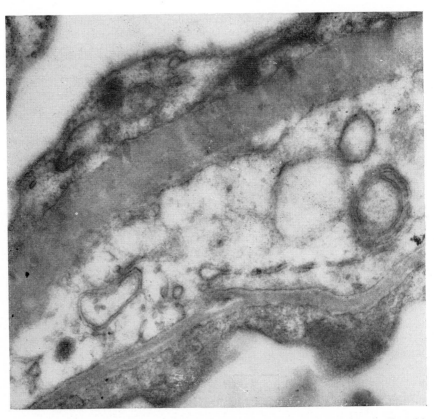

Figure 4.15. Electron micrograph of the near-term placental membrane (chorio-allantoic) of the grey seal[99]

At the top left is a maternal sinusoid lined by endothelium. Note the thickened perivascular 'membrane'. Trophoblast intervenes between it and the thinner membrane surrounding the foetal capillary with its endothelium at the bottom right.   × 29,000 (Reduced 2/3 when reproduced)

sinusoids and escape of blood into the spaces can be seen. There does not appear to be any circulation of maternal blood through the marginal region. The debris contains much bilirubin and cholesterol esters. The trophoblast cells possess long, branched microvilli at their apices and contain aggregates which appear to be remnants of phagocytosed maternal red cells as well as irregular crystalline objects. These appearances indicate a mechanism for transferring iron to the foetus: it is indeed present in other carnivores, but appears to be quantitatively well developed in seals. With its higher blood volume, greater red cell count and larger red cells than most mammalian foetuses, the pinniped foetus would appear to have a marked demand for iron. It is perhaps relevant that the cow frequently eats the placenta almost immediately after parturition, presumably thus replenishing the cow's bilirubin stores.

There have been few authoritative, detailed descriptions of the cetacean placenta and none that have made use of modern techniques of investigation. Most descriptions are based on the early and scanty observations of William Turner: Wislocki[103] gives a more useful account of the placenta of *Phocaena*.

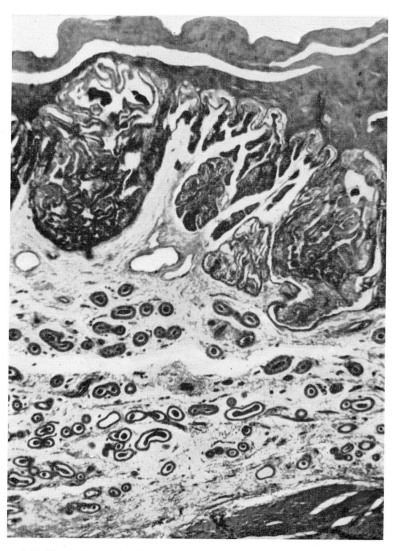

Figure 4.16. Photomicrograph of placenta of *Globicephala* showing tufts of chorionic villi fitting into the corresponding crypts in the uterine mucosa[104]
In the lower part of the picture are numerous coiled uterine glands which appear to open into the bases of the crypts.   × 76 (Reduced 2/3 when reproduced)

The cetacean placenta is diffuse in form with short villi and the foetal–maternal relationship is epitheliochorial. There has been no suggestion so far that any particular feature in the cetacean placenta can be associated with an aquatic existence.

Morton and Mulholland[104] have recently given a brief account of the placenta in *Globicephala*. It is diffuse with the chorion covered by small villous tufts 2 to 3 cm high which fit into corresponding crypts in the uterine wall (*Figure 4.16*). Coiled uterine glands are present in much of the sub-epithelial zone and appear to open at the bases of some maternal crypts. The relationship of maternal to foetal tissues is epitheliochorial, although maternal capillaries are frequently intra-epithelial. The trophoblast is thin and foetal capillaries lie immediately beneath it. These features may certainly facilitate transport across the placenta, but they are not necessarily aquatic adaptations. Similar characteristics are seen in epitheliochorial placentae of terrestrial mammals. Those trophoblast cells adjacent to the mouths of the uterine glands have appearances suggesting that they are actively absorbing the glandular secretions.

The placenta of the manatee[105] is zonary, labyrinthine and haemochorial, though possibly partly endotheliochorial. Small accessory nodules of placental tissue are present at the edge of the main band. The dugong has a placenta that is diffuse in early stages becoming zonary later. It is villous and epitheliochorial.

THE BRAIN

'The brains of the seal and whales (mammals belonging to widely different groups) have taken a common form due to adaptation to a common medium and differ very greatly from other mammals'[106].

Whether or not one is in agreement with this statement, there is little doubt that the brains of these aquatic mammals have many similarities and show many interesting features. Since Hunter's classic work[49], a considerable literature has arisen, mainly concerned with the cetacean brain. This has been reviewed by Breathnach[107] who should be consulted for detailed references.

The cetacean brain is very large, and varies from 500 g in *Phocaena* to 9,200 g in *Physeter*[108]. The relation of brain to body weight, however, is very low, 0·4 per cent in the porpoise and 0·01 per cent in the fin whale[109], although the question of the amount of blubber carried by the larger species would prevent any real conclusions being drawn from these data. The general morphology of the whale brain shows a foreshortening antero-posteriorly and a widening laterally, resulting in a deep or high brain. This is most likely due to adaptations in skull configuration, termed telescoping by Kellogg[110] and explained by Langworthy[111] as the overlapping of the vault bones. The cerebral hemispheres are well developed, and show marked convolution—more highly differentiated in this respect than man[112]. The Sylvian fissure is vertical, caused by rotation of the forebrain consequent on telescoping; the occipital lobe is small, the temporal lobe very large. The acoustic nerve, particularly the cochlear division, is very well developed as are the acoustic centres in the brain, especially the inferior colliculi[113]. The brain stem has been described by Wilson[114] who remarks on the small pyramidal tracts, as does Jansen[115] and Kojima[108]. Two other striking features of the cetacean brain are the large cerebellum, and the reduction of the olfactory apparatus.

In an 8 cm foetus of the hump-back whale *Megaptera*, Riese[116] describes well formed olfactory lobes, and olfactory tracts can be recognized in whalebone whales, but are mere rudiments embedded in the meninges in toothed whales[117]. Edinger[118] considers olfactory bulbs to exist in adult whalebone whales, but suggests they may be missed due to being torn when the brain is removed from the skull. Breathnach[119] describes olfactory peduncles containing nerve fibres in *Megaptera*. The authors have been unable to find any account of incontrovertible bulbs and peduncles in adult toothed whales, and they are certainly absent in adult specimens of *Tursiops*, *Delphinus* and *Phocaena* examined by us.

In spite of the poor development of the superficial olfactory parts of the brain, various authors have shown that some of the other structures which have been implicated in olfactory functioning, *e.g.* habenular nuclei and tracts, do not necessarily show a comparable state. In the last 20 years views on the parts of the brain concerned in olfactory functions have undergone a considerable revision[120,121] and it is difficult as yet to draw any firm conclusions with regard to function from the configuration and degree of development of these structures in macrosmatic as compared with allegedly anosmatic species. Breathnach and Goldby[122] have pointed out that the condition of the cetacean hippocampus might be used to support either the olfactory or non-olfactory view of its function. It seems certain that cetacea in general must have a poor sense of smell, if indeed they have any, and it has been suggested that this is probably due to a failure to adapt a peripheral olfactory apparatus, designed for functioning in air, to an aquatic environment[107]. Water is said not to come into contact with the sinuses to which the olfactory nerves are distributed[110].

Studies on the cetacean cerebellum have been extensive and have been responsible, in a large measure, for elucidating the present views on the morphology and function of this organ. It is well developed in all cetacean species; in toothed whales it comprises 15 per cent, in whalebone whales 20 per cent, of the total brain weight as compared with an average of 10 per cent in other mammals[123].

In a detailed and impressive study of the cerebellum of fin whale foetuses, varying from 10·5 cm to 450 cm in crown–rump length, Jansen[124] described certain typical features of the whale cerebellum. They include a well developed vermis to the anterior lobe, with rudimentary associated hemispheres; a large lobulus simplex and paramedian lobule; a small ansiform lobule; a small rudimentary flocculo-nodular lobe, and an enormous paraflocculus divided into dorsal, accessory and ventral portions, of which the latter, homologous with the tonsil in man[123], is markedly the most developed. The same characteristics were present in an adult bottle-nose whale cerebellum. Jansen considered that the large lobulus simplex was consistent with the view that it received tactile projection from the head area, that the parafloccular development pointed to a functional relationship with the tail and trunk, and that the rudimentary flocculo-nodular lobe indicated little demand for equilibration in whales 'which live, and one might well say float, in the water'. The difficulties of formulating any definitive functional significations with regard to the mammalian cerebellum in general are great[123],[125]. Much is known of its connections *per se*, but little of how they are related to each other. Cetacea, with their marked adaptations in cerebellar morphology, undoubtedly offer considerable scope in this direction when their general morphology and mode of life are considered, but, at the moment, lack of precise knowledge of the source of many cerebellar afferent impulses renders the cetacean cerebellar 'adaptations' an enigma[107]. The configuration of the cerebellar nuclei has been described by Ogawa[126]; the cerebellar cortex, which contains relatively few Purkinje cells, but a number of even larger cells, is described by Addison[127] and Ogawa[128].

Views on the degree of visual development and function in whales are conflicting[107], but it is not unlikely that their vision is better than was previously believed. In fact the idea of an animal, half-blind, anosmatic and unable to taste, with low tactile sensibility and not over-burdened with intelligence is now undergoing considerable revision.

As has been stated, one of the striking features of cetacean brains is the development of those parts associated with hearing. Theories of how whales 'hear' under water differ, but it may be that the view argued by Fraser and Purves[129]—via the external auditory meatus and by modification of typical mammalian structures—will be the one to prevail. Their paper should be consulted for details and discussion.

The cetacean cerebral cortex shows very marked and complex con-volutions. Early workers commented on the poor differentiation of cell layers and the paucity of neurons[130] (isocortex neuron density 6,500 to 7,100/mm³). Kojima[108] describes a five-layered cortex, with a decrease in cell density in all layers as one progresses anteriorly in the frontal lobe. The allocortex, however, shows a degree of differentiation not conspicuously different from most mammals and as well developed as in microsmatic man[131].

The fact that captive dolphins and porpoises can be quite highly trained to perform complicated marine manoeuvres and what might be called 'circus tricks' has been extensively exploited in recent years, and there can be little doubt that their intelligence entitles them to a high position in the mammalian scale in this respect. The methods by which dolphins position themselves underwater before 'jumping' through hoops or taking objects held as high as 20 feet above water and by which they appear to 'communi-cate' with each other are beyond the scope of this review.

The brain of the seal has received much less attention than that of whales. The brain weight varies considerably—266 g in *Phoca*, 375 g in *Zalophus*. The general morphology is recorded by Flateau and Jacobsohn[132] who give references to earlier work. The general configuration, with considerable detail of fissure topography, can be found in Fish[133], who compares the brains of different species; the surface morphology and histology is described by Jelgersma[134]. Some experiments have been carried out on the cerebral cortex[135–137], and reference is made to the cerebellar morphology by Bolk[138] and Jansen and Brodal[123]. The cerebral hemispheres show a degree of foreshortening, more marked in the common seal than in either the fur or monk seals, together with an increased width. They are large with considerable cortical convolutions. The excito-motor cortex is placed well anteriorly and somewhat ventrally between the coronal, cruciate and pre-Sylvian sulci. It shows histological appearances, characteristic of motor cortices in other animals, and the seal's body is represented approximately upside down upon it. Stimulation produces body movements simulating swimming. The auditory and trigeminal sensory areas of the cortex have been mapped[137], the former being situated in part of the posterior, the latter in the anterior, Sylvian gyrus. The degree of development of the superficial olfactory apparatus varies, being well developed in the fur seal and sea lion, less so in the common seal[133]. The cerebellum and, as might therefore be expected, the pons also, are very large compared with other carnivores. The lobulus simplex is small (it is large in whales) as is the ansiform lobule; there is a moderate sized paramedian lobule, and a large paraflocculus, particularly the ventral part. There is a relatively larger flocculo-nodular lobe than obtains in Cetacea[123]. We are unaware of any description of the pinniped brain stem.

It is surprising that so little investigation of the pinniped brain has been made, particularly as seals are relatively easy to catch and keep in most parts of the world. Seals and sea lions do not perform such spectacular acrobatics as dolphins, but they can be trained to perform 'tricks', their equilibratory powers with a bottle of Guinness are universally appreciated, and they are attracted by music.

REFERENCES

1. MELVILLE, H. *The Whale* (3 Vols.): Bentley, London, 1851; *Moby Dick or the Whale:* Cresset Press, London, 1946
2. HOWELL, A. B. *Aquatic Mammals:* C. C. Thomas, Baltimore, 1930
3. SLIJPER, E. J. 'Die Cetaceen, vergleichend-anatomisch und systematisch'. *Capita zool.* 1936, **7,** 1–590
4. KELLOGG, R. 'Adaptation of structure and function in whales'. *Publ. Carneg. Instn.* 1938, **501,** 649–682
5. BOHR, C. 'Bidrag til Syømmefuglenes Fysiologi'. *Overs. danske Videnst. Selsk. Forh.* 1897, No. 2
6. SCHOLANDER, P. F. 'Experimental investigation on the respiratory function in diving mammals and birds'. *Hvalråd. Skr.* 1940, **22,** 1–131
7. RICHET, C. 'De la résistance des canards à l'asphyxie'. *J. Physiol. Path. gén.* 1899, **1,** 641–650
8. BURRELL, H. *The Platypus:* Angus and Robertson, Sydney, 1927
9. BERT, P. *Physiologie de la Respiration:* Paris, 1870
10. IRVING, L. 'Respiration in diving mammals'. *Physiol. Rev.* 1939, **19,** 112–134
11. HARRISON, R. J. 'Experiments with diving seals'. *Nature, Lond.* 1960, **188,** 1068–1070
12. MATTHEWS, L. H. *British Mammals:* Collins, London, 1952
13. FREUCHEN, P. *Report of Fifth Thule Expedition,* 1921–1924. Vol. 2: Nordisk Forlag, Copenhagen, 1935
14. PAULIAN, P. 'Note sur les phoques des îles Amsterdam et Saint-Paul'. *Mammalia* 1957, **21,** 210–225
15. PARKER, G. H. 'The breathing of the florida manatee (*Trichechus latirostris*)'. *J. Mammal.* 1922, **3,** 127–135

16. HARRISON, R. J. and TOMLINSON, J. D. W. 'Observations on the venous systems in certain Pinnipedia and Cetacea'. *Proc. zool. Soc. Lond.* 1956, **126**, 205–233

17. COLLETT, R. 'On *Halichoerus grypus* and its breeding on the Fro Island off Trondhjems-fjord in Norway'. *Proc. zool. Soc. Lond.* 1881, 380–387

18. BERTRAM, G. C. L. 'The biology of the Weddell and crabeater seals, with a study of the comparative behaviour of the Pinnipedia'. *Sci. Rep. Brit. Grahamld. Exped. 1934–1937* 1940, **1**, 1–139

19. NANSEN, F. *Hunting and Adventure in the Arctic:* London, 1925

20. KENYON, K. W. 'Diving depths of the Steller sea lion and Alaska fur seal'. *J. Mammal.* 1952, **33**, 245–246

21. LAURIE, A. H. 'Some aspects of respiration in blue and fin whales'. *'Discovery' Rep.* 1933, **7**, 363–406

22. DAVIS, R. H. *Deep Diving and Submarine Operations:* 6th edn: Siebe, Gorman, London, 1955

23. HARRISON, R. J. and TOMLINSON, J. D. W. 'Normal and experimental diving in the common seal (*Phoca vitulina*)'. *Mammalia* 1960, **24**, 386–399

24. *Handbook of Biological Data* (1956)

25. KOPPÁNYI, T. and DOOLEY, M. S. 'Submergence and postural apnea in the muskrat (*Fiber zibethicus* L.)'. *Amer. J. Physiol.* 1929, **88**, 592–595

26. IRVING, L. and ORR, M. D. 'The diving habits of the beaver'. *Science* 1935, **82**, 569

27. *Essex Countryside*, Nov. 1961

28. SCHEFFER, V. B. *Seals, Sea Lions and Walruses:* Stanford University Press, California, 1958

29. KERMACK, K. A. 'The propulsive powers of blue and fin whales'. *J. exp. Biol.* 1948, **25**, 237–240

30. FEJER, A. A. and BACKUS, R. H. 'Porpoises and the bow-riding of ships under way'. *Nature, Lond.* 1960, **188**, 700–703

31. PERRY, B., ACOSTA, A. J. and KICENIUK, T. 'Simulated wave-riding dolphins'. *Nature, Lond.* 1961, **192**, 148–150

32. BACKHOUSE, K. M. and SMART, P. J. G. 'The mechanism of wave riding in porpoises'. *Proc. zool. Soc. Lond.* 1961, **136**, 197–200

33. PARRY, D. A. 'The structure of whale blubber, and a discussion of its thermal properties'. *Quart. J. micr. Sci.* 1949, **90**, 13–25

34. BARTHOLOMEW, G. A. and WILKE, F. 'Body temperature in the northern fur seal *Callorhinus ursinus*'. *J. Mammal.* 1956, **37**, 327–337

35. SCHOLANDER, P. F., IRVING, L. and GRINNELL, S. W. 'On the temperature and metabolism of the seal during diving'. *J. cell. comp. Physiol.* 1942, **19**, 67–78

36. BARNETT, C. H., HARRISON, R. J. and TOMLINSON, J. D. W. 'Variations in the venous systems of mammals'. *Biol. Rev.* 1958, **33**, 442–487

37. MURIE, J. 'Research upon the anatomy of the Pinnipedia. Pt. III. Descriptive anatomy of the sea-lion (*Otaria jubata*)'. *Trans. zool. Soc. Lond.* 1874, **8**, 501–582

38. FAWCETT, D. W. 'A comparative study of blood vascular bundles in the Florida manatee and in certain cetaceans and edentates'. *J. Morph.* 1942, **71**, 105–133

39. OSMAN HILL, W. C.—personal communication

40. CAVE, A. J. E. and AUMONIER, F. J. 'The visceral histology of the primitive cetacean *Caperea* (*Neobalaena*)'. *J. R. micr. Soc.* 1961, **80**, 25–33

41. GERVAIS, H. P. 'Sur la circulation péri-rénale de l'*Hyperoodon rostratus*'. *Bull. Mus. Hist. nat., Paris* 1895, **1**, 146–150

42. BOULART, M. 'Note sur les plexus thoraciques veineux du Phoque commun (*Phoca vitulina*)'. *Bull. Mus. Hist. nat., Paris* 1895, **1**, 45–46

43. OMMANNEY, F. D. 'The vascular networks (*Retia mirabilia*) of the fin whale (*Balaenoptera physalus*)'. '*Discovery*' *Rep.* 1932, **5,** 327–465

44. BEAUREGARD, H. and BOULART, R. 'Recherches sur les appareils genito-urinaires des Balaenides'. *J. Anat. Paris* 1882, **18,** 158–201

45. DAVIES, D. V. 'The cardiovascular system of the slow loris (*Nycticebus tardigradus malaianus*)'. *Proc. zool. Soc. Lond.* 1947, **117,** 377–410

46. HARRIS, H. A. 'A note on the clinical anatomy of the veins, with special reference to the spinal veins'. *Brain* 1941, **64,** 291–300

47. WALMSLEY, R. 'Some observations on the vascular system of a foetal female finback'. *Contr. Embryol. Carneg. Instn* 1938, **27,** 107–178

48. BATSON, O. V. 'The vertebral vein system'. *Amer. J. Roentgenol.* 1957, **78,** 195–212

49. HUNTER, J. 'Observations on the structure and oeconomy of whales'. *Phil. Trans.* 1787, **77,** 371–450

50. BUROW, A. 'Über das Gefässystem der Robben'. *Müller's Arch. Anat. Physiol.* 1838, 230–258

51. BOWSHER, D. 'A comparative study of the azygos venous system in man, monkey, dog, cat, rat and rabbit'. *J. Anat., Lond.* 1954, **88,** 400–406

52. FRANKLIN, K. J. *A Monograph on Veins:* Thomas, Baltimore, 1937

53. GRATIOLET, L. P. *Recherches sur l'anatomie de l'Hippopotame:* Masson, Paris, 1867

54. CAVE, A. J. E. (1957)—personal communication

55. BURNE, R. H. 'Notes on the viscera of a walrus (*Odobaenus rosmarus*)'. *Proc. zool. Soc. Lond.* 1909, 732–738

56. FRANKLIN, K. J. 'Observations on the venae cavae of certain mammals'. *J. Anat., Lond.* 1933, **67,** 382–386

57. MITCHELL, G. A. G., SAMUEL, E. P. and WARWICK, R. 'The roots and spinal origin of the phrenic nerve in the rhesus monkey'. *J. Anat., Lond.* 1954, **88,** 562 Proc

58. TYSON, E. *Phocaena or the Anatomy of a Porpess:* (Printed for Benj. Tooke), London, 1680

59. OWEN, R. *On the anatomy of vertebrates:* Longmans, Green, London, 1868

60. WISLOCKI, G. B. and STRAUS, W. L. 'On the blood vascular bundles in the limbs of certain edentates and lemurs'. *Bull. Mus. comp. Zool. Harv.* 1933, **74,** 1–15

61. DE KOCK, L. L. 'The arterial vessels of the neck in the pilot-whale (*Globicephala melaena Traill*) and the porpoise (*Phocaena phocaena L*) in relation to the carotid body'. *Acta anat., Basel.* 1959, **36,** 274–292

62. BURNE, R. H. *Handbook of Cetacean Dissections:* British Museum, London, 1952

63. DANIEL, P. M., DAWES, J. D. K. and PRICHARD, M. M. L. 'Studies on the carotid rete and its associated arteries'. *Phil. Trans.* 1953, **B237,** 173–208

64. CARLISLE, A. 'An account of a peculiarity in the distribution of the arteries sent to the limbs of slow moving animals'. *Phil. Trans.* 1800, p. 601; 1804, p. 17

65. MACKAY, J. Y. 'The arteries of the head and neck and the rete mirabile of the porpoise (*Phocaena communis*)'. *Proc. roy. phil. Soc., Glasg.* 1886, **17,** 366–377

66. LAURIE, A. H. 'Physiology of whales'. *Nature, Lond.* 1935, **135,** 823

67. HYRTL, J. 'Das arterielle Gefässystem der Edentaten'. *Denkschr. Akad. Wiss. Wien* 1854, **6,** 21–64

68. SCHOLANDER, P. F. and SCHEVILL, W. E. 'Countercurrent vascular heat exchange in the fins of whales'. *J. appl. Physiol.* 1955, **8,** 279–282

69. FIEBIGER, J. 'Über Eigentümlichkeiten im Aufbau der Delphinlunge und ihre physiologische Bedeutung'. *Anat. Anz.* 1916, **48,** 540–565

70. LACOSTE, A. and BAUDRIMONT, A. 'Sur quelques peculiarités histologiques du poumon du Dauphin et leur adaptation fonctionnelle à la plongée'. *Bull. Soc. sci. Arcachon* 1926, **23,** 87–140

71. LACOSTE, A. and BAUDRIMONT, A. 'Dispositifs d'adaption fonctionnelle á la plongée dans l'appareil respiratoire du marsouin (*Phoca communis* Less.)'. *Arch. Anat., Strasbourg* 1933, **17**, 1–48

72. WISLOCKI, G. B. 'On the structure of the lungs of the porpoise (*Tursiops truncatus*)'. *Amer. J. Anat.* 1929, **44**, 47–77

73. BONIN, W. and BÉLANGER, L. F. 'Sur la structure du poumon de *Delphinapterus leucas*'. *Trans. roy. Soc. Can.* 1939, **33**, 19–22

74. BÉLANGER, L. F. 'A study of the histological structure of the respiratory portion of the lungs of aquatic mammals'. *Amer. J. Anat.* 1940, **67**, 437–461

75. WISLOCKI, G. B. 'The lungs of the Cetacea, with special reference to the harbor porpoise (*Phocaena phocaena* L.)'. *Anat. Rec.* 1942, **84**, 117–121

76. WISLOCKI, G. B. and BÉLANGER, L. F. 'The lungs of the larger Cetacea compared to those of smaller species'. *Biol. Bull.* 1940, **78**, 289–297

77. SLIJPER, E. J. *Walvissen*: Centen, Amsterdam, 1958

78. GOUDAPPEL, J. R. and SLIJPER, E. J. 'Microscopic structure of the lungs of the bottle-nosed dolphin'. *Nature, Lond.* 1958, **182**, 479

79. TOMLINSON, J. D. W. and HARRISON, R. J. 'Venous modifications in two rare marine mammals'. *J. Anat., Lond.* 1961, **95**, 453 Proc

80. KING. J. E. and HARRISON, R. J. 'Some notes on the Hawaiian Monk seal'. *Pacif. Sci.* 1961, **15**, 282–293

81. BROWN, D. 'The bronchial tree in aquatic mammals'. *J. Anat., Lond.* 1958, **92**, 656 Proc

82. PICK, F. K. 'Zur feineren Anatomie der Lunge von *Halichore dugong*'. *Arch. Naturgesch.* 1907, **73**, 245–272

83. WISLOCKI, G. B. 'The lungs of the manatee (*Trichechus latirostris*) compared with those of other aquatic mammals'. *Biol. Bull. Wood's Hole* 1935, **68**, 385–396

84. SLIJPER, E. J. 'Organ weights and symmetry problems in porpoises and seals'. *Arch. néerl. Zool.* 1958, **13**, 97–113

85. SMITH, H. W. 'The composition of the urine in the seal'. *J. cell. comp. Physiol.* 1936, **7**, 465–474

86. HIATT, E. P. and HIATT, R. B. 'The effect of food on the glomerular filtration rate and renal blood flow in the harbor seal (*Phoca vitulina* L.)'. *J. cell. comp. Physiol.* 1942, **19**, 221–227

87. PAGE, L. B., SCOTT-BAKER, J. C., ZAK, G. A., BECKER, E. L. and BAXTER, C. F. 'The effects of variation in filtration rate on the urinary concentrating mechanism in the seal (*Phoca vitulina* L.)'. *J. cell. comp. Physiol.* 1954, **43**, 257–269

88. SCHMIDT-NIELSEN, B., MURDAUGH, H. V. Jr., O'DELL, R. and BACSANYI, J. 'Urea excretion and diving in the seal (*Phoca vitulina* L.)'. *J. cell. comp. Physiol.* 1959, **53**, 393–411

89. HILL, W. C. O. 'Notes on the dissection of two dugongs'. *J. Mammal.* 1945, **26**, 153–175

90. SLIJPER, E. J. 'On the thickness of the layer of blubber in Antarctic blue and fin whales. I, II and III'. *Proc. Akad. Sci. Amst.* 1948, **51**, 1033–1045, 114–1124, 1310–1316

91. BERGERSEN, B. 'Beiträge zur Kenntnis der Haut einiger Pinnipedien unter besonderer Berücksichtigung der Haut der *Phoca grölandica*'. *Skr. norske Vidensk Akad. Mat-Naturv. Klasse.* 1931

92. MOHR, E. 'Behaarung und Haarwechsel der Robben'. *Neue Ergeb. Probleme Zool.* (Klatt-Festschrift, Leipzig) 1950, 602–614

93. MONTAGNA, W. and HARRISON, R. J. 'Specializations in the skin of the seal (*Phoca vitulina*)'. *Amer. J. Anat.* 1957, **100**, 81–114

94. ROTHMAN, S. *Physiology and Biochemistry of Skin*: University of Chicago Press, Chicago, 1954

95. MONTAGNA, W. 'The brown inguinal glands of the rabbit'. *Amer. J. Anat.* 1950, **87,** 213–238

96. VAN UTRECHT, W. L. 'Temperaturregulierende Gefässysteme in der Haut und anderen epidermalen Strukturen bei Cetaceen'. *Zool. Anz.* 1958, **161,** 77–82

97. HILDITCH, T. P. and PATHAK, S. P. 'The use of low-temperature crystallization in the determination of component acids of liquid fats. IV. Marine animal oils. The component acids and glycerides of a grey (atlantic)seal'. *J. Soc. chem. Ind., Lond.* 1947, **66,** 421–425

98. WINTER, G. and NUNN, W. 'The composition of the blubber fat of crabeater seal'. *J. Sci. Food Agric.* 1953, **4,** 439–442

99. HARRISON, R. J. and YOUNG, B. A. 'Specializations in the pinniped placenta'. *J. Anat., Lond.* 1961, **95,** 450 Proc

100. DEMPSEY, E. W. and WISLOCKI, G. B. 'Electron microscopic observations on the placenta of the cat'. *J. biophys. biochem. Cytol.* 1956, **2,** 743–754

101. AMOROSO, E. C., HARRISON, R. J., MATTHEWS, L. H. and ROWLANDS, I. W. 'Reproductive organs of near term and newborn seals'. *Nature, Lond.* 1951, **168,** 771–772

102. HARRISON, R. J. 'Reproduction and reproductive organs in common seals (*Phoca vitulina*) in the Wash, East Anglia'. *Mammalia* 1960, **24,** 372–385

103. WISLOCKI, G. B. 'On the placentation of the harbour porpoise (*Phocaena phocaena* L.)'. *Biol. Bull., Wood's Hole* 1933, **65,** 80–98

104. MORTON, W. R. M. and MULHOLLAND, H. C. 'The placenta of the ca'ing whale, *Globicephala melaena* (Traill)'. *J. Anat., Lond.* 1961, **95,** 605 Proc

105. WISLOCKI, G. B. 'The placentation of the manatee (*Trichechus latirostris*)'. *Mem. Mus. comp. Zool. Harv.* 1935, **54,** 159–178

106. RIESE, W. 'Adaptations and convergence in the brain'. *Naturwissenschaften* 1927, **15,** 814–881

107. BREATHNACH, A. S. 'The cetacean central nervous system'. *Biol. Rev.* 1960, **35,** 187–230

108. KOJIMA, T. 'On the brain of the sperm whale (*Physeter catodon* L.)'. *Sci. Rep. Whale Res. Inst., Tokyo* 1951, **6,** 49–72

109. BJARNASON, I. and LINGAAS, P. 'Some weight measurements of whales'. *Norsk Hvalfangsttid.* 1954, **43,** 8–11

110. KELLOGG, R. 'The history of whales—their adaptation to life in the water'. *Quart. Rev. Biol.* 1928, **3,** 174–208

111. LANGWORTHY, O. R. 'The brain of the whalebone whale *Balaenoptera physalus*'. *Johns Hopk. Hosp. Bull.* 1935, **57,** 143–147

112. LANGWORTHY, O. R. 'A description of the central nervous system of the porpoise (*Tursiops truncatus*)'. *J. comp. Neurol.* 1932, **54,** 437–499

113. LANGWORTHY, O. R. 'Factors determining the differentiation of the cerebral cortex in sea-living mammals (the cetacea). A study of the brain of the porpoise, *Tursiops truncatus*'. *Brain* 1931, **54,** 225–236

114. WILSON, R. B. 'The anatomy of the brain of the whale (*Balaenoptera sulphurea*)'. *J. comp. Neurol.* 1933, **58,** 419–480

115. JANSEN, J. 'Studies on the cetacean brain. The gross anatomy of the rhombencephalon of the fin whale (*Balaenoptera physalus* L)'. *Hvalråd. Skr.* 1953, **37,** 1–35

116. RIESE, W. 'Über des Vorderhirn des Walfötus (*Megaptera boops*)'. *Anat. Anz.* 1928, **65,** 255–260

117. RIES, F. A. and LANGWORTHY, O. R. 'A study of the surface structure of the brain of the whale (*Balaenoptera physalus* and *Physeter catodon*)'. *J. comp. Neurol.* 1937, **68,** 1–36

118. EDINGER, T. 'Hearing and smell in cetacean history'. *Mschr. Psychiat. Neurol.* 1955, **129,** 37–58

119. BREATHNACH, A. S. 'The surface features of the brain of the humpback whale (*Megaptera novaeangliae*)'. *J. Anat., Lond.* 1955, **89**, 343–354

120. BRODAL, A. *Neurological Anatomy:* Clarendon Press, Oxford, 1948

121. MEYER, M. and ALLISON, A. C. 'An experimental investigation of the connexions of the olfactory tracts in the monkey'. *J. Neurol. Psychiat., N.S.* 1949, **12**, 274–286

122. BREATHNACH, A. S. and GOLDBY, F. 'The amygdaloid nuclei, hippocampus and other parts of the rhinencephalon in the porpoise (*Phocaena phocaena*)'. *J. Anat., Lond.* 1954, **88**, 267–291

123. JANSEN, J. and BRODAL, A. *Aspects of Cerebellar Anatomy:* Grundt Tanum, Oslo, 1954

124. JANSEN, J. 'The morphogenesis of the cetacean cerebellum'. *J. comp. Neurol.* 1950, **93**, 341–400

125. DOW, R. S. and MORUZZI, G. *The Physiology and Pathology of the Cerebellum:* University of Minnesota Press, Minneapolis, 1958

126. OGAWA, T. 'Beiträge zur vergleichenden Anatomie des Zentralnervensystems der Wassersäugetiere. Über die Kleinhirnkerne der Pinnipedien und Cetacea'. *Arb. anat. Inst. Sendai* 1935, **17**, 63–136

127. ADDISON, W. H. F. 'Unusual large nerve cells in the cerebellar cortex of several aquatic mammals'. *Psychiat. neurol. bl., Amst.* 1934, **3/4**, 587–595

128. OGAWA, T. 'Beiträge zur vergleichenden Anatomie des Zentralnervensystems der Wassersäugetiere'. *Arb. anat. Inst. Sendai* 1934, **16**, 83–96

129. FRASER, F. C. and PURVES, P. E. 'Hearing in cetaceans'. *Bull. Brit. Mus. (nat. Hist.)* 1960, **7**, 1–140

130. TOWER, D. B. 'Structural and functional organization of the mammalian cerebral cortex: the correlation of neurone density with brain size'. *J. comp. Neurol.* 1954, **101**, 19–51

131. BREATHNACH, A. S. 'The olfactory tubercle, prepyriform cortex and precommisural region of the porpoise (*Phocaena phocaena*)'. *J. Anat., Lond.* 1953, **87**, 96–113

132. FLATEAU, E. and JACOBSOHN, L. *Handbuch der Anatomie und vergleichenden Anatomie der Centralnervensystems der Säugetiere:* Karger, Berlin, 1899

133. FISH, P. A. 'The brain of the fur seal, *Callorhinus ursinus*; with a comparative description of those of *Zalophus californianus*, *Phoca vitulina*, *Ursus americanus* and *Monachus tropicalis*'. *J. comp. Neurol.* 1898, **8**, 57–91

134. JELGERSMA, G. *Das Gehirn der Wassersäugetiere:* Barth, Leipsig, 1934

135. RIOCH, D. M. 'A physiological and histological study of the frontal cortex of the seal (*Phoca vitulina*)'. *Biol. Bull., Wood's Hole* 1937, **73**, 591–602

136. LANGWORTHY, O. R., HESSER, F. H. and KOLB, L. C. 'A physiological study of the cerebral cortex of the hair seal (*Phoca vitulina*)'. *J. comp. Neurol.* 1938, **69**, 351–369

137. ALDERSON, A. M., DIAMANTOPOULOS, E. and DOWMAN, C. B. B. 'Auditory cortex of the seal (*Phoca vitulina*)'. *J. Anat., Lond.* 1960, **94**, 506–511

138. BOLK, L. *Das cerebellum der Säugetiere:* E. F. Bohn, Haarlem, 1906

5

KINETIC ASPECTS OF ION REGULATION IN AQUATIC ANIMALS

J. Shaw

INTRODUCTION

One characteristic feature of higher animals is that the majority of their cells and tissues are isolated from direct contact with the environment by the presence of a circulating body fluid which surrounds them. There are a large number of marine animals in which this fluid is almost identical in composition with the surrounding sea water, with respect to its main inorganic constituents (Na^+, Cl^-, K^+, Ca^{2+}, Mg^{2+}, and SO_4^{2-}). It has been known for many years, however, that certain aquatic animals are able to maintain distinct concentration differences of one or more of these solute ions between their body fluid and the external medium. In the majority of animals, sodium and chloride ions are numerically the most important inorganic constituents of the body fluid and, hence, where large concentration gradients of these ions are encountered, differences in osmotic pressure between the two solutions are also found.

The maintenance of ionic concentration or osmotic pressure gradients is clearly a property of the body surface of the animal and of the membranes of which it is composed[1]. The body surface is complex in nature and differentiated into a number of special regions such as the integument, the respiratory surface, the gut, and the excretory system. It is now clear that at least one of the constituent surface membranes is permeable to water and to ions, so that it is impossible to explain the maintenance of ionic and osmotic gradients in terms of the action of purely physical forces. Part of the body surface has properties not possessed by inanimate membranes, and conferred on it by its constitution from living cells.

Aquatic animals as a whole exhibit a wide range of ability in maintaining the body fluid different from that of the external medium. It is useful, therefore, to group them together according to the extent to which this ability is developed. Thus, following in the main the classification adopted by Pantin[1], animals may be placed into one of five main categories. The division is, however, to a large extent an arbitrary one and many intermediate forms are known.

(a) *Iso-osmotic animals*—This group includes many marine animals in which the body fluid is practically iso-osmotic with the surrounding sea water and contains almost the same relative proportions of inorganic ions. The body fluid thus approximates to a fluid in true equilibrium with the external medium, although this is probably never exactly so. A few typical examples are shown in *Table 5.1.*

163

(b) *Iso-osmotic animals showing ionic regulation*—Here we have marine animals which are also nearly iso-osmotic with their environment, but in which is found some degree of divergence in ionic composition. This applies particularly to the concentrations of potassium, magnesium and sulphate ions, but in certain cases the retention of organic molecules in the blood, such as urea in the Elasmobranchs, allows the maintenance of low concentrations of all the major inorganic ions. A number of examples from this group are also shown in *Table 5.1.*

Table 5.1. The composition of the body fluids of some iso-osmotic animals
A. *Iso-osmotic animals*

Species	Na	K	Ca	Mg	Cl	SO₄	Reference
Echinodermata							
Echinus esculenta	100	102	101	100	100	101	2
Holothuria tubulosa	101	103	102	104	100	100	4
Annelida							
Arenicola marina	100	103	100	100	98	92	3
Mollusca							
Mya arenaria*	101	107	107	99	100	101	3

B. *Iso-osmotic animals showing ionic regulation*

Species	Na	K	Ca	Mg	Cl	SO₄	Reference
Annelida							
Aphrodite aculeata	99	126	100	99	100	100	3
Mollusca							
Ensis ensis*	99	155	108	99	99	86	3
Buccinum undatum*	97	142	104	103	100	90	3
Loligo forbesi*	95	219	102	102	103	29	3
Arthropoda							
Lithodus maia*	104	128	113	97	103	96	3
Nephrops norvegicus*	113	77	124	17	99	69	3
Homarus vulgaris*	110	85	131	14	101	32	2
Vertebrata							
Myxine glutinosa	110	90	56	33	97	22	5

Values expressed as a percentage of the corresponding values in sea water or, in those animals marked with an asterisk, as a percentage of the values in the plasma dialysed against sea water.

(c) *Hyperosmotic animals from brackish water*—In this group are placed animals which are able to maintain the concentration of sodium ions and chloride ions in their body fluids above that of the external medium and thus preserve a permanent osmotic gradient. The concentration of other ions may also be regulated, but the preservation of ion balance and of the osmotic pressure difference requires the presence of some sea water in the medium. The crab, *Carcinus maenas*, is a well-known example of this group and the composition of its blood in dilute sea water is shown in *Table 5.2.*

(d) *Hyperosmotic animals from fresh water*—The composition of fresh water is characterized by its low total ionic content and its relative proportions of ions being different from those in sea water. Animals which live in fresh water all maintain a very high total osmotic pressure compared with that of the medium, although its value is extremely variable from one species to another and is generally lower than that of brackish water and marine animals (see *Table 5.2*).

(e) *Hypo-osmotic animals*—This group includes a number of animals, probably derived originally from fresh water forms, but inhabiting marine or other saline waters, which possess the special ability to keep the body fluid osmotic pressure well below that of the environment. The best known examples are the marine Teleosts, other examples being a few insect larvae, such as *Aedes detritus*, and Crustacea, such as *Artemia salina*.

Over thirty years ago it was clearly realized that the maintenance of gradients of ionic concentration and osmotic pressure required the expenditure of energy by the animal. Further, in view of the permeability of the

Table 5.2. The composition of the body fluids of some hyperosmotic animals
(Concns. in mM/l.)

Species	Total concn. $= Na \, Cl$soln.	Na	K	Ca	Mg	Cl	SO$_4$	Reference
Crustacea								
Carcinus maenas (from 67% SW)	—	418	9·5	9·1	11·3	454	8·7	6
Eriocheir sinensis	318	—	5	10	3·5	282	—	7
Astacus sp.	230	203	5·2	10·4	2·7	194	—	7, 8
Insecta								
Aedes aegypti larva	145	110	3	—	—	43	—	9, 10
Annelida								
Lumbricus terrestris	91	—	—	—	—	47	—	11
Mollusca								
Anodonta cygnea	23	15·5	0·5	8·4	0·2	11·7	0·8	12
Teleostei								
Coregonus clupeiodes	157	141	3·8	5·3	1·7	117	2·3	5
Amphibia								
Rana esculenta	130	104	2·5	2·0	1·2	74	1·9	13

surface membrane to ions, this energy could not be utilized solely for osmotic work in transporting water molecules. Subsequent experience has shown that in the majority of animals the active transport of water (*i.e.* transport of water against an osmotic gradient) plays little or no part in the maintenance of the observed gradients, and that they are maintained by active processes located in the surface membranes and specifically concerned with the transport of solute ions.

During the nineteen thirties, great strides were made in locating the membranes responsible for ion transport and in elucidating their role in ionic regulation. Thus, in 1930, Homer Smith demonstrated that in the hypo-osmotic marine Teleosts, water losses due to outward diffusion under the action of the osmotic gradient, were made good by drinking sea-water. Monovalent ions and water are absorbed iso-osmotically from the intestine, but salt balance is maintained by the secretion of the absorbed ions against a concentration gradient from the anterior part of the animal, presumably through the gill membranes[14]. Nagel clearly showed that the crab *Carcinus maenas* is able to absorb chloride ions against a gradient from dilute sea water and to secrete them into the body fluid, again almost certainly through the gill surface[15]. In fresh water animals the maintenance of a large osmotic gradient is assisted by the production of a dilute urine in many species. Richards and his colleagues proved that the formation of this fluid in the Amphibia also involved the uptake of sodium chloride against a large gradient in the distal convoluted region of the nephric tubule[16,17]. Finally, Krogh extended Nagel's discovery by showing that many fresh water animals, previously salt-depleted by washing in running distilled water, were able to absorb sodium and chloride ions from the very dilute solutions in which they normally live[18-21]. *Table 5.3* gives a few examples of those animals which are known to be able to do this and the location of the membranes responsible, where these are known.

It is apparent from this list that the ability to take up sodium and chloride ions against a concentration gradient is widespread among the hyperosmotic

Table 5.3. The active uptake of ions against a concentration gradient by salt-depleted animals

Species	Ions absorbed	Location of uptake mechanisms	Reference
Amphibia			
Rana esculenta	Na, Cl	Skin	18, 21
Teleostei			
Carassius auratus	Na, Cl	Anterior end (gill chamber)	19, 21
Crustacea			
Eriocheir sinensis	Na, K, Cl	Gills	20, 21, 22
Carcinus maenas	Cl	Not gut (gill chamber)	15
Potamon niloticus	Na, K.	—	23
Astacus sp.	Na, Cl	Gill chamber	21, 24
Insecta			
Culex and *Chironomus* larvae	Cl	Anal papillae	25
Aedes aegypti larva	Na, K.	Anal papillae	10
Mollusca			
Anodonta cygnea	Cl	—	21
Annelida			
Haemopsis sanguisuga	Na, Cl	—	21

coelomate animals, and among the examples quoted there are representatives from most of the major Phyla. In the Arthropods, too, the ability to take up potassium is also apparent. Although the location of the site of uptake has yet to be determined with sufficient precision to implicate special cells, it is clear that in general animals do not utilize special membranes for this purpose but they make use of the respiratory epithelium. It is only in certain aquatic insect larvae, such as the larva of the mosquito, *Aedes aegypti*, that special structures like the anal papillae have been found to have this specific function[10,25].

Despite the wide-spread occurrence of the active uptake of ions, there are a few fresh water animals in which this appears to be absent. Krogh was unable to detect it in the Branchiopod Crustacea *Branchipus* and *Lepidurus* and, similarly, the occurrence is doubtful in some fresh water fish, especially in the eel, *Anguilla vulgaris*. In the aquatic larva of the insect, *Sialis lutaria*, no evidence of chloride uptake from dilute solutions could be found[26]. In cases where active uptake is definitely ruled out, it is reasonable to assume that salt loss is balanced by an uptake of ions from the food, but this has yet to be formally demonstrated.

By 1939 the active uptake or secretion of ions against a concentration gradient, as a mechanism for the maintenance of ionic and osmotic gradients, had been firmly established, and the location of these processes was known in general terms. Taken together with a knowledge of urine production rate and urine composition, a clear general picture had emerged of the way in which the composition of the body fluids was maintained[21].

During this period another important concept was developing. In 1925 Duval demonstrated that aquatic animals differed widely in their abilities to regulate the composition of their body fluids in the face of changes in the composition of the external medium[27]. The ability to regulate the composition of the body fluid is found to be clearly related to the ability to maintain concentration gradients in a constant environment. Thus, in general, marine animals iso-osmotic with their environment remain so when transferred to a more dilute solution. On the other hand, hyperosmotic animals from brackish water can maintain their internal medium relatively constant for limited changes in the concentration of their external environment. Fresh water animals show a high degree of regulation in a wide range of very dilute media, regulation only breaking down when the concentration of the external medium approaches that of the animal's original blood concentration.

In this review no attempt will be made at a comprehensive account of the regulatory abilities of the wide variety of aquatic animals which have now been studied. Much of this information has been collected together in Krogh's excellent monograph[21] and in previous review articles[28,29], and the more recent work surveyed by Ramsay[31], Beadle[32], Robertson[33], and Shaw[34], and in Prosser and Brown's text-book[35].

In recent years a different approach to the study of ionic regulation has been made possible by the use of radioactive tracers. Although this technique in no way supplants older methods of analysis—indeed it must be used in conjunction with them—its application allows a study of the kinetics of ion movement across the surface membranes of an animal and, hence, the possibility of building up a dynamic picture of the regulation processes.

THE CONCEPT OF THE DYNAMIC STEADY STATE

In an aquatic animal whose body fluid is separated from the external medium by a membrane permeable to water and ions, there is a continuous interchange of ions between the two solutions. For a particular ion, the ion flux is a measure of the rate at which this ion is crossing the membrane—thus the influx (M_{in}) may be defined as the rate at which the ion moves from the external to the internal solution, and the efflux (M_{out}), the rate of movement in the opposite direction. If the animal is in a steady state with its environment for this ion, there is no net movement of the ion across the surface and the two fluxes are equal (*i.e.* $M_{in} = M_{out}$). The measurement of these fluxes is made by means of the isotopic tracer technique. From this additional information (a) it is possible to decide which ions are actively transported and the proportion of the total flux which can be ascribed to active movement, and (b) by subdivision of the fluxes into their major components, such as active transport, passive influx and efflux through the body surface and efflux through the excretory organ, the extent to which each is determined by external factors or regulated in relation to the internal

Table 5.4. Equations for the measurement of ion fluxes.

Isotope introduced initially into:	Radioactivity measured in:	General solution	Special solution
1. External medium	External medium	$y = y_0 \dfrac{A_2}{A_1 + A_2}\left(\exp(-Bt) + \dfrac{A_1}{A_2}\right)$	$A_1 \ll A_2; \quad y = y_0 \exp\left(-\dfrac{M}{A_1}t\right)$
2. External medium	Internal medium	$y' = y_0 \dfrac{C_2}{C_1}\dfrac{A_1}{A_1 + A_2}\{1 - \exp(-Bt)\}$	$A_1 \gg A_2; \quad y' = y_0 \dfrac{C_2}{C_1}\left\{1 - \exp\left(-\dfrac{M}{A_2}t\right)\right\}$
3. Internal medium	External medium	$y = y_0' \dfrac{C_1}{C_2}\dfrac{A_2}{A_1 + A_2}\{1 - \exp(-Bt)\}$	$A_1 \ll A_2; \quad y = y_0' \dfrac{C_1}{C_2}\left\{1 - \exp\left(-\dfrac{M}{A_1}t\right)\right\}$
4. Internal medium	Internal medium	$y' = y_0' \dfrac{A_1}{A_1 + A_2}\left\{\dfrac{A_2}{A_1} + \exp(-Bt)\right\}$	$A_1 \gg A_2; \quad y' = y_0' \exp\left(-\dfrac{M}{A_2}t\right)$

$$B = \frac{M}{A_1} + \frac{M}{A_2}$$

ion concentration can be examined. The effectiveness of the regulation of the concentration of the ion in the body fluid clearly depends on the extent to which at least one of these flux components is under physiological control.

THE MEASUREMENT OF ION FLUXES

The flux of an ion across the surface of an aquatic animal can easily be measured providing that the ion, within the animal, is confined to the body fluid. The system can then be considered as consisting of two compartments, the external solution and the body fluid, separated by a single membrane. This is generally true for sodium and chloride ions and studies on the kinetics of the penetration of labelled sodium in *Aedes aegypti* larvae[36,37] and the crayfish, *Astacus pallipes* (= *fluviatilis*)[8] are consistent with this view. Exceptions, however, may be found (*e.g.* in the crustacean *Asellus aquaticus*[38]), and before fluxes are calculated from the equations based on a two-compartment analysis, it is necessary to show that these equations are obeyed. The derivation of such equations is a simple matter providing it is assumed that the membrane is composed of a single layer, and that the solutions on both sides are well stirred. Considering such a system which is in a steady state with respect to a certain ion, let the total number of these ions in the external and internal solutions be A_1 and A_2 respectively, the solution volumes be v_1 and v_2, and the ion concentrations, C_1 and C_2. Let an ion label, in the form of a radioactive isotope of the ion and of negligible mass, be introduced initially into one solution or the other and be in the process of reaching a steady state. If the concentration of radioactive ions in the external solution is y and that in the internal solution is y', after time, t, then:

$$\frac{dy}{dt} = \frac{Mv_2}{A_2 v_1}y' - \frac{M}{A_1}y \quad \text{and} \quad \frac{dy'}{dt} = \frac{Mv_1}{A_1 v_2}y - \frac{M}{A_2}y'$$

where M is the ion flux.

These equations can be readily solved either for y or y' for the two cases where the isotope is introduced initially into the external medium (initial radioactive ion concentration $= y_0$), and where it is introduced into the internal medium (initial concentration $= y'_0$). *Table 5.4* shows the four required solutions. Generally the special solutions (where A_1 is either much greater or much smaller than A_2) have been employed for flux measurement, although the general solutions may be more suitable in certain cases. The flux is calculated from the slope of the straight line obtained from the appropriate semi-logarithmic plot against time. *Figure 5.1* shows one method which has been used to measure the decrease in radioactivity of the external medium after introduction of the isotope. The ion influx can then be calculated from the first equation in *Table 5.4*[39]. This method has the advantage that a continuous record of the concentration of radioactive ions is obtained, and avoids the necessity for continually sampling the external or internal medium. The values of the steady state fluxes for a number of aquatic animals are given in *Table 5.5*.

The flux equations can also be used for the measurement of fluxes under non-steady state conditions, providing that the duration of the experiment is such that only relatively small changes in A_1 and A_2 are produced.

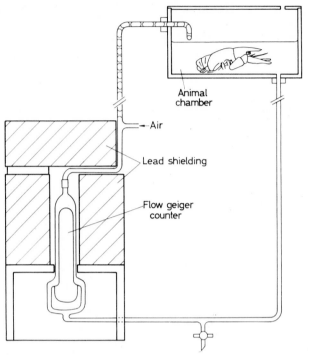

Figure 5.1. One method which can be used to measure ion fluxes by continuously recording the change in the concentration of radio-active ions in the external medium[39].

Table 5.5. Steady state fluxes, as measured by radio isotopes, in some aquatic animals.

Species	Isotope	Flux (mean value)	Concentration of external soln. (mM/l. NaCl)	Reference
Amphibia				
Amblystoma mexicanum	²⁴Na	2·9 μM/hr/90 g	1–3	40
Rana temporaria	²⁴Na	5·6 μM/hr/100 cm² surface	3	41
Rana esculenta	³⁶Cl	5 μM/hr/100 g		42
Bufo bufo	²⁴Na	4·9 μM/hr	3	43
	³⁶Cl	5·2 μM/hr		
Teleostei				
Carassius auratus	²²Na	24 μM/hr/30 g	1	44
Crustacea				
Astacus pallipes	²⁴Na	1·5 μM/hr/10 g	0·3	46
(= A. fluviatilis)	²²Na	0·87 μM/hr/ml blood	2	8
Gammarus pulex	²⁴Na	0·16 μM/hr/40 mg	0·3	48
Eriocheir sinensis	²²Na	360 μM/hr/165 g	6	45
Carcinus maenas	²⁴Na	1267 μM/hr/50 g	Sea water	47
Artemia salina	²⁴Na	85 μM/hr/ml blood	Sea water	49
Insecta				
Aedes aegypti larva				
fed	²²Na	8 μM/hr/ml blood	2	37
starved	²²Na	1·09 μM/hr/ml blood	2	37

THE CHARACTERIZATION OF ACTIVE ION TRANSPORT

Active transport of an ion across a cellular membrane occurs when the ion moves in the opposite direction from that determined by the presence of physical forces which act upon it. The free energy of the ion is increased during this process and the additional energy required is supplied by the metabolic activity of the cells. Active transport appears to be a characteristic feature of cell membranes, although the means by which it is achieved is completely unknown and the essential link with the cell's metabolism only dimly understood. Active transport systems for ions are often referred to as 'ion pumps': this is a descriptive term and has the dubious advantage of disguising our ignorance of the underlying mechanism.

Krogh's work firmly established that many hyperosmotic animals are able to take up ions against a concentration gradient: but this is not proof that the ions are actively transported, since forces other than diffusion may influence their movement. The ion may be dragged through water-filled pores in the membrane when there is a net bulk flow of water through them, due to an osmotic or hydrostatic pressure gradient and also, since they are electrically charged, force may be exerted on them by the presence of an electrical potential gradient across the membrane[50-52]. In the case of aquatic animals which have been examined, the net flow of water is small compared with the ion flux and the effect of water drag can be safely ignored[21,43] but the electrical potential gradient certainly cannot. Since the gradients of electrical and chemical potential can usually be measured without much difficulty, it is possible to predict the behaviour of an ion if this is purely passive (*i.e.* if it crosses the membrane by a process analogous to diffusion in free solution). Although the magnitude of the passive ion flux itself cannot be determined from these measurements, the ratio of the two fluxes (M_{in}/M_{out}) can be calculated[50].

$$\frac{M_{in}}{M_{out}} = \frac{c_1 f_1}{c_2 f_2} \exp \frac{zFE}{RT} \qquad (1)$$

where c_1 and c_2 are the concentrations of the ion in the external and internal solutions respectively, f_1 and f_2 are their activity coefficients, z is the valency of the ion, F Faraday's constant (96,490 coulombs), R the gas constant (8·314 joules/degree/mole), T the absolute temperature, and E the electrical potential difference across the membrane.

For the fluxes to be equal (*i.e.* $M_{in}/M_{out} = 1$) the diffusion gradient must be balanced by the electrical potential gradient and hence, from (1)

$$E_{eq} = \frac{RT}{zF} \ln \frac{c_2 f_2}{c_1 f_1} \qquad (2)$$

where E_{eq} is the equilibrium potential for passive movement of the ion.

If the measured flux ratio $(M_{in}/M_{out})_{obs}$ is equal to that predicted from equation (1), then it reasonable to assume that the ion is moving across the membrane in a purely passive manner. If passive movement and active transport are the only means by which an ion can cross the membrane, then a departure of the measured flux ratio from that predicted from (1) is evidence for the presence of active transport. In practice, flux measurements on aquatic animals show that other components of the flux such as an exchange component, may be present (see p. 183). Although the exchange component appears to be linked with active transport, evidence for active transport based solely on flux ratio measurements must be viewed with caution. Additional evidence, such as the net transport of ion against the prevailing electrochemical potential gradient, must also be sought.

Studies on the isolated skin of the frog by Ussing and others has been of the greatest importance in providing a clear proof of the existence of a mechanism for actively transporting sodium ions in this organ[53]. The skin, mounted as a membrane separating solutions bathing the outer and inner surface respectively, is especially favourable for analysis, as the composition of the bathing solutions can be controlled and the electrical potential difference across the membrane easily measured. With Ringer solution on either side of the skin a steady potential of some 30–110 mV (inside solution positive) is maintained for many hours. From equation (1) it follows that the predicted flux ratio for passive sodium movement is between 0·3 and 0·01 for this range of potentials. The measured flux ratio as determined by tracers is always much greater than 1 (usually about 10) and hence the net movement of sodium is in the opposite direction from that predicted. Active transport of sodium across the skin is clearly indicated. Confirmation comes from measurement of the current flow across the skin while the potential is short-circuited. Simultaneous flux measurements show that this current is practically identical with the net sodium flux[54] and hence the current drawn from the skin comes from active sodium transport, there being no other possible processes which involve the transfer of charge across the membrane. These experiments also indicate that the normal potential difference across the skin is generated by active sodium transport—a conclusion previously deduced from the correlation between the fall in potential difference and in sodium influx brought about by metabolic inhibitors or by a change in pH[53].

A study of the movement of chloride ions by the same methods led to a different conclusion[55]. In skins mounted with 10 per cent Ringer solution on the outside and normal Ringer on the other, the measured flux ratios for the chloride ion are in good agreement with those calculated on the assumption that the ion was behaving passively (*i.e.* as predicted from (1)). Thus there is no evidence of active chloride transport under these conditions—a conclusion which is supported by the identity of the short circuit current and the net sodium flux.

IONIC REGULATION IN HYPEROSMOTIC ANIMALS

The Active Transport of Sodium and Chloride Ions

The analytical method outlined above is applicable to the study of active ion transport in intact animals, although the system is obviously not as simple as that provided by the isolated frog skin. Since the surface membrane of a whole animal is differentiated into a number of regions, the total measured flux is made up of the sum of the fluxes through these different regions. In general, the influx may consist of components through the permeable parts of the body surface and through the gut, and the efflux of components through

172

the body surface and through the excretory organ. Often the flux through the gut and the excretory organ is quite small (see p. 186) and a large fraction of the measured flux must occur through the regions known to be concerned with active uptake. This appears to be the case in the frog[43], in the crayfish[8,24,46] and in *Carcinus*[47] under normal conditions. In cases where this is not so, studies can be made after blockage of one or other of these organs.

In fresh water Amphibians, such as the frog, the ability to transport sodium actively from its environment is strongly suggested by the fact that salt-depleted animals show a net uptake of sodium from dilute sodium chloride solutions, and from the persistence of active sodium transport in the isolated skin. This has been confirmed in the toad, *Bufo bufo*, by simultaneous measurements of sodium fluxes and of the potential difference across the skin in normal animals acclimatized to a 3 mM/l. sodium chloride solution[43]. The mean value of the potential difference was 85 mV, and the measured flux ratio ranged from 0·32 to 1·4. These values greatly exceed the passive flux ratio calculated according to equation (1) and in some of the animals a net uptake of sodium took place against the electrochemical potential gradient.

Active sodium transport is also apparent as a major component of the sodium influx in *Astacus*. For animals in a steady state in artificial tap water containing 2 mM/l. sodium chloride, the measured sodium fluxes are equal and the mean potential difference, measured between the body fluid and the external medium, is 4·1 mV[8]. The predicted passive flux ratio for these conditions is only 0·01 (putting $c_1 = 2$ mM/l., $f_1 = 0.96$, $c_2 = 203$ mM/l. and and $f_2 = 0.73$ in equation (1)). Thus a maximum of 99 per cent of the influx might be ascribed to active transport. Confirmation comes from the fact that the salt-depleted animal shows a large net uptake of sodium from the same solution, although the potential difference is not significantly changed[24].

In *Carcinus maenas*, acclimatized to 40 per cent sea water, the measured potential difference is $-1·0$ mV and the concentration gradient $c_2/c_1 = 1·7$[47,56]. To maintain this gradient without active sodium transport would require a potential difference of -13 mV.

It is likely that studies on other animals, such as those listed in *Table 5.3*, would show that active sodium transport is widespread. This is already indicated by Krogh's demonstration that the crab, *Eriocheir sinensis*, and the goldfish, *Carassius auratus*, after salt depletion, are able to take up sodium from sodium chloride and also from other sodium salts such as sulphate, bicarbonate and nitrate. Final proof of this must await measurements of the electrochemical gradient.

The view that chloride ions behave passively in their movement across the isolated frog skin is apparently at variance with the fact that salt-depleted frogs can take up chloride against a concentration gradient without the simultaneous uptake of sodium[18]. There is, moreover, convincing evidence for the presence of active chloride transport in the intact toad derived from simultaneous chloride flux and potential difference measurements. In normal frogs and toads (*i.e.* animals acclimatized to tap water) placed in 3 mM/l potassium chloride solutions, the measured skin potential is lower than in a sodium chloride solution and often negative[43]. In the toad a net uptake of chloride takes place from the potassium chloride solution. *Figure*

5.2a shows the observed flux ratios compared with those calculated for purely passive chloride movement. The observed flux ratios exceed unity in every case, whereas the calculated ratios are much smaller. *Figure 5.2b* gives the range of potentials recorded during the experiments, together with the equilibrium potential for chloride and the potential required to achieve the observed flux ratios by passive movement of the ions. The measured

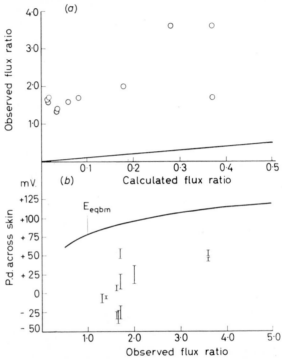

Figure 5.2. The demonstration of active chloride transport by *Bufo bufo* in 3 mM/1 KCl[43]. (*a*) The relation between the observed chloride flux ratios and those calculated for passive movement. The line represents identity between the two ratios. (*b*) The relation between the observed flux ratios and the skin p.d., measured during the experiment. The curve represents the relation between the p.d. and the flux ratio for passive movement.

potentials are not only below the calculated potentials but also below the equilibrium potential. These results can only be explained by the presence of active chloride transport.

In the frog, *Rana esculenta*, deficient in chloride but not sodium, there is a net uptake of chloride from both 3 mM/l. potassium and sodium chloride, and in the latter the net uptake of chloride exceeds that of sodium[43]. This is not proof of active chloride transport since the potential difference was not measured, but it is clear that the transport of chloride is not necessarily dependent on the simultaneous transport of sodium, even when this is present. Taken together with the results for the toad, there is little doubt that active chloride transport is a reality in these animals.

The presence of a chloride pump has also been demonstrated in *Astacus*[57]. In sodium chloride-deficient animals, chloride is only absorbed slowly from a 0·3 mM/l. potassium chloride solution. But, if the animals are allowed to make good their sodium deficit by the uptake of sodium from a sodium sulphate solution and then replaced in potassium chloride, the net chloride flux is greatly increased. Under these conditions a mean chloride flux ratio of 4·8 was observed: this would require a potential difference of 197 mV if the fluxes were passive, whereas the mean recorded potential was −28 mV. The clear indication of active chloride transport is substantiated by the fact that 5 per cent CO_2 in air, introduced into the external medium, reduced both the net flux and the potential towards zero.

Active chloride transport may well be found in many other animals if it is looked for. Krogh's observations on the net uptake of chloride from solutions of potassium, calcium and ammonium chlorides by *Eriocheir*, *Carassius* and by the larva of the dragon-fly *Aeschna*, after salt-depletion, are suggestive of the presence of such a mechanism in these animals.

The Simultaneous Uptake of Sodium and Chloride Ions

With the clear demonstration of active transport of sodium, from a sodium chloride solution, and of chloride, from a potassium chloride solution, in Amphibians and in the crayfish, the question now arises as to whether the two ion pumps operate simultaneously in a normal external medium containing both ions. In *Astacus* it appears that this must be the case. Under steady state conditions in 2 mM/l. sodium chloride, there corded potential difference is only 4 mV and, hence, chloride must be actively transported as well as sodium[8]. Further, in salt-deficient animals a net uptake of both ions takes place from a similar sodium chloride solution, yet the potential difference does not rise above a mean figure of 9 mV[24,57]. Similarly in *Carcinus* the recorded p.d. of −1·0 mV for animals acclimatized to 40 per cent sea water is insufficient to account for the passive movement of either sodium or chloride ions.

In the Amphibia, however, the situation is not so clear. Measurements of chloride flux and potential difference in toads acclimatized to 3 mM/l. sodium chloride established the presence of active chloride transport in only a few cases[43]. *Figure 5.3a* shows the measured chloride flux ratios compared with those calculated for passive movement. *Figure 5.3b* gives the measured potentials during these experiments, together with those calculated as necessary to account for the observed flux ratios in passive terms. It is evident that in the majority of cases active chloride transport is not demonstrated and there are only two cases where this is so. Thus, in the main, these results are in accord with those obtained on the isolated frog skin.

The reason for the different mode of chloride transport, depending on the presence of potassium or sodium in the external solution, is not clear. It cannot be due to the nature of the cation itself, since in the chloride-deficient frog the rate of chloride uptake is the same in a 3 mM/l. solution of either sodium or potassium chloride[43]. From inspection of *Figures 5.2a* and *5.3a*, and from the fact that the potential difference measured on the isolated skin[55] always exceeded the chloride equilibrium potential, it appears that when the potential across the skin is greater than the chloride-equilibrium potential, then the chloride ion behaves passively, whereas if it is less, then active chloride transport is in evidence. One possible explanation may lie in the fact that sodium transport itself generates a positive potential across the skin[53]. If this potential is large enough to exceed the chloride-equilibrium potential, current must be drawn through the chloride pump and may put

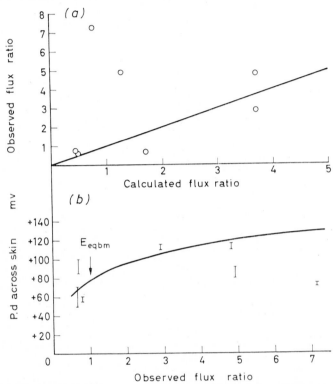

Figure 5.3. The uptake of chloride by *Bufo bufo* in 3 mM/l NaCl[43]. (*a*) The relation between the observed chloride flux ratios and those calculated for passive movement. The line represents identity between the two ratios. (*b*) The relation between the observed flux ratios and the recorded skin p.d. The curve represents the relation between p.d. and the flux ratio for passive movement.

it out of operation, perhaps by a process analogous to polarization in a galvanic cell.

Clear evidence, then, of the simultaneous operation of sodium and chloride pumps in the Amphibia is not forthcoming. The possibility of their operation in animals acclimatized to more dilute solutions is, however, not ruled out—indeed, since the potential required for passive movement increases with the dilution of the external solution, it is not unlikely that a critical external concentration would be found at which a switch to active chloride transport occurs.

The present evidence favours the view that in *Astacus* and in *Carcinus* the maintenance of a sodium chloride concentration gradient between the external and internal media is effected by the simultaneous operation of balanced sodium and chloride pumps, whereas in the Amphibia the sodium pump may predominate. The Amphibia may well be specialized in this respect. If chloride is held in balance by the maintenance of a potential difference generated by sodium transport, then it is necessary that the membrane shall be impermeable to other cations. If it were not so, the outward movement of these ions would short-circuit the potential and cause the chloride influx to lag behind that of sodium. It is doubtful if impermeability to cations is ever completely realized in practice, even in the Amphibia, and it is not surprising that these animals can bring a chloride pump into operation when conditions demand it.

The Active Transport of Other Ions

By analogy with the behaviour of sodium ions, it would not be unreasonable to assume that concentration gradients of other cations could be maintained by the inward transport of these ions in a similar manner.

The movement of ions, other than Na^+ and Cl^-, has not yet been examined by tracer methods, and conclusive proof of the presence of other cation pumps is still lacking. However, indirect evidence points strongly to the presence of a potassium transporting mechanism in certain Arthropods (see *Table 5.3*). The crustaceans *Eriocheir* and *Potamon* after salt depletion, show a net uptake of potassium from dilute potassium chloride solutions[20,23]. In *Aedes aegypti*, salt-depleted larvae increased their blood potassium concentration from 3·1 to 4·2 mM/l when placed in a 1·7 mM/l. potassium chloride solution[10]. *Carcinus* is clearly permeable to potassium since the blood potassium concentration falls in dilute sea water, yet it is maintained above that of the medium[6]. Webb has suggested that sodium and potassium may be taken up by a transport system which does not discriminate between the two[6]. However, a potassium gradient of similar size is maintained even in normal sea water (where sodium uptake is greatly diminished), if the potassium concentration of the sea water is reduced[56].

On the other hand it appears that active uptake of potassium is absent in the aquatic Vertebrates. Krogh was unable to detect a net uptake of this ion from potassium chloride solutions by the goldfish or by the frog, after salt depletion. In the isolated frog skin, bathed by Ringer on the inside and on the outside by a Ringer solution with 35 per cent of the sodium replaced by potassium, the short-circuit current can still be accounted for by the net sodium flux and there is no evidence of active potassium transport[51].

The active uptake of calcium is still in doubt. Krogh failed to detect a net uptake of the ion by the frog or by *Eriocheir* and in only one experiment was calcium uptake observed in *Carassius*. In *Carcinus*, active absorption of calcium has been claimed[6]. The calcium concentration of the blood is found to be above that of the medium in normal sea water and also in dilute sea water and sea water with a reduced calcium content[6,58]. The permeability of the body surface to calcium is well established[58,59]. But in normal animals about 17 per cent of the blood calcium is present in an indiffusible form, probably bound to the blood proteins[58]. Taking this into account, the ratio of the diffusible blood calcium to that in sea water only slightly exceeds unity and calcium balance may be maintained by the small negative potential which is found across the surface[56]. There is some evidence in the case of *Carcinus*, however, that active calcium uptake may come into operation during the later stages of the moulting cycle[60].

The active uptake of magnesium and sulphate ions is also unknown. However, many marine and brackish water animals maintain the concentrations of these ions in the blood below that of the medium (see *Tables 5.1* and *5.2*). In cases where the urine composition of these animals has been examined, the concentration of magnesium and sulphate ions in the excretory fluid exceeds that of the blood[2-4,6,47]. It is reasonable to assume that these ions enter the body fluid by diffusion through the body surface and that their concentration is regulated by secretion in the urine[2-4,6,47].

The Properties of the Sodium and Chloride Active Transport Systems

We have seen that in fresh water animals, such as the frog and the crayfish, only a small percentage of the total number of sodium ions which enter the animal do so passively: and the same is true of the chloride influx where a balanced chloride pump is in operation, and may be true of other ions. A large proportion of the total ion influx is often due to active transport (see p. 183). This not only clearly establishes the vital role which transport mechanisms play in the maintenance of the internal ion concentrations, but it also shows that their effective regulation will depend upon the activity of these mechanisms under different conditions and the extent to which the rate of transport can be controlled by the animal itself.

The factors which control the rates of active transport of sodium and chloride will now be considered.

Control of active transport rate in relation to the internal salt content

The first demonstration of changes in sodium influx in relation to the internal sodium content were made on the Amphibians, *Bufo bufo* and *Rana temporaria*[41]. A comparison of the sodium influx and the net sodium uptake from 3 mM/l. sodium chloride solution in animals acclimatized to tap water and in animals salt-depleted by washing in distilled water, showed that both were increased by salt depletion. In the frog the sodium influx was doubled, and in the toad an even greater increase was found[41].

Regulation of the rate of active sodium transport is also clearly seen in *Astacus*. For animals acclimatized to 0·3 mM/l. sodium chloride, a loss of only 5 to 10 per cent of the internal sodium increased the sodium influx to about four times the normal level. Additional sodium loss did not induce a further increase, and it appeared that the transport system had achieved its maximum rate[46]. Similarly an increase in the blood sodium concentration leads to a suppression of the influx. Raising the blood concentration from the normal value of 200 mM/l. to 300 mM/l. reduced the influx virtually to zero[61]. Thus sodium influx in *Astacus* appears to be determined by the blood sodium concentration.

Flux measurements on other fresh water animals suggests that the physiological control of sodium uptake may be widespread, although the extent of the control varies in different animals. For example, in the mosquito larva, *Aedes aegypti*, the sodium influx from 2 mM/l. sodium chloride in fed sodium-deficient larvae exceeds that of normal larvae by a factor of about 13. The same is true of starved larvae, although both fluxes are an order of magnitude lower than in the feeding animals[37,62]. On the other hand, in the crustacean *Gammarus pulex*, acclimatized to 0·3 mM/l. sodium chloride, the sodium influx at this concentration was only increased by a factor of 1·5 in animals previously salt-depleted[48]. In *Asellus aquaticus* the sodium uptake rate is approximately doubled by a fall in blood sodium concentration[38].

Regulation of the rate of active chloride transport is also possible. In *Rana esculenta*, the chloride influx from 3 mM/l. potassium chloride in salt-deficient animals is roughly twice that of animals with the chloride level restored by treatment with 2 mM/l. calcium chloride. Further the net chloride flux accounts for about half the influx in the salt-depleted animals, but it drops practically to zero after restoration of their chloride deficit[43]. In *Astacus*, chloride transport is not increased by sodium chloride deficiency though a great increase in its rate is found in animals deficient in chloride but not in sodium[57].

The fact that in animals such as *Astacus*, sodium and chloride pumps may operate simultaneously and yet can be activated independently, suggests that each may be concerned with the regulation of the concentration of its respective ion in the blood independently of the other. This, however, may be an oversimplification of the situation. The maintenance of the normal sodium concentration, under conditions of chloride deficiency, might be possible by the retention of a metabolic anion, such as bicarbonate, to maintain electroneutrality. However, the maintenance of the normal chloride level under conditions of sodium deficiency may be more difficult to achieve. In view of their physiological effects the retention of other cations may only be possible to a very limited extent. It has been suggested that in *Astacus* the chloride concentration of the blood is regulated in relation to the prevailing sodium concentration[57].

Saturation of the ion transport systems

The rate of active transport depends not only on the body fluid concentration but also on the concentration of the ion in the external solution. Measurements of the sodium influx immediately after changing the external concentration from that to which the animal was acclimatized, indicate that the rate of transport is limited and the system becomes saturated at higher concentrations. This has been found in *Astacus*, *Gammarus pulex*, and *G. duebeni*, and in *Eriocheir*[45,47,48]. The relation between the sodium influx and the external sodium concentration for *Astacus* and *G. duebeni* is shown in *Figure 5.4*. The relation follows a Michaelis–Menten type curve, which is typical of many rate-limited processes. In *Astacus*, saturation of the transport system is approached at a low concentration of about 1 mM/l. In the goldfish the concentration may be even lower, as the influx remains practically constant over a concentration range of 0·1 to 0·6 mM/l.[63]. On the other hand, measurements on the isolated frog skin show that the sodium influx does not begin to level off until an external sodium concentration of about 40 mM/l. is reached[64].

179

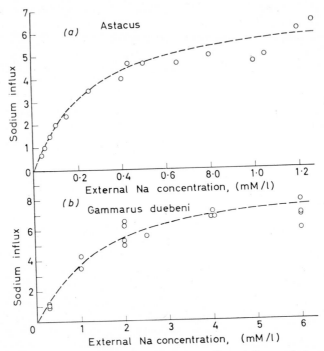

Figure 5.4. The relation between the sodium influx and the external sodium concentration in (*a*) *Astacus*[46] and in (*b*) *Gammarus duebeni*[48].

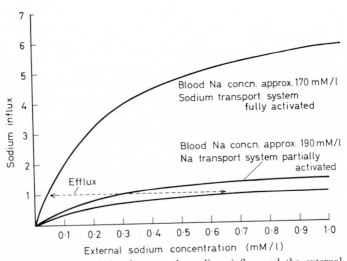

Figure 5.5. The relation between the sodium influx and the external sodium concentration in *Astacus* at different levels of internal sodium concentration. A reduction in blood concentration activates the sodium transport system and allows balance to be maintained at a lower external concentration[46].

The Factors Determining the Efflux of Sodium and Chloride Ions

Measurements of the total efflux in a whole animal represent the sum of fluxes through different regions of the body surface. In hyperosmotic animals efflux occurs mainly through the more permeable regions of the body surface and through the excretory organs. The possible role of the gut will be considered later. First, on the assumption that the gut plays a minor role, the partition of the efflux between the body surface and the excretory organ will be considered.

Efflux through the excretory organ

Efflux through the excretory organ normally forms only a small part of the total efflux (see p. 186). Therefore tracer measurements of efflux cannot

Table 5.7. The composition of the urine and the rate of urine production in some hyperosmotic animals (concentrations in mM/l.)

Species	Osmotic pressure $\equiv$ NaCl soln.	Na	K	Ca	Mg	Cl	SO₄	Rate of production % body wt/day	Reference
Crustacea									
Eriocheir sinensis	330	—	7·0	4·7	0·7	264	—	4	7
Potamon niloticus	246	240	3·7	13·0	—	238	—	<0·6	23
Astacus sp.	26	6	0·6	2·7	1·2	10	—	8·2	7, 8
Gammarus pulex	27	—	—	—	—	—	—	37	76
Annelida									
Lumbricus terrestris	17	—	—	—	—	3·4	—	—	11
Insecta									
Aedes aegypti larva	12	4	25	—	—	—	—	—	10, 77
Teleostei									
Ameirus nebulosus	7	—	—	—	—	—	—	4–8	80
Anguilla rostrata	22	—	—	—	0·7	—	1·3	4–10	78
Elasmobranch									
Pristis microdon	29	—	2·0	3·2	1·5	8·2	0·4	15–46	79
Amphibia									
Rana esculenta	31	2·4	0·9	0·8	0·4	1·9	0·5	25	21, 81

readily detect this. The efflux can be calculated, however, from a knowledge of the ionic composition of the urine and its rate of production. Hyperosmotic animals may be divided into two groups according to whether they produce an excretory fluid iso-osmotic with the body fluid or whether they are able to elaborate a dilute urine. As far as is known at present, animals of the first group are confined to the Crustacea and include brackish water forms, such as Carcinus[15] and a number of fresh water species, such as Eriocheir[7], Potamon edule, and P. niloticus[23,73], and the prawn, Palaemonetes antennarius[74].

The second group, on the other hand, has representatives from many phyla. Fresh water animals known to produce a dilute urine include, among the invertebrates, Astacus[75], Gammarus pulex[76], the larvae of Aedes aegypti[77], and the earthworm, Lumbricus terrestris[11], and among the vertebrates, the frog, the freshwater teleosts[78], and the freshwater elasmobranch, Pristis microdon[79]. The composition of the excretory fluid in relation to the body fluid composition is shown in *Table 5.7*. In those animals where the mode of formation of the excretory fluid has been studied, it is invariably found that the process of dilution occurs in the distal part of the excretory tubule. Thus in the

Amphibia, dilution takes place in the distal convoluted tubule of the nephron[16], in *Astacus* it occurs in the nephridial canal[82], in *Lumbricus* in the distally-situated wide tube of the nephridium[83], and in *Aedes* in the rectum[77]. In the case of the Amphibia, it is well established that the composition of the primary excretory fluid closely resembles that of the blood and is produced by pressure ultra-filtration through the glomerulus. Dilution in the distal tubule takes place by the active absorption of sodium chloride against a large concentration gradient[16,17]. In *Astacus* and in *Lumbricus*, the fluid in the proximal regions of the excretory organ resembles the body fluid in total osmotic pressure and in chloride concentration[82,83]. The occurrence of pressure filtration in the initial stages of urine production in the invertebrates is still in doubt[84] but if the primary fluid is practically iso-osmotic with, and of a similar composition to, the body fluid, little work is involved in its formation. The only known exception to this among hyperosmotic animals is in the insects. In these animals the primary fluid is produced in the Malpighian tubules, and although its osmotic pressure is the same or slightly lower than that of the body fluid, its composition is strikingly different[85]. The characteristic feature of the tubule fluid is the very high potassium concentration which it contains[86]. In *Aedes aegypti* larvae, the potassium concentration is about thirty times that of the haemolymph, whereas the sodium concentration is less than that of the haemolymph[10]. The formation of fluid involves the active secretion of potassium ions into the fluid from the haemolymph[86].

In the freshwater invertebrates which produce a dilute urine, it seems extremely probable that the process of dilution involves the active reabsorption of sodium and chloride ions from the primary iso-osmotic fluid, as it does in the Amphibia. In *Aedes* larvae the reabsorption of large amounts of potassium must also take place[10]. It is clear that regulation of the efflux through the excretory organ may be determined by the extent of the distal reabsorption.

The normal rate of urine production, where it is known, is also shown in *Table 5.7*. By use of the values given in the Table, the efflux of an ion through the excretory organ for a number of these animals can be calculated.

Partition of the efflux

For some of the animals listed in *Table 5.7* the total efflux or the passive efflux (which is assumed to be equal to the loss rate in deionized water and, hence, includes urine losses) for sodium or chloride ions has been measured. Where the normal rate of urine production is also known it is possible to estimate the relative contribution of the efflux through the excretory organ to the total flux. This is illustrated in *Table 5.8*. It can be clearly seen that in those animals which produced a dilute urine, the efflux through the excretory organ accounts for only a small fraction of the total efflux. In the animals producing an iso-osmotic urine the contribution may be larger. In *Carcinus*, the rate of urine production and, hence, the urine efflux is larger in 50 per cent than in normal sea water; this is due to the larger osmotic gradient between the blood and the external medium. However, in *Eriocheir*, from 2 per cent sea water, the osmotic gradient is also very large, but the efflux still only accounts for 22 per cent of the total. In *Potamon* the efflux

186

each other and also of other ions in the external solution, it follows that any net influx of the ion must be balanced by outward movement of similarly charged ions from the body fluid. Although it might be expected that the exchange would involve metabolic ions, such as H^+ or NH_4^+ for sodium and HCO_3^- for chloride, experimental proof is still lacking. Even in the absence of a net flux of sodium or chloride, these ions may appear in external solution as a result of excretion of CO_2 and ammonia by the animal. In *Astacus* it was found that during net uptake of sodium from sodium sulphate there was no increase in ammonia excretion and, in some cases, the net sodium flux exceeded the total ammonium loss. There was no significant exchange with metallic cations such as K^+ or Ca^{2+}, so that an exchange for H^+ was indicated[39]. The possibility of some exchange with NH_4^+ normally excreted was not ruled out. In the case of the goldfish and frog, Krogh gives some evidence of exchange with NH_4^+[,21].

There is a similar uncertainty with regard to chloride. In *Astacus*, uptake of chloride from potassium chloride by chloride-deficient animals was not accompanied by cation uptake, and at least 75 per cent of the exchange was for an anion of a weak acid[66]. This may well be bicarbonate, but the possibility of exchange with other weak acid anions is not excluded.

The components of the influx

It has been seen that in fresh water animals which maintain a steady state in dilute solutions by the active uptake of sodium and chloride ions, the component of the influx due to passive movement is very small and that active transport contributes largely to the measured flux. The question now arises as to whether active transport can account for the whole of the non-passive flux. If this were the case, it follows that during net uptake the measured influx must equal the sum of the net flux and the passive efflux—the latter measured in the absence of the ion from the external solution. Measurements of sodium fluxes in salt-depleted *Astacus* showed that at low external sodium concentrations this was roughly true. At higher concentrations, however, the net flux was lower than that predicted from the difference between the measured influx and passive efflux, and the discrepancy was largest at the highest external concentration studied (about 26 per cent of the influx at 0·8 mm/l. external sodium concentration)[46]. It follows, therefore, that the measured influx must contain a component which is balanced by a non-passive efflux component of the same magnitude. The presence of such a component in the efflux was demonstrated independently and was found to account for about 36 per cent of the total efflux in animals acclimatized to 2 mm/l. sodium chloride[24]. The magnitude of this component is greatly increased during net sodium uptake by salt-depleted animals in the same solution, hence its size does not depend on the external concentration as such, but on the rate of active transport. The balanced influx and efflux components must represent a 1:1 exchange between sodium ions from the external and internal solutions and, therefore, can only be observed in tracer experiments. An exchange of this nature is clearly analogous to 'exchange diffusion' as postulated by Ussing[70,71], but differs from it in that it is linked with, or forms an integral part of, the active transport system and becomes more obvious as the system approaches saturation.

The presence of an exchange component is also apparent in the larvae of *Aedes aegypti*. For starved animals in a steady state in a medium containing 2 mm/l. NaCl, the total sodium flux is at least three times the passive efflux—the latter measured by the initial sodium loss rate in deionized water. In fed larvae[37] the sodium fluxes are increased by a factor of about 7 and, if the passive efflux remains unchanged, the exchange component may account for as much as 95 per cent of the total efflux. Probable linkage with active sodium transport is indicated by the fact that in sodium-deficient larvae in 2 mm/l. NaCl, the fluxes are much greater than the steady state values[62]. Again, if the passive efflux is not increased, the exchange component increases roughly in proportion to the increase in active uptake rate.

In *Asellus aquaticus*, only about a half of the total sodium efflux is accounted for by passive loss and an exchange component of the flux is, again, indicated[38].

The presence of an exchange component in the chloride flux is also apparent in *Astacus*. In sodium chloride-deficient animals the chloride influx greatly exceeds the sum of the net flux and the passive efflux[57]. The exchange component may account for 70 per cent of the influx. There is some evidence that in chloride-deficient animals the exchange component may be switched to active transport without an increase in total influx[57].

At this stage it is convenient to summarize the main conclusions concerning the importance of ion transporting systems and their properties in maintaining ionic balance in hyperosmotic animals.

At present, active sodium transport is the only known mechanism by which starving animals can balance their tendency to lose sodium. Since the transport mechanism shows a high degree of selectivity and is largely independent of the transport of other ions, it follows that variations in the composition of the environment, such as changes in the relative proportions of ions such as K^+, Ca^{2+}, Mg^{2+}, Cl^-, HCO_3^-, and SO_4^{2-}, will have little effect on sodium balance. Balance is only upset by factors which change the rate of active transport. The rate may be altered by a reduction in the metabolism of the transporting cells (for example, by lack of oxygen[22,23] or by a fall in temperature[23,38,72]), by a fall in pH of the external medium or by a change in its sodium concentration. Variations in the rate of transport lead to a loss or gain of sodium and, hence, to a change in the internal sodium content. However, the internal sodium level also influences the rate of transport by a compensatory activation or suppression of the transport mechanism. It is upon this property of internal control of the sodium uptake rate that the efficiency of the regulation ultimately depends.

A similar control system is apparent in the regulation of active chloride transport, but the independence of the system is less clearly marked. Thus chloride transport may be influenced by simultaneous sodium regulation, both as regards the effect of the external sodium concentration (in the Amphibia) and the internal sodium concentration (in *Astacus*).

To build up a picture of ion regulation solely in terms of control of the active transport rate presupposes that the rate of ion loss is constant. There are, however, conditions when this is not so. The factors which determine and regulate the ion efflux must now be considered.

184

The Factors Determining the Efflux of Sodium and Chloride Ions

Measurements of the total efflux in a whole animal represent the sum of fluxes through different regions of the body surface. In hyperosmotic animals efflux occurs mainly through the more permeable regions of the body surface and through the excretory organs. The possible role of the gut will be considered later. First, on the assumption that the gut plays a minor role, the partition of the efflux between the body surface and the excretory organ will be considered.

Efflux through the excretory organ

Efflux through the excretory organ normally forms only a small part of the total efflux (see p. 186). Therefore tracer measurements of efflux cannot

Table 5.7. The composition of the urine and the rate of urine production in some hyperosmotic animals (concentrations in mM/l.)

Species	Osmotic pressure ≡ NaCl soln.	Na	K	Ca	Mg	Cl	SO₄	Rate of production % body wt/day	Reference
Crustacea									
Eriocheir sinensis	330	—	7·0	4·7	0·7	264	—	4	7
Potamon niloticus	246	240	3·7	13·0	—	238	—	<0·6	23
Astacus sp.	26	6	0·6	2·7	1·2	10	—	8·2	7, 8
Gammarus pulex	27	—	—	—	—	—	—	37	76
Annelida									
Lumbricus terrestris	17	—	—	—	—	3·4	—	—	11
Insecta									
Aedes aegypti larva	12	4	25	—	—	—	—	—	10, 77
Teleostei									
Ameirus nebulosus	7	—	—	—	—	—	—	4–8	80
Anguilla rostrata	22	—	—	—	0·7	—	1·3	4–10	78
Elasmobranch									
Pristis microdon	29	—	2·0	3·2	1·5	8·2	0·4	15–46	79
Amphibia									
Rana esculenta	31	2·4	0·9	0·8	0·4	1·9	0·5	25	21, 81

readily detect this. The efflux can be calculated, however, from a knowledge of the ionic composition of the urine and its rate of production. Hyperosmotic animals may be divided into two groups according to whether they produce an excretory fluid iso-osmotic with the body fluid or whether they are able to elaborate a dilute urine. As far as is known at present, animals of the first group are confined to the Crustacea and include brackish water forms, such as Carcinus[15] and a number of fresh water species, such as Eriocheir[7], Potamon edule, and P. niloticus[23,73], and the prawn, Palaemonetes antennarius[74].

The second group, on the other hand, has representatives from many phyla. Fresh water animals known to produce a dilute urine include, among the invertebrates, Astacus[75], Gammarus pulex[76], the larvae of Aedes aegypti[77], and the earthworm, Lumbricus terrestris[11], and among the vertebrates, the frog, the freshwater teleosts[78], and the freshwater elasmobranch, Pristis microdon[79]. The composition of the excretory fluid in relation to the body fluid composition is shown in Table 5.7. In those animals where the mode of formation of the excretory fluid has been studied, it is invariably found that the process of dilution occurs in the distal part of the excretory tubule. Thus in the

Amphibia, dilution takes place in the distal convoluted tubule of the nephron[16], in *Astacus* it occurs in the nephridial canal[82], in *Lumbricus* in the distally-situated wide tube of the nephridium[83], and in *Aedes* in the rectum[77]. In the case of the Amphibia, it is well established that the composition of the primary excretory fluid closely resembles that of the blood and is produced by pressure ultra-filtration through the glomerulus. Dilution in the distal tubule takes place by the active absorption of sodium chloride against a large concentration gradient[16,17]. In *Astacus* and in *Lumbricus*, the fluid in the proximal regions of the excretory organ resembles the body fluid in total osmotic pressure and in chloride concentration[82,83]. The occurrence of pressure filtration in the initial stages of urine production in the invertebrates is still in doubt[84] but if the primary fluid is practically iso-osmotic with, and of a similar composition to, the body fluid, little work is involved in its formation. The only known exception to this among hyperosmotic animals is in the insects. In these animals the primary fluid is produced in the Malpighian tubules, and although its osmotic pressure is the same or slightly lower than that of the body fluid, its composition is strikingly different[85]. The characteristic feature of the tubule fluid is the very high potassium concentration which it contains[86]. In *Aedes aegypti* larvae, the potassium concentration is about thirty times that of the haemolymph, whereas the sodium concentration is less than that of the haemolymph[10]. The formation of fluid involves the active secretion of potassium ions into the fluid from the haemolymph[86].

In the freshwater invertebrates which produce a dilute urine, it seems extremely probable that the process of dilution involves the active reabsorption of sodium and chloride ions from the primary iso-osmotic fluid, as it does in the Amphibia. In *Aedes* larvae the reabsorption of large amounts of potassium must also take place[10]. It is clear that regulation of the efflux through the excretory organ may be determined by the extent of the distal reabsorption.

The normal rate of urine production, where it is known, is also shown in *Table 5.7*. By use of the values given in the Table, the efflux of an ion through the excretory organ for a number of these animals can be calculated.

Partition of the efflux

For some of the animals listed in *Table 5.7* the total efflux or the passive efflux (which is assumed to be equal to the loss rate in deionized water and, hence, includes urine losses) for sodium or chloride ions has been measured. Where the normal rate of urine production is also known it is possible to estimate the relative contribution of the efflux through the excretory organ to the total flux. This is illustrated in *Table 5.8*. It can be clearly seen that in those animals which produced a dilute urine, the efflux through the excretory organ accounts for only a small fraction of the total efflux. In the animals producing an iso-osmotic urine the contribution may be larger. In *Carcinus*, the rate of urine production and, hence, the urine efflux is larger in 50 per cent than in normal sea water; this is due to the larger osmotic gradient between the blood and the external medium. However, in *Eriocheir*, from 2 per cent sea water, the osmotic gradient is also very large, but the efflux still only accounts for 22 per cent of the total. In *Potamon* the efflux

Table 5.8. The contribution of the urine efflux to the total efflux in some hyperosmotic animals

Species	External Medium	Ion	Flux units	Total efflux	Passive efflux	Urine efflux	Urine efflux as % passive efflux	Urine efflux as % total efflux	Reference
Carcinus maenas	Sea-water	Na	μM/hr/50 g	1267	—	34·5	—	2·7	47
	50% SW	Na	μM/hr/50 g	1009	—	163	—	16·1	47
Eriocheir sinensis	2% SW	Na	μM/hr/153 g	—	323	71	22	—	45
Astacus pallipes	2 mM/l. NaCl	Na	μM/hr/ml blood	0·87	0·56	0·049	8·8	5·6	8
Gammarus pulex	0·3 mM/l. NaCl	Na	μM/hr/40 mg	0·16	—	0·016	—	10	48, 76
Rana esculenta (salt depleted)	3 mM/l. NaCl	Cl	μM/hr/100 g	35	—	0·6	—	1·7	21, 43
Potamon niloticus	0·5 mM/l. NaCl	Na	μM/10 g/hr	—	8·0	<0·6	<7·5	—	23

is even lower, and it is clear that the relatively small contribution of the urine to the total efflux, in these forms, is due to the low permeability of the body surface to water compared with that to ions.

Regulation of efflux through the excretory organ

In animals which produce an iso-osmotic urine containing concentrations of sodium and chloride approximately equal to those in the blood, there is no reason to believe that the regulation of the concentration of these ions

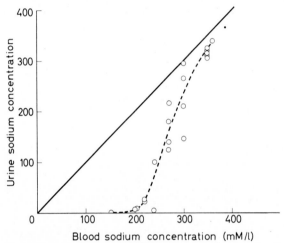

Figure 5.6. The relation between the sodium concentration of the blood and that of the excretory fluid in *Astacus*[61].

in the blood can be assisted by changes in urine efflux. Indeed the only known way by which the efflux is altered significantly is by a change in the osmotic gradient between the body fluid and the external medium, which, in turn, alters the rate of urine production (for example, in *Carcinus*—see *Table 5.8*): but this change is in the opposite direction from that required to assist the process of regulation. For other ions, such as magnesium and sulphate, variations in the urine concentration may be more important and may constitute the only means by which the blood concentration of these ions is regulated (see p. 178).

On the other hand, in several animals which normally produce a dilute urine, there is clear evidence that the urine sodium or chloride concentration is increased in response to an increase in blood concentration induced either by acclimatization of the animals to a more concentrated external medium or by injection of sodium chloride. Thus in *Aedes aegypti* larvae, reared in 85 mM/l. NaCl, the rectal fluid sodium increases to 100 mM/l. from 4 mM/l. for larvae from distilled water[10]. In *Lumbricus*, in tap water, the chloride concentration of the urine is very low, but it is increased in animals kept in Ringer solution[11]. A similar behaviour is found for chloride in the urine of *Rana esculenta*[87]. In *Astacus*, the urine sodium concentration increases steeply when the blood sodium concentration exceeds about 220 mM/l., and becomes almost identical with it when it has reached about 350 mM/l. (see *Figure 5.6*)[61].

If the blood concentration is raised by increasing the concentration of the external medium, it does not follow that the efflux through the excretory organ is increased, since the osmotic gradient is reduced, and hence the urine production rate will fall. If the external medium becomes iso-osmotic with the body fluid, the urine production rate may fall to zero[75]. The importance of variations in the sodium and chloride concentrations of urine is evident, however, for animals in their normal environment (*i.e.*

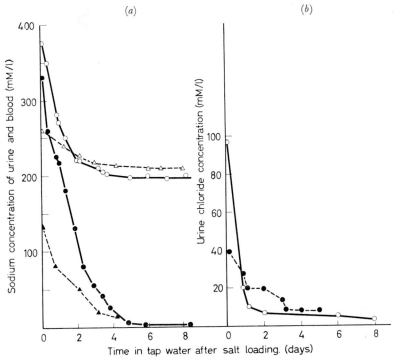

Figure 5.7. The rate of fall of blood and urine concentrations in salt-loaded animals placed in tap water. (*a*) *Astacus*. ○ and △ are measurements of the blood sodium concentration in two different animals; ● and ▲ are the mean values of sodium concentration of the fluid from both excretory organs[61]. (*b*) *Bufo*. ○ and ● are the values of the chloride concentration of the urine of two different animals[87].

when they are producing urine at the normal rate) after the blood concentration has been raised by pretreatment in a concentrated external medium or by injection of salt. Initially the urine concentration is high, and the greatly increased urine efflux leads to a rapid restoration of the blood concentration to its normal level. At the same time the urine concentration declines, with the fall in blood concentration, until the normal level is reached. This is illustrated in *Figure 5.7* which shows the decline in blood and urine sodium in *Astacus*, and for urine chloride in *Bufo bufo*[87]. In *Astacus*, with the blood sodium concentration raised initially to about 300 mM/l., the initial efflux through the excretory organ when the animal is in tapwater accounts for about 70 per cent of the total efflux, compared with only 6 per cent in the normal animal[61] (see *Table 5.8*). Further the total efflux during this period is about six times its normal value. This mechanism clearly allows for the speedy removal of excess sodium which would otherwise diffuse out at rather a slow rate, even after suppression of the active transport system.

If active transport systems are present in the distal regions of the excretory organ and are responsible for the production of the normally dilute urine, then an increase in the urine concentration may be brought about by a decrease in the active transport rate in response to an increase in blood concentration. If this is the case, then control of active transport systems in the excretory organ is analogous to the control of such systems at the body surface and may be brought about by the same agency[61].

Regulation of efflux through the body surface

It is reasonable to assume that the outward movement of ions across the body surface (excluding the excretory organ) in hyperosmotic animals is due to passive diffusion in the direction of the electrochemical gradient, although the measured efflux may also include an exchange component if active transport inwards is present (see p. 183). The passive efflux is determined by the permeability of the body surface, and the possibility that this may represent another variable factor must not be overlooked. At present there is no unequivocal evidence of this, but certain observations are suggestive of this being the case: or, at any rate, that the possibility deserves a closer investigation. In *Astacus* the passive sodium efflux through the body surface is greater in salt-loaded animals than in normal ones. This can be largely accounted for by the increase in blood sodium concentration, but it is possible that the permeability constant is slightly increased[61]. There is also evidence of an increased loss of chloride through the skin, after salt-loading, in both *Rana temporaria* and *Bufo bufo*[87]. On the other hand, the possibility of a reduction in permeability is suggested by the fact that in *Aedes aegypti* larvae the rate of sodium loss in deionized water is greatly reduced as the blood sodium concentration falls[36,37]. A similar reduction in loss rate is observed in *Gammarus duebeni* when animals previously adapted to 2 per cent sea water are acclimatized to 0·25 mM/l. NaCl[48]. In the last two cases, however, the relative contribution of loss through the urine is not known. These observations are, as yet, far from conclusive but the possibility of variations in permeability should be kept in mind. Reduction in surface permeability could play an important part in the acclimatization of some animals to very dilute solutions.

The main conclusions of efflux measurements on hyperosmotic animals can now be summarized. The efflux of sodium and chloride ions is made up of two major components: one through the permeable part of the body surface, the other through the excretory organ, the latter component generally being much the smaller. The former consists of a passive component together with an exchange component, where active transport across the membrane is found. The permeability of the body surface is a possible variable in some animals. In animals which produce a dilute urine, increase in the urine concentration occurs in response to an increase in blood concentration, possibly by a reduction in active reabsorption. Under conditions in which urine is produced at the normal rate, an increase in urine concentration greatly increases the total efflux and allows a rapid elimination of excess salt.

The Role of the Gut in Hyperosmotic Regulation

In considering the dynamics of ionic regulation so far, no account has been taken of the part played by the gut. In animals where no active transport systems are present, the uptake of salts through the gut wall from ingested food must presumably be sufficient to balance the normal salt losses. The majority of hyperosmotic animals, however, can maintain a steady state with their environment in the absence of food, and there are sound reasons for believing that the gut cannot play more than a minor role in the regulatory process. In fresh water animals, the uptake of ions from a very dilute solution by the means of the gut is inherently inefficient. Consider the case of *Astacus* in a steady state in a 0·3 mM/l. NaCl solution at 12°C, where the sodium influx is 1·5 μM/hr/10 g body weight[46]. If the measured influx is due to uptake through the gut, the animal would have to drink the medium at a rate equivalent to about twelve times its own weight per day. An equivalent ion-free solution must then be eliminated, or, if the water is also absorbed through the gut wall, urine must be produced at the same rate (*i.e.* at about 150 times the observed value). In fact, the observed rate of drinking by *Astacus*, using phenol red in the external medium as an indicator, is very low[8] and, hence, the contribution to the influx by this means is negligible. Observations on frogs and fresh water teleosts, also, show that they drink very little in fresh water[87,88].

In the larva of *Aedes aegypti* a comparison of the sodium influx in normal larvae and in larvae with their anal papillae destroyed by treatment with 5 per cent sodium chloride, showed that 90 per cent of the observed flux took place through these organs in both fed and starved animals[36,37]. Blocking the mouth showed that the influx through the rest of the body surface is very small[36], so it may be concluded that the remainder of the influx occurred through the gut. Here the uptake through the gut is a small but not insignificant part of the total flux: the water intake into the gut is rather large and probably associated with their specialized feeding habits.

It is a requirement, then, for a transport system to operate efficiently from a dilute solution, that the membrane should be in free contact with the external solution, and that the solution should circulate freely past it. It is only in rare cases that the gut membrane might be expected to fulfil this role. In fact, as we have seen (p. 166), transport mechanisms are generally located in the respiratory epithelium where these conditions are fulfilled.

Sodium and Chloride Regulation in Hyperosmotic Animals

By combining the results of influx and efflux measurements it is possible to build up a reasonably complete picture of the process of sodium regulation in certain hyperosmotic animals. If the animal maintains a steady state with its environment with respect to sodium ions, then the total influx must equal the total efflux. The influx consists of components due to active transport (M_{in}^{a}), to passive movement (M_{in}^{p}) and to exchange (M_{in}^{e}). The efflux has a passive component (M_{out}^{p}), a component due to urine loss (M_{out}^{u})

and an exchange component, equal to that in the influx (*i.e.* $= M_{in}^{e}$). Hence in the steady state,

$$M_{in}^{a} + M_{in}^{p} + M_{in}^{e} = M_{out}^{p} + M_{out}^{u} + M_{in}^{e} \qquad (3)$$

In animals which produce an iso-osmotic urine, the available evidence indicates that the active transport rate (M_{in}^{a}) is the only variable flux component which can serve to regulate the internal sodium concentration. In animals which normally excrete a dilute urine, regulation may be assisted by variations in M_{out}^{u}. *Astacus*, for example, regulates its internal sodium

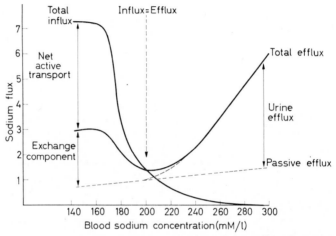

Figure 5.8. A diagrammatic representation of the sodium fluxes in *Astacus* in tap water containing 2mM/1 Na Cl. A steady state is maintained with the blood sodium concentration = 200 mM/1. A fall in blood sodium leads to an increase in the influx and a net gain of sodium: a rise in the blood level leads to a decrease in the influx and an increase in the efflux and, hence, a net loss of sodium. (From Bryan[61], slightly modified.)

content by controlling both M_{in}^{a} and M_{out}^{u}. This is illustrated in *Figure 5.8*. A fall in the internal sodium concentration leads to an increase in M_{in}^{a} and, hence, to a net gain in sodium. This continues until the normal sodium level is restored. On the other hand, if the internal content rises, M_{in}^{a} is decreased and M_{out}^{u} is increased, the combined effects leading to a substantial net loss of sodium until the internal concentration has returned to its normal value again. This gives an adequate description of regulation of the internal sodium concentration for the animal in a constant environment. Regulation is, however, more generally considered in relation to changes in the concentration of the external medium. The same control mechanisms operate but, in addition, the external concentration itself affects both M_{in}^{a} and M_{in}^{p}. The relation between M_{in}^{a} and the external sodium concentration has already been considered (see *Figure 5.4*). This relationship is such that effective regulation cannot be maintained below an external concentration at which balance is just held with the transport system fully activated. Below this critical concentration (about 0·04 mM/l. in *Astacus*) the blood sodium must fall in proportion to that of the external medium. At high external concentrations M_{in}^p becomes significant and M_{out}^u is reduced as the osmotic gradient becomes smaller. As a result the blood sodium concentration rises. Nevertheless the range of the external concentration over which internal regulation is effective may be extremely wide. In *Astacus*, the range extends from 0·04 to 100 mM/l. Na+ for only a ±10 per cent change in the blood sodium concentration[46,61]. Thus a change in the external concentration by a factor of 2,500 over this range only induces an internal change by a factor of 1·2.

From what is known of the factors determining the sodium flux components in other hyperosmotic animals, it is not improbable that sodium regulation is achieved in a similar manner. The extent of the regulation plateau, and the range of external concentrations over which it extends, clearly depends on the properties of the flux components. These will depend on (*a*) the permeability of the body surface to sodium and its possible control, (*b*) the maximum rate of active transport, (*c*) the relation of the active transport rate to the external and internal sodium concentrations, (*d*) its independence of other environmental factors and (*e*) the urine efflux and its relation to the internal sodium level and to the osmotic gradient.

In *Carcinus*, for example, the maximum rate of sodium transport is greater than in *Astacus*, but the surface permeability is also much higher (see *Table 5.8*). As a result, effective regulation of the blood sodium concentration is restricted to a range of external concentrations between about 300 and 400 mM/l. Na. Below 300 mM/l. the blood sodium falls in proportion to the external concentration[47].

In general, it appears that chloride regulation follows the same pattern as that of sodium, but further work is required to establish to what extent chloride and sodium regulation are independent of each other.

The fact that ionic regulation is achieved, in the main, by controlling the activity of ion transport systems, suggests that hormones circulating in the body fluid may provide the necessary link. As yet, there is no direct evidence of hormonal control of ion transport in the invertebrates, but in the aquatic vertebrates, especially in the Amphibia, there seems little doubt that this is the case.

In the Amphibia, total hypophysectomy results in a fall in the blood sodium chloride concentration[89]. The same effect is produced by the removal of the adenohypophysis alone[90]. Measurement of sodium and chloride fluxes in the hypophysectomized animals shows that the loss of sodium chloride can be explained partly by the increase in the permeability of the skin to ions[90,91]. However, at the same time, there is also either a decrease in the active transport rate across the skin, or the rate fails to increase in response to the fall in blood concentration[89,91]. The effects produced by adenohypophysis removal can be largely reversed by the injection of ACTH or aldosterone[91]. Similar effects are also produced by the removal of the inter-renal bodies and, again, conditions can be partially restored to normal by injection of aldosterone, but not by ACTH[92]. However, the maintenance of salt balance in the Amphibia cannot be explained solely in terms of adenohypophysis-interrenal secretion. In hypophysectomized animals, restoration of the active transport rate can be achieved by the implantation of neurohypophysial tissue[89]. Salt balance is not restored, however, as the urine output is increased and the blood concentration is maintained at the previous low level[89]. The fact that hormones from the neurohypophysis can definitely stimulate active transport through the skin seems to be now well established. Earlier experiments on the effect of the injection of preparations of mammalian neurohypophysial hormones were inconclusive because of lack of purity of the material. Such preparations may contain ACTH or adenohypophysis-stimulating hormones. Convincing evidence comes from the fact that certain of the neurohypophysial hormones stimulate active transport, *in vitro*, on isolated skin preparations. Thus, in *Rana esculenta*, oxytocin stimulates active sodium transport, whereas vasopressin (pitressin, ADH) has little effect[93]. Extracts of the neurohypophysis of amphibians or fish are very much more effective than mammalian preparations, and a new hormone complex—'natriferrin'—with a very powerful effect on sodium transport has been prepared from these glands[94,95]. Fractionation of the complex shows that it is made up of two hormones: one is arginine-vasotocin[96], and the other is an, as yet, unidentified hormone of equal activity[97].

The part that these hormones play *in vivo* has yet to be established. Clearly both the neuro- and the adenohypophysis may be involved, and the role of the individual hormones in the overall balance system is not clear. The situation is further complicated by the presence of independent sodium and chloride transporting systems. The possibility of specific hormones concerned with regulating the transport of particular ions must be considered.

IONIC REGULATION IN HYPO-OSMOTIC ANIMALS

Comparatively few measurements of ion fluxes have been made in hypo-osmotic animals and the picture, at present, is far from complete. The classical studies of H. W. Smith[14] established the mechanism by which the hypo-osmotic condition of marine Teleosts is maintained. In *Anguilla* and *Myoxocephalus*, for example, sea water is taken in to the gut at a rate of between 5–20 per cent of the body weight per day. Of the ingested water, about 75 per cent is absorbed iso-osmotically in the intestine, together with sodium, chloride, and potassium ions; magnesium and sulphate are largely retained in the gut. Urine production is small (about 1–5 per cent of the rate in fresh water Teleosts) but sufficient to remove those divalent ions which are absorbed. About 90 per cent of the absorbed monovalent ions are secreted extrarenally, against a concentration gradient. The outward transport of ions takes place in the head region—presumably through the gill epithelium. Control of the transport mechanism is indicated by the fact that the rate of chloride secretion, in the perfused head preparation of the eel, is determined by the concentration of the perfusing fluid[98]. In such a perfused preparation with Ringer solution on both sides, the potential difference across the gill membrane is not greater than 10 mV. The flux ratio (M_{out}/M_{in}) for both sodium and chloride ions is greater than 40, so that active secretion of both ions is suggested[99].

The kinetics of ion movement in some fish, such as *Gasterosteus*, are of especial interest in view of the fact that they can maintain either a hyper-osmotic or hypo-osmotic state, depending on the concentration of the

194

external environment. The sodium influx in *Gasterosteus* is much greater from 50 per cent sea water than from freshwater, due to ingestion of the medium in the former solution[100]. There is probably a switch from active uptake to active secretion of sodium with a change of medium.

In the hypo-osmotic crustacean, *Artemia salina*, there is evidence of a similar mechanism. This species can maintain its blood concentration relatively constant and below that of the medium over a wide range of external concentration from 25 per cent to 100 per cent sea water. Below 25 per cent sea water the blood is hyperosmotic to the medium. The blood osmotic pressure is due largely to sodium and chloride ions, and evidence of their secretion comes from the fact that transference of the animals from a concentrated medium to one which is less concentrated but still greater than that of the blood, leads to a fall in blood concentration. Transport probably occurs through the gills since, after their destruction with potassium permanganate, the blood becomes iso-osmotic with the medium. The permeability of the body surface is largely restricted to the gut and there is evidence of extensive drinking of the medium, with active uptake of sodium chloride, and possibly also of water, from the gut[101-103]. Sodium and chloride fluxes are very high and not changed significantly by the prevention of drinking. The efflux is greatly reduced if the medium is changed from sea water to distilled water or to an iso-osmotic erythritol solution. A very large proportion of the flux must be accounted for by the presence of a large exchange component. The sodium exchange rate is increased at higher external concentrations and has the peculiar property that it is not specific for sodium ions. Sodium ions in the blood can be exchanged for potassium ions in the external medium if the K^+/Na^+ ratio of the latter is high[49].

Insect larvae from saline waters have some of the same properties as the other hypo-osmotic forms. In the mosquito larva, *Aedes detritus*, the outer surface is rather impermeable to water and salts, and the anal papillae are greatly reduced in size[104]. The gut is more permeable and water losses due to exosmosis and excretion are made good by drinking. There is no evidence of extra-renal excretion but a hyperosmotic excretory fluid is produced, probably by active uptake in the rectum[77]. The ability to produce a concentrated urine is also found in other hypo-osmotic insects[105].

GENERAL CONCLUSIONS

The main conclusions drawn from studies on the kinetics of ion movement in aquatic animals have been summarized during the course of this review. There is no doubt that flux measurements on other animals will reveal many variations in the relative importance and in the properties of the various membranes involved in ionic regulation as a whole. However, it is clear that the development of powers of ionic regulation in animals depends on the exploitation of the fundamental property of cell membranes actively to transport solute ions. For a further understanding of the mechanism of ion regulation, attention must be focussed on the nature and properties of the cells which compose the membranes in which the transporting mechanisms are located. Already, for the frogs' skin, Ussing and his associates[106-108] have produced evidence for the location of the sodium pump on the inner facing membrane of the transporting cells, and have defined the permeability characteristics of both inner and outer membranes of the cell which would permit the transport of sodium in one direction across the cell.

However, sodium is not the only ion which is actively transported. Active chloride transport is certain. Transport of potassium, and perhaps also of calcium, are important in arthropods and possibly in other animals. One must, therefore, consider whether a transporting membrane contains special cells, which have the specific function of transporting a particular ion, or whether each cell contains a number of transport systems.

Any theory as to the nature and properties of cell membranes which is developed to explain their function in an ion-regulatory capacity, will be inadequate if it fails to account for the transport of all the ions which are observed to move across them. Further, it must explain those properties of the active transport systems which are observed under normal physiological conditions—namely, their independent activation, their ability to operate from extremely dilute solutions, and the fact that the movement of one ion, independent of others, may occur by exchange for ions of similar charge. Finally it must account for the presence of an exchange component in the ion flux, for which there is evidence, at least in *Astacus*, of close linkage with the process of active transport.

There is every reason to believe that a study of transporting membranes in aquatic invertebrates may lead to an understanding of the evolution of transporting mechanisms. Among the wide variety of animals available there is every gradation, even among close relations, between forms which possess an external bounding membrane which is bathed on both sides by a solution of similar composition and which shows little ability to transport ions, and forms where the membranes separate solutions of widely different composition and where the ability to transport several ions is highly developed.

REFERENCES

1. PANTIN, C. F. A. 'Origin of the composition of the body fluids in animals'. *Biol. Rev.* 1931, **6,** 459–482
2. ROBERTSON, J. D. 'The inorganic composition of the body fluids of three marine invertebrates'. *J. exp. Biol.* 1939, **16,** 387–397
3. ROBERTSON, J. D. 'Ionic regulation in some marine invertebrates'. *J. exp. Biol.* 1949, **26,** 182–200
4. ROBERTSON, J. D. 'Further studies on ionic regulation in marine invertebrates'. *J. exp. Biol.* 1953, **30,** 277–296
5. ROBERTSON, J. D. 'The chemical composition of the blood of some aquatic chordates, including members of the Tunicata, Cyclosomata and Osteichthyes'. *J. exp. Biol.* 1954, **31,** 424–442
6. WEBB, D. A. 'Ionic regulation in *Carcinus maenas*'. *Proc. Roy. Soc.* B 1940, **129,** 107–135
7. SCHOLLES, W. 'Ueber die Mineralregulation wasserlebender Evertebraten'. *Z. vergl. Physiol.* 1933, **19,** 522–554
8. BRYAN, G. W. 'Sodium regulation in the crayfish, *Astacus fluviatilis* 1. The normal animal'. *J. exp. Biol.* 1960, **37,** 83–99
9. WIGGLESWORTH, V. B. 'The regulation of osmotic pressure and chloride concentration in the haemolymph of the mosquito larva'. *J. exp. Biol.* 1938, **15,** 235–247

10. RAMSAY, J. A. 'Exchanges of sodium and potassium in mosquito larvae'. *J. exp. Biol.* 1953, **30**, 79–89

11. RAMSAY, J. A. 'The osmotic relations of the earthworm'. *J. exp. Biol.* 1949, **26**, 46–56

12. POTTS, W. T. W. 'The inorganic composition of the blood of *Mytilus edulis* and *Anodonta cygnea*'. *J. exp. Biol.* 1954, **31**, 376–385

13. CONWAY, E. J. 'The physiological significance of inorganic levels in the internal medium of animals'. *Biol. Rev.* 1945, **20**, 56–72

14. SMITH, H. W. 'The absorption and excretion of water and salts by marine teleosts'. *Amer. J. Physiol.* 1930, **93**, 480–505

15. NAGEL, H. 'Die Aufgaben der Exkretionsorgane und der Kiemen bei der Osmoregulation von *Carcinus maenas*'. *Z. vergl. Physiol.* 1934, **21**, 468–491

16. WALKER, A. M., HUDSON, C. L., FINDLEY, T. and RICHARDS, A. N. 'The total molecular concentration and the chloride concentration of fluid from different segments of the renal tubule of Amphibia'. *Amer. J. Physiol.* 1937, **118**, 121–129

17. WALKER, A. M. and HUDSON, C. L. 'The reabsorption of glucose from the renal tubule in Amphibia and the action of phlorhizin upon it'. *Amer. J. Physiol.* 1937, **118**, 130–141

18. KROGH, A. 'Osmotic regulation in the frog (*R. esculenta*) by active absorption of chloride ions'. *Skand. Arch. Physiol.* 1937, **76**, 60–73

19. KROGH, A. 'Osmotic regulation in fresh water fishes by active absorption of chloride ions'. *Z. vergl. Physiol.* 1937, **24**, 656–666

20. KROGH, A. 'The active absorption of ions in some freshwater animals' *Z. vergl. Physiol.* 1938, **25**, 335–350

21. KROGH, A. *Osmotic Regulation in Aquatic Animals*: Cambridge University Press, 1939

22. KOCH, H. J., EVANS, J. and SCHICKS, E. 'The active absorption of ions by the isolated gills of the crab, *Eriocheir sinensis* (M. Edw.)'. *Mededel. Koninkl. Vlaam. Acad. Wetenschap, Kl. Wetenschap* 1954, **16**, No. 5

23. SHAW, J. 'Salt and water balance in the East African fresh-water crab, *Potamon niloticus*'. *J. exp. Biol.* 1959, **36**, 157–176

24. BRYAN, G. W. 'Sodium regulation in the crayfish, *Astacus fluviatilis*. 11. Experiments with sodium-depleted animals'. *J. exp. Biol.* 1960, **37**, 100–112

25. KOCH, H. J. 'The absorption of chloride ions by the anal papillae of diptera larvae'. *J. exp. Biol.* 1938, **15**, 152–160

26. BEADLE, L. C. and SHAW, J. 'The retention of salt and the regulation of the non-protein nitrogen fraction in the blood of the aquatic larva, *Sialis lutaria*'. *J. exp. Biol.* 1950, **27**, 96–109

27. DUVAL, M. 'Recherches physico-chimiques et physiologiques sur le milieu intérieur des animaux aquatiques. Modifications sous l'influence du milieu extérieur'. *Ann. Inst. océanogr.* 1925, **2**, 232–407

28. SCHLIEPER, C. 'Die Osmoregulation wasserlebender Tiere'. *Biol. Rev.* 1930, **5**, 309–356

29. SCHLIEPER, C. 'Neue Ergebnisse und Problem aus dem Gebiet der Osmoregulation wasserlebender Tiere'. *Biol. Rev.* 1935, **10**, 334–360

30. BEADLE, L. C. 'Osmotic regulation and the faunas of inland waters'. *Biol. Rev.* 1943, **18**, 172–183

31. RAMSAY, J. A. 'Movements of water and electrolytes in invertebrates'. *Symp. Soc. exp. Biol.* 1954, **8**, 1–15

32. BEADLE, L. C. 'Osmotic and ionic regulation (Comparative Physiology)'. *Ann. Rev. Physiol.* 1957, **19**, 329–358

33. ROBERTSON, J. D. 'Osmotic and ionic regulation in aquatic invertebrates'. *Recent Advances in Invertebrate Physiology*: University of Oregon Publications, 1957.

34. SHAW, J. 'The Mechanisms of Osmoregulation'. *Comparative Biochemistry*, Vol. 2: Academic Press, 1960.

35. PROSSER, C. L. and BROWN, F. A. *Comparative Animal Physiology* 2nd edn: W. B. Saunders, 1961

36. TREHERNE, J. E. 'The exchange of labelled sodium in the larva of *Aedes aegypti* L'. *J. exp. Biol.* 1954, **31**, 386–401

37. STOBBART, R. H. 'Studies on the exchange and regulation of sodium in the larva of *Aedes aegypti* (L.). 1. The steady state exchange'. *J. exp. Biol.* 1959, **36**, 641–653

38. LOCKWOOD, A. P. M. 'Some effects of temperature and concentration of the medium on the ionic regulation of the isopod, *Asellus aquaticus* (L.)'. *J. exp. Biol.* 1960, **37**, 614–630

39. SHAW, J. 'The absorption of sodium ions by the crayfish *Astacus pallipes* Lereboullet. 11. The effect of external anion'. *J. exp. Biol.* 1960, **37**, 534–547

40. JØRGENSEN, C. B., LEVI, H. and USSING, H. H. 'On the influence of the neuro-hypophyseal principles on the sodium metabolism in the Axolotl (*Amblystoma mexicanum*)'. *Acta. physiol. Scand.* 1946, **12**, 350–371

41. JØRGENSEN, C. B. 'The influence of salt loss on the osmotic regulation in Anurans'. *Acta physiol. Scand.* 1950, **20**, 56–61

42. JØRGENSEN, C. B. and ROSENKILDE, P. 'Chloride balance in hypophysecto-mized frogs'. *Endocrinology* 1957, **60**, 219–224

43. JØRGENSEN, C. B., LEVI, H. and ZERAHN, K. 'On active uptake of sodium and chloride ions in Anurans'. *Acta Physiol. Scand.* 1954, **30**, 178–190

44. MEYER, D. K. 'Sodium flux through the gills of the goldfish'. *Amer. J. Physiol.* 1951, **165**, 580–587

45. SHAW, J. 'Sodium balance in *Eriocheir sinensis* (M. Edw.). The adaptation of the Crustacea to fresh water'. *J. exp. Biol.* 1961, **38**, 153–162

46. SHAW, J. 'The absorption of sodium ions by the crayfish, *Astacus pallipes* Lereboullet. 1. The effect of external and internal sodium concentrations'. *J. exp. Biol.* 1959, **36**, 126–144

47. SHAW, J. 'Studies on ionic regulation in *Carcinus maenas* (L.) 1. Sodium balance'. *J. exp. Biol.* 1961, **38**, 135–152

48. SHAW, J. and SUTCLIFFE, D. W. 'Studies on sodium balance in *Gammarus duebeni* Lilljeborg and *G. pulex pulex* (L.)'. *J. exp. Biol.* 1961, **38**, 1–15.

49. CROGHAN, P. C. 'Ionic fluxes in *Artemia salina* (L.)'. *J. exp. Biol.* 1958, **35**, 425–436

50. USSING, H. H. 'The distinction by means of tracers between active transport and diffusion. The transfer of iodide across the isolated frog skin'. *Acta. physiol. Scand.* 1949, **19**, 43–56

51. USSING, H. H. 'Active transport of inorganic ions'. *Symp. Soc. exp. Biol.* 1954, **8**, 407–422

52. ANDERSEN, B. and USSING, H. H. 'Active transport'. *Comparative Biochemistry* Vol. 2: Academic Press, New York and London. 1960

53. USSING, H. H. 'The active ion transport through the isolated frog skin in the light of tracer studies'. *Acta physiol. Scand.* 1949, **17**, 1–37

54. USSING, H. H. and ZERAHN, K. 'Active transport of sodium as the source of electric current in the short-circuited isolated frog skin'. *Acta physiol. Scand.* 1951, **23**, 110–127

55. KOEFOED-JOHNSEN, V., LEVI, H. and USSING, H. H. 'The mode of passage of chloride ions through the isolated frog skin'. *Acta physiol. Scand.* 1952, **25**, 150–163

56. SHAW, J.–unpublished observations

57. SHAW, J. 'The absorption of chloride ions by the crayfish, *Astacus pallipes* Lereboullet'. *J. exp. Biol.* 1960, **37**, 557–572

58. ROBERTSON, J. D. 'Some features of the calcium metabolism of the shore crab *Carcinus maenas* (Pennant)'. *Proc. roy. Soc.* B 1937, **124,** 162–182

59. BETHE, A. 'Ionendurchlässigkeit der Körperoberfläche von wirbellosen Tieren des Meeres als Ursache der Giftigkeit von Seewasser abnormer Zusammensetzung'. *Pflüg. Arch. ges. Physiol.* 1928, **221,** 344

60. ROBERTSON, J. D. 'Ionic regulation in the crab *Carcinus maenas* (L.) in relation to the moulting cycle'. *Comp. Biochem. Physiol.* 1960, **1,** 183–212

61. BRYAN, G. W. 'Sodium regulation in the crayfish *Astacus fluviatilis* III. Experiments with NaCl-loaded animals'. *J. exp. Biol.* 1960, **37,** 113–128

62. STOBBART, R. H. 'Studies on the exchange and regulation of sodium in the larva of *Aedes aegypti* (L.) II. The net transport and the fluxes associated with it'. *J. exp. Biol.* 1960, **37,** 594–608

63. MAETZ, J. 'Les échanges de sodium chez le poisson *Carassius auratus* L. Action d'un inhibiteur de l'anhydrase carbonique'. *J. Physiol. Path. gén.* 1956, **48,** 1085–1099

64. KIRSCHNER, L. B. 'On the mechanism of active Na transport across frog skin'. *J. cell. comp. Physiol.* 1955, **45,** 61–88

65. KOCH, H. J. and EVANS, J. 'On the influence of lithium on the uptake of sodium and potassium by the crab *Eriocheir sinensis* (M. Edw.)'. *Mededel. Koninkl. Vlaam. Acad. Wetenschap, Kl. Wetenschap* 1956 No. 6, 3–10

66. SHAW, J. 'The absorption of sodium ions by the crayfish *Astacus pallipes* Lereboullet. III. The effect of other cations in the external solution'. *J. exp. Biol.* 1960, **37,** 548–556

67. SEXTON, A. W. and MEYER, D. K. 'Effects of potassium, calcium and lithium ions on sodium transport through the gills of goldfish'. *Fed. Proc.* 1955, **14,** 137

68. ZERAHN, K. 'Studies on the active transport of lithium in the isolated frog skin'. *Acta physiol. Scand.* 1955, **33,** 347–358

69. SCHOFFENIELS, E. 'Influence du pH sur le transport actif de sodium à travers la peau de grenouille'. *Arch. Int. Physiol. Biochim.* 1955, **63,** 513–530

70. USSING, H. H. 'Interpretation of the exchange of radio-sodium in isolated muscle'. *Nature, Lond.* 1947, **160,** 262

71. LEVI, H. and USSING, H. H. 'The exchange of sodium and chloride ions across the fibre membrane of the isolated frog sartorius'. *Acta physiol. Scand.* 1948, **16,** 232–249

72. WIKGREN, B. 'Osmotic regulation in some aquatic animals with special reference to the influence of temperature'. *Acta zool. fenn.* 1953, **71,** 1–102

73. SCHLIEPER, C. and HERRMANN, F. 'Beziehungen zwischen Bau und Funktion bei den Exkretionsorganen dekapoder Crustacien'. *Zool. Jb. Abt. Anat. Ontog.* 1930, **52,** 624–630

74. PARRY, G. 'Osmoregulation in some freshwater prawns'. *J. exp. Biol.* 1957, **34,** 417–423

75. HERRMANN, F. 'Uber den Wasserhaushalt des Flusskrebses'. *Z. vergl. Physiol.* 1931, **14,** 479–524

76. LOCKWOOD, A. P. M. 'The urine of *Gammarus duebeni* and *G. pulex*'. *J. exp. Biol.* 1961, **38,** 647–658

77. RAMSAY, J. A. 'Osmotic regulation in mosquito larvae'. *J. exp. Biol.* 1950, **27,** 145–157

78. SMITH, H. W. 'Water regulation and its evolution in fishes'. *Quart. Rev. Biol.* 1932, **7,** 1–26

79. SMITH, H. W. and SMITH, C. 'The absorption and excretion of water and salts by the elasmobranch fishes. 1. Fresh-water Elasmobranchs'. *Amer. J. Physiol.* 1931, **98,** 279–295

80. Haywood, C. and Clapp, M. J. 'A note on the freezing-points of the urines of two fresh-water fishes: the catfish (*Ameiurus nebulosus*) and the sucker (*Catostomus commersonii*)'. *Biol. Bull.* 1942, **83**, 363–367

81. Toda, S. and Taguchi, L. 'Untersuchungen über die physikalischen Eigenschaften und die chemische Zusammensetzung des Froschharns'. 1. Mitteilung. *Z. physiol. Chem.* 1913, **87**, 371–378

82. Peters, H. 'Ueber den Einfluss des Salzgehaltes im Aussenmedium auf den Bau und die Funktion der Exkretionsorgane dekapoder Crustacien (nach Untersuchungen an *Potamobius fluviatilis* und *Homarus vulgaris*)'. *Z. Morph. Ökol. Tiere* 1935, **30**, 355–381

83. Ramsay, J. A. 'The site of the formation of hypotonic urine in the nephridium of *Lumbricus*'. *J. exp. Biol.* 1949, **26**, 65–75

84. Ramsay, J. A. 'The comparative physiology of renal function in invertebrates'. *The Cell and the Organism.* Cambridge University Press. 1962

85. Ramsay, J. A. 'Osmotic regulation in mosquito larvae: the role of the Malpighian tubules'. *J. exp. Biol.* 1951, **28**, 62–73

86. Ramsay, J. A. 'Active transport of potassium by the Malpighian tubules of insects'. *J. exp. Biol.* 1953, **30**, 358–369

87. Jørgensen, C. B. 'On excretion of chloride in sodium chloride-loaded Frogs and Toads'. *Acta physiol. Scand.* 1954, **30**, 171–177

88. Jørgensen, C. B. and Rosenkilde, P. 'On regulation of concentration and content of chloride in goldfish'. *Biol. Bull.* 1956, **110**, 300–305

89. Jørgensen, C. B. and Rosenkilde, P. 'Chloride balance in hypophysectomized frogs'. *Endocrinology* 1957, **60**, 219–224

90. Jørgensen, C. B. 'Influence of adenohypophysectomy on the transfer of salt across the frog skin'. *Nature, Lond.* 1947, **160**, 872

91. Myers, R. M., Bishop, W. R. and Scheer, B. T. 'Anterior pituitary control of active sodium transport across frog skin'. *Amer. J. Physiol.* 1961, **200**, 444–450

92. Bishop, W. R., Mumbach, M. W. and Scheer, B. T. 'Interrenal control of sodium transport across frog skin'. *Amer. J. Physiol.* 1961, **200**, 451–453

93. Morel, F., Maetz, J. and Lucarain, Cl. 'Action des deux peptides neurohypophysaires sur le transport actif de sodium et le flux net d'eau à travers la peau de diverses espèces de Batraciens anoures'. *Biochim. biophys. Acta.* 1958, **28**, 619–626

94. Maetz, J., Morel, F. and Lahlouh, B. 'Natriferrin: A new hormonal principle in the neurohypophysis of certain vertebrates'. *Nature, Lond.* 1959, **184**, 1236

95. Maetz, J., Morel, F. and Race, B. 'Mise en évidence dans la neurohypophyse de *Rana esculenta* L. d'un facteur hormonal nouveau stimulant le transport actif de sodium à travers la peau'. *Biochim. biophys. Acta.* 1959, **36**, 317–326

96. Sawyer, W. H. 'Evidence for the Identity of Natriferrin, the frog water. balance principle and Arginine Vasotocin'. *Nature, Lond.* 1960, **187**, 1030–1031

97. Morel, F., Maetz, J., Archer, R., Chauvet, R. and Lenci, M. T. 'A "Natriferic" principle other than Arginine-Vasotocin in the Frog Neurohypophysis'. *Nature, Lond.* 1961, **190**, 828–829

98. Keys, A. B. 'Chloride and water secretion and absorption by the gills of the eel'. *Z. vergl. Physiol.* 1931, **15**, 364–388

99. Toteson, D. C., Spirack, S. and Nelson, D. 'Sodium and chloride transport by the isolated perfused eel gill'. *J. gen. Physiol.* 1962, **45**, 620A

100. Mullins, L. J. 'Osmotic regulation in fish as studied with radio isotopes'. *Acta physiol. Scand.* 1950, **21**, 303–314

101. Croghan, P. C. 'The osmotic and ionic regulation of *Artemia salina* (L.)'. *J. exp. Biol.* 1958, **35**, 219–233

102. CROGHAN, P. C. 'The mechanism of osmotic regulation in *Artemia salina* (L.): the physiology of the branchiae'. *J. exp. Biol.* 1958, **35,** 234–242

103. CROGHAN, P. C. 'The mechanism of osmotic regulation in *Artemia salina* (L.): the physiology of the gut'. *J. exp. Biol.* 1958, **35,** 243–250

104. BEADLE, L. C. 'Regulation of the haemolymph in the saline water mosquito larva *Aedes detritus* Edw'. *J. exp. Biol.* 1939, **16,** 346–362

105. SUTCLIFFE, D. W. 'Osmotic regulation in the larvae of some euryhaline Diptera'. *Nature, Lond.* 1960, **187,** 331–332

106. KOEFOED-JOHNSEN, V. and USSING, H. H. 'The nature of the frog skin potential'. *Acta physiol. Scand.* 1958, **42,** 298–308

107. HOSHIKO, T. and USSING, H. H. 'The kinetics of Na^{24} flux across amphibian skin and bladder'. *Acta physiol. Scand.* 1960, **49,** 74–81

108. MACROBBIE, E. A. C. and USSING, H. H. 'Osmotic behaviour of the epithelial cells of frog skin'. *Acta. physiol. Scand.* 1961, **53,** 348–365

PALAEOBOTANICAL TECHNIQUES

William S. Lacey

INTRODUCTION

Palaeobotany is the study of the history of plant life. It is concerned with the plants of former times preserved as fossils and therefore embraces both botanical and geological principles, its various aspects combining to provide evidence which throws light on the evolution of the present vegetation of the earth. The pursuit of this study by successive generations of palaeobotanists has given not only much information on the history and past geographical distribution of groups of living plants, but also has revealed the former existence of many other groups not represented today.

It is a study fraught with unusual difficulties. The student of living plants can use whole specimens, replenish his stocks of material, repeat experiments, refer to excellent herbarium collections, and readily consult many other workers in his field. By contrast, the palaeobotanist almost invariably deals with fragments of plants, often in small quantity or indifferently preserved, and when he wishes to compare his material with previously described specimens he finds all too frequently that the earlier collections are scattered, badly housed or no longer available. He is, moreover, a member of a comparatively small band of investigators in any one country, who are often widely separated from one another. Thus the very nature of his material provides the palaeobotanist with an exceptional challenge.

The story of the great advance that has been made in palaeobotany during the last century and a half is largely the story of the way this challenge has been met, of man's ingenuity and increasing skill in applying to the study of fossil plants new physical and chemical methods as they became available. Old methods of study have been continually improved, new ones have been developed, so that nowadays, with very many techniques from which to choose, it is possible to wrest from the rocks the secrets that they have held for so many millions of years. Few things are more exciting than the gradual piecing together of the fragments of evidence extracted in this way.

The present article will briefly review the history of this technological advance in palaeobotany, provide practical details of methods in current use and, in conclusion, indicate the field for future palaeobotanical research. Before these aims are attempted, however, a short description will be given of the ways in which plants are preserved as fossils, since the kind of fossilization which a plant has undergone will determine which methods of examination are to be employed.

KINDS OF FOSSIL PLANTS

The ultimate form of a fossil plant depends on a number of factors. The most important of these are the nature of the original plant material, the nature of the matrix in which it is embedded, the amount of decomposition which takes place before or during the process of fossilization, and the way in which the plant organ lies when it originally settles in the surrounding sediments. Interaction in varying degree of these and other factors (such as subsequent physical forces and chemical changes) results in a great diversity of forms, so numerous as almost to defy rigid classification. Reference to the various descriptive terms used by Walton[1,2], Crookall[3], Arnold[4], Lacey[5], Darrah[6] and Andrews[7,8] will illustrate this point. Photographs of various fossil plants are shown in *Figures 6.1* to *6.6*.

In the present survey the scheme of classification adopted is that of Lacey[5], itself modified from Crookall[3]. Four main kinds of preservation are recognized—*Directly preserved hard parts, Compressions, Petrifactions* and *Mummifications*.

Directly Preserved Hard Parts

Some plants, chiefly algae, possess a hard exoskeleton composed most commonly of calcium carbonate or of silica. The rock-building calcareous algae and the diatoms with their siliceous valves may be quoted as examples. When such plants are fossilized, their protoplasmic contents rapidly disappear but their resistant outer parts are preserved with little or no chemical or physical change. They retain various structural features which are sufficiently characteristic to permit identification and classification.

Compressions

Fragments of roots, stems, leaves, and fructifications find their way through the agency of streams or fall directly into lakes, estuaries or lagoons. In time the partly decomposed plant débris becomes waterlogged and sinks to the bottom where it is embedded in the sand or mud continually brought in by inflowing streams. The surrounding sand or mud is gradually converted by the pressure of overlying deposits into sandstone, clay or shale and the enclosed plant fragments, continuing to undergo both decomposition and flattening, finally form fossils known as Compressions. Several kinds occur, depending on the amount of decomposition and flattening which takes place. Also, as Walton[9] has demonstrated, the orientation of the plant organ when it settles in the sediments is an important form-determining factor which applies particularly to Compressions.

In some cases, especially leaves, decomposition may proceed until little or no organic substance remains (perhaps only a thin black film of coal) and the plant fragment is usually completely flattened. All that remains is an outline or pattern of the plant impressed in the rock matrix. Such Compressions are termed Impressions.

In other cases decomposition does not go so far and, although the plant organ may be considerably compressed, a certain amount of the original organic matter persists (such as cuticles, lignin, some cellulose) and has the appearance of being incrusted on the rock matrix. Compressions of this form are called Incrustations (Walton[1], Crookall[3]) and are equivalent to the Compressions as understood by Walton[2], Arnold[4], Darrah[6] and Andrews[7,8].

Figure 6.1. Alethopteris serli Bgt. from the Upper Coal Measures, Radstock, Somerset. A compression photographed with unilateral illumination from the top end. (Photo: F. A. Hibbert)

Figure 6.2. Stigmarian axis from the Lower Carboniferous of Dyserth, Flintshire. A cast photographed with unilateral illumination from the right hand side. (Photo: H. T. Davies)

Figure 6.3. Lepidodendron perforatum Lacey from the Lower Carboniferous of Denbighshire. A compression of the incrustation type photographed under xylol. (Photo: H. T. Davies)

Figure 6.4. Clwydia decussata Lacey from the Lower Carboniferous of Denbighshire. A compression of the incrustation type prepared by the Walton Balsam Transfer Method. (Photo: F. A. Hibbert)

205

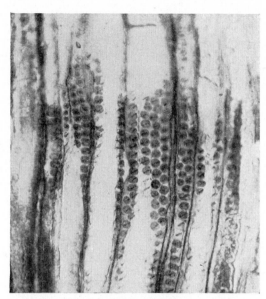

Figure 6.5. Eristophyton waltoni Lacey from the Lower Carboniferous of Dunbartonshire. Radial longitudinal section of the secondary wood showing details of the multiseriate bordered pitting of the tracheids. A peel-section prepared from a silicified petrifaction. (Photo: L. C. Willis)

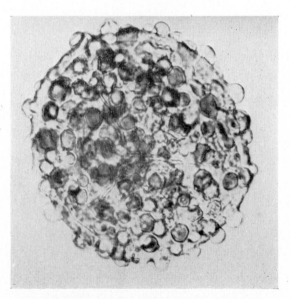

Figure 6.6. Raistrickia sp., a microspore from the Lower Carboniferous of Caernarvonshire, obtained by the Bulk Maceration of shales exposed in the Menai Straits. (Photo: F. A. Hibbert)

Stems and roots, being composed partly of delicate tissues (pith, cortex) and partly of more resistant tissues (wood), frequently decay unequally. Often a naturally-occurring pith-cavity or one formed by the decay of the softer tissues becomes filled by the surrounding sediment which later hardens to form a Pith-cast, showing the features of the inside of the plant organ. In a similar way sediments round the outside can eventually harden into a Mould, the equivalent of the Incrustation of Walton[2], Darrah[6], Andrews[7] and Encrustation of Andrews[8]. A Mould shows the markings of the outer surface in reverse, that is elevations in the plant appear as depressions in the mould and vice-versa. After subsequent decay of the plant, infilling sediments may take on an impression from the mould and form a Stem-cast.

Rounded and angular seeds, with layers of resistant tissues in their seed-coats, frequently form Seed-casts and Moulds, while soft and platyspermic (flattened) seeds form Compressions of the Incrustation or Impression type.

Usually the degree of flattening in Casts and Moulds is slight compared with that found in Impressions and Incrustations. In interpreting Impressions, Casts and Moulds, it is important to remember that different appearances are presented by different surfaces (for example, the epidermis, cortex or wood). The early palaeobotanists not infrequently founded separate species and sometimes even genera on different states of preservation of the same plant.

Petrifactions

Sometimes plant remains are submerged directly in water rich in dissolved minerals or are buried in coarse waterborne sediments or in volcanic ash through which water containing minerals in solution subsequently percolates. In such cases the tissues of the plant are preserved by being gradually infiltrated with, or sometimes actually replaced by, the minerals deposited from solution. Calcium carbonate and silica are the most frequent petrifying minerals but sometimes preservation is in magnesium and calcium carbonates combined (dolomite) or in carbonates, hydrated oxides and sulphides of iron (pyrite, marcasite). Fossils preserved in this manner are known as Petrifactions or Mineralizations.

Perhaps the most familiar examples are the 'coal-balls' or plant-containing calcareous nodules found in certain Upper Carboniferous (Pennsylvanian) coal-seams in Britain, Europe and the United States, but important petrifaction horizons are also found in older rocks. The Calciferous Sandstone Series (Lower Carboniferous or Mississippian) of Scotland and the north of England and the Devonian Rhynie Chert of Aberdeenshire are two good examples.

Petrifactions in general are characterized by relatively little compression and distortion of the plant organ and by the preservation of the finest details of cellular structure, sometimes even including the nuclei within the cells. Such fossils are of the greatest importance, not only in providing valuable information on the possible relationships between groups of plants but also, quite often, in suggesting the general climatic or environmental conditions under which the plants lived.

The most useful petrifactions are those that show the external features in addition to the details of the inner tissues, so that they can be correlated with those plants which are preserved as compressions. This type of preservation is unfortunately rather rare.

Mummifications

Under normal conditions, that is in the presence of warmth, moisture and oxygen, plants decay rapidly after death. If any one of these three factors is lacking, decay is slowed down or stopped before it is complete. With fossil plants absence of oxygen is the most important factor preventing decay. Therefore only partially decomposed plant remains are most commonly found under conditions of deposition which tend to exclude oxygen. Two such conditions are provided by the inclusion of plant fragments in extremely fine-grained sediments (muds) and by the accumulation of plant material in thick, compact masses. In both cases oxygen is almost completely excluded and bacterial or autolytic break-down processes are limited to those which can take place under anaerobic conditions. As a result, cuticles and the waxy materials of cork, lignin and some cellulose, persist. Fossils preserved in this way have been called Mummifications, equivalent in part to the Compactions of Darrah[6].

A number of different types of Mummification are known and four widely differing examples are given here.

Mummification in fine-grained sediments

When very fine sediments settle under tranquil anaerobic conditions, leading to the formation of shales, mudstones and soapstones, mummified plant remains are frequently enclosed. The earliest known Bryophytes were preserved in this manner (Walton[10,11])*. It must be admitted, however, that the distinction between Mummifications in shale and Compressions of the Incrustation type is rather an arbitrary one.

Peat

This is formed by the rapid accumulation of large quantities of plant material under wet, mineral deficient, and largely anaerobic conditions. Oxidation is slow and the plant fragments persist, relatively little changed, in the mummified condition.

Coal

This is a rather special case of Mummification. Thick masses of plant débris, together with a small amount of mineral matter, are compressed by the weight of overlying deposits and are partly mummified, partly carbonized, by subsequent chemical and physical changes.

Baltic amber

The preservation of insects and plant remains in fossilized resin is again a special type of Mummification.

HISTORICAL REVIEW

Although there are no records to show that fossil plants received any serious attention from the philosophers of pre-Classical civilizations, it is probably

* Hueber has recently discovered earlier bryophytes in the Upper Devonian of New York (*Ann. Miss. Bot. Gard. 1961*).

true to say that they have fascinated man ever since he became capable of taking an intelligent interest in his natural surroundings. Certainly fossils were dealt with by the natural historians among the Greeks and Romans. Pliny (A.D. 23–79), for example, wrote about fossils and attempted to connect their occurrence, albeit vaguely, with the plants and animals of former times. But Pliny was exceptional in this respect. Most writings about fossils in these early times were little more than superstitions.

In the following centuries fossils doubtless continued to arouse curiosity, although there is little recorded evidence of this until the fifteenth century. In such meagre writings as there are, there is no attempt to explain fossils as the remains of an orderly succession of earlier faunas and floras. They are explained away either as curious rock formations, 'mineral accidents', as they have sometimes been called, or as the result of the Noachian Flood which was supposed to have so mixed up the earth's surface and its inhabitants that the plants and animals became enclosed in mud, later to appear as fossils in the solid rock.

In the fifteenth century Leonardo da Vinci stands out as one who clearly understood that fossils were the remains of previously living creatures. With masterly reasoning he pointed out that the presence of growth lines on fossil shells and the occurrence of individuals of different sizes implied growth, feeding and movement. The fossils could not, therefore, be the results of 'mineral accidents'. But Leonardo da Vinci also was much before his time; few were ready for his wisdom and the 'accident theory' of the origin of fossils persisted for another two hundred years. Belief in the Deluge as an explanation of the occurrence of fossils embedded in rocks lasted even longer, indeed right into the first half of the nineteenth century.

The first work of importance dealing primarily with fossil plants is the *Herbarium Diluvianum* of Johann Scheuchzer (1672–1773) published in 1709. The illustrations in this book are excellent and there is no difficulty in recognizing many well-known genera among his drawings. But, as the title of the work indicates, Scheuchzer held to the Flood theory as an explanation of the origin of fossils.

The early years of the nineteenth century saw a great expansion of interest in fossil plants and the development of palaeobotany as a truly scientific study may be said to date from this time. The published works of many British and Continental palaeontologists bear witness to this fact. James Parkinson, for example, wrote his *Organic Remains of a Former World*, the first two volumes (1808, 1811) dealing with animals and the third volume, published in 1820, with plants. About the same time books on fossil plants by the two German workers, C. von Sternberg and E. von Schlotheim, appeared, and soon afterwards (1828) the Frenchman, Adolphe Brongniart, the 'father of palaeobotany', published his *Prodrome d'une histoire des végétaux fossiles* as well as the first part of his great *Histoire des végétaux fossiles*, a most impressive undertaking which was to occupy him during the next ten years.

All these early palaeobotanists (and many others whom limitation of space forbids a mention) dealt only with those fossils that were preserved as impressions, incrustations, casts, and moulds. Petrifactions were almost completely ignored and the presence of cuticles in certain kinds of compressions and mummifications was not suspected.

Thus, until after the first quarter of the nineteenth century, the primary stage in the development of palaeobotany remained largely descriptive—and descriptive of surface features at that. The fossils were taken literally at their face value, and there was no attempt to make preparations from them for detailed examination under the microscope. Very often this led to erroneous conclusions and the use of quite unsuitable names. For example, in 1820 Schlotheim proposed the name *Poacites* for leaves which he supposed to belong to grasses. His *Poacites* leaves were Carboniferous in age and certainly not grasses. The genus has been shown subsequently to include both lycopod leaves and calamite stems. This example could be repeated many times, for the literature of palaeobotany is burdened with such misnomers, mostly dating from the early phase of description of superficial features.

Although the microscope had been developed in the seventeenth century by the Dutchman, Anton van Leeuwenhoek (1632–1723), and had long been in use, no progress was made in the study of the internal structure of petrified fossil plants until the discovery of the technique for cutting and grinding thin sections of rocks. The invention of this technique is usually attributed to William Nicol of Edinburgh, just before 1830, but, in fact, the method had been known for some years previously. Nicol himself acknowledged in 1834[12] that his method was a development of the earlier work of another lapidary and fellow Scot, George Sanderson, also of Edinburgh.

By the time of Sanderson and Nicol, the microscope had become a refined scientific instrument and thin sections of rocks and petrified fossils were very suitable objects for study by its use. Thus, by a combination of two important inventions, separated by more than a hundred years, real progress in the investigation of the internal anatomy of fossil plants and their correlation with groups of living plants was at last possible.

The great potentialities of the rock-cutting technique were soon realized by Henry Witham, who as early as 1831 published his *Observations on Fossil Vegetables, accompanied by Representations of their Internal Structure as seen through the Microscope*. This work, republished in 1833 under the title *The Internal Structure of Fossil Vegetables found in the Carboniferous and Oolitic Deposits of Great Britain, described and illustrated* is justifiably regarded as the pioneer investigation of the anatomy of fossil plants. Its publication marked the beginning of a 'grand period' in structural palaeobotany which was to last for almost a hundred years. Few branches of a science have advanced so rapidly as a result of the discovery of a single technique. Mention of the names of only a few of the 'giants' of palaeobotany who were active at this time will serve to illustrate this point.

In 1868–1875 E. W. Binney published his *Observations on the Structure of Fossil Plants Found in the Carboniferous Strata*. These papers dealt with British Coal Measure lycopods and calamites. They were followed by a long series of papers between 1871 and 1896 by W. C. Williamson, sometimes collaborating with D. H. Scott, also on the internal structure of British Carboniferous plants.

Between 1898 and 1919 A. C. Seward published his well-known four-volume work, *Fossil Plants*, while between 1915 and 1921 R. Kidston and W. H. Lang produced their monographs on the exquisitely preserved Devonian Rhynie Chert flora. In 1920–1923 appeared the last edition of

Scott's invaluable two-volume *Studies in Fossil Botany*, the culmination of a prodigious output of memoirs dealing chiefly with Carboniferous plants.

These early British palaeobotanists often relied upon professional lapidaries to prepare the thin sections of their petrified plants. Tribute must be paid to J. Lomax, of Bolton, and W. Hemingway, of Derby, two such men who were outstanding in their skill. Hemingway was perhaps exceptional among professional rock-cutters for he had a keen botanical interest in the material he was preparing and he did, in fact, publish several papers on Coal Measure plants.

From what has been said above the impression may be gained that Britain led the way in the investigation of petrifactions by ground rock sections. This was, indeed, the case. Nevertheless, during the same period rapid progress was also made on the Continent. Brongniart, who had worked on compressions many years earlier, before the development of the rock-cutting technique, turned his attention to petrifactions. Quite late in his life he wrote his *Recherches sur les graines fossiles silicifiées*, published posthumously in 1881. This fine work still provides the background to knowledge of the anatomy of upper Palaeozoic seeds. W. P. Schimper also must be mentioned. His beautifully illustrated *Traité de Paléontologie Végétale*, published in four volumes between 1869 and 1874, summarized the whole extent of palaeobotanical knowledge resulting from work in the nineteenth century. Another great Continental palaeobotanist was Bernard Renault, the French counterpart of Williamson; from about 1875 onwards he also produced an invaluable series of books and memoirs on Carboniferous petrifactions.

In America practically no palaeobotanical work was accomplished before the middle of the nineteenth century, largely due to the fact that botanists were preoccupied with the vast numbers of new and undescribed living plants which were continually discovered as civilization spread westwards. As a consequence, the study of petrified fossil plants began much later in America than in Europe. L. Lesquereux and F. H. Knowlton, two of the greatest early American palaeobotanists, worked mainly on compressions (although it is true that Knowlton described the petrified trees of the Yellowstone Park). The detailed investigation of petrified plants only really began with the studies of A. C. Noé in the early 1920s on coal-balls from Midwestern coal-fields. It is a little curious that American coal-ball work should have been so slow in starting, for the occurrence of coal-balls in various parts of America had been reported by geologists nearly twenty-five years earlier.

During the same period of the nineteenth and early twentieth centuries, which saw the rapid expansion in the study of petrified plants due to the use of the rock-cutting technique, steady, if less spectacular, progress was made in the field of cuticle studies from compressions and mummifications. Just as in the case of petrifactions, full use of the microscope was not possible until a means was found to prepare thin rock sections, so also in the case of compressions and mummifications the full potentialities of the microscope could not be realized until the discovery of methods of isolating plant fossils from the rock matrix and of preparing their cuticles. This time the initiative lay with Continental rather than with British workers. H. R. Goeppert, about 1840, had already used acids to remove the rock matrix from petrified specimens and had been successful in obtaining organic fragments of the original plants, but it was the discovery by Schulze[13] about 1855 of the oxidizing fluid which still bears his name that really advanced cuticle studies. 'Schulze's Macerating Fluid' was, in fact, first devised for the maceration of bituminous coals, but it was very soon used for the isolation of spores, pollen, seeds, and other cutinized membranes from incrustations and mummifications of many kinds.

J. G. Bornemann about 1856 was the first to use Schulze's solution to prepare the cuticles of fossil fronds, and it may be noted also that he was the first to make a comparative study of recent and fossil forms. Since his time the oxidative maceration method has been used very successfully by a great many palaeobotanists. Notable advances in the knowledge of cuticle structure were effected for example by A. Schenk and R. Zeiller between 1867 and 1906 and especially by A. G. Nathorst in a series of papers between 1907 and 1912. Nathorst was the first to give detailed descriptions of the cuticles of Mesozoic seeds, a field of investigation which Harris[14] was later to make very much his own.

Among British workers on fossil cuticles Seward was early in the field; for example, descriptions and figures of cuticles are included in his *Jurassic Flora of the Yorkshire Coast* which was published by the British Museum in 1900.

In 1913 a paper of outstanding interest appeared. This was the comparative account of the cuticles of recent and fossil cycadean fronds published by Hamshaw Thomas and Bancroft[15]. This work was on similar lines to that undertaken by Bornemann nearly sixty years earlier, but its treatment of the fossils was much more thorough. It demonstrated very clearly for the first time the essential differences in epidermal structure between Bennettitalean and Cycadalean fronds.

In America E. H. Sellards was one of the first to attempt maceration preparations. As early as 1903 he was successful in obtaining spores from fructifications preserved as incrustations. The general principles of the early maceration techniques in use at about the end of the first decade of the present century have been summarized by Bather[16], Nathorst[17] and Hamshaw Thomas[18].

In 1916 the study of fossil pollen by maceration methods acquired a new importance when L. von Post first demonstrated the significance of the varying percentages of pollen in peat.

The period from about 1830 to 1920 which has just been reviewed can be considered as a second stage in the development of palaeobotany. No longer content to rely solely on superficial features like their eighteenth and early nineteenth century predecessors, the palaeobotanists of this second phase used to good advantage such new technical aids as were available to them to elucidate the anatomy and histology of their material.

In the early 1920s the second stage may be said to have passed into the third or modern scientific stage in the development of palaeobotanical technology. This period right up to the present day has been characterized by the application of an extraordinary number of new techniques to palaeobotanical problems as well as by the improvement of older ones.

In 1923 Walton[1] developed the Canada balsam transfer technique. This method, modified soon afterwards by Lang[19], and by Walton himself[20], revolutionized the study of incrustations. It has proved invaluable, not only for revealing those features which are normally hidden in the matrix, but also in obtaining, free from the matrix, pieces suitable for investigation by other means. At about the same time, Harris[21] described the Bulk Maceration Method of preparing plant fragments preserved in shales. This also yields material which can be examined further by other methods.

The study of petrifactions received a new impetus with the development by Walton[22,23] in 1928 and 1930 of the peel method of making serial sections. Since the early 1930s these peel techniques have been intensively applied, especially in America. In consequence, while it was once true that the study of petrifactions in America lagged behind that in Europe, this is no longer the case. American palaeobotanists are now making good this deficiency and are rapidly catching up on their back-log of excellent petrified material.

It was during this same period around 1930 that Hamshaw Thomas[24] and Halle[25] described methods of preparing microtome sections of incrustations. Microtome sectioning was not a new technique however. It had already been used some years earlier by Hollick and Jeffrey[26] in the investigation of Cretaceous lignites.

Since the Second World War the old rock-cutting method of examining petrifactions has become easier to use and more valuable as a result of great improvements in the efficiency of cutting and polishing machines. Changes have also been made in several of the newer techniques. Thus the transfer method of investigating incrustations has been modified by Abbott and Abbott[27,28] and by Danzé[29], while a rapid peel technique for the examination of petrifactions has been described recently by Joy, Willis and Lacey[30].

In the last decade new discoveries have also been applied to the study of palaeobotanical materials. For example, Wesley and Kuyper[31] have used the electron microscope in the study of petrifactions, Danzé[29] has employed the phase-contrast microscope to examine incrustations and the use of radiocarbon (carbon-14) has become well established in dating fossil materials.

PRACTICAL DETAILS

In the following pages an account is given of the various techniques used in the investigation of the different kinds of fossil plants. In most cases sufficient practical detail is provided to enable the reader to try out the techniques for himself (although this clearly may not be possible in a few instances where special apparatus is required).

As far as possible, the modifications of the various techniques applicable to each kind of fossil are given in order of discovery (except in those cases where the modifications are so numerous as to necessitate an arbitrary selection). In this way a more complete idea of the advance of palaeo-botanical technology will be gained, amplifying what has already been given in the brief historical review.

Directly Preserved Hard Parts

Calcareous algae can be investigated by several of the methods used for Petrifactions, in particular by the examination of thin ground rock sections with transmitted light and of polished surfaces with reflected light (see Petrifactions, page 220).

The fructifications (oogonia) of Charophytes are also calcareous structures. Those found in hard rocks are examined by the same methods as for the rock-building calcareous algae, while those occurring in soft sediments (marl, clays, silts) are usually extracted by careful washing in water through a sieve, followed by cleaning and mounting as opaque objects on a dark background for examination by reflected light. If the sample is not readily broken down by water alone it may be necessary to use a dilute solution of washing soda.

Diatoms can be isolated from the surrounding matrix by boiling in strong mineral acids and, after thorough washing, are subsequently mounted in a medium of high refractive index. The actual process depends on whether the sample to be examined is a hard rock or a soft diatomaceous earth. While some botanists rely simply on boiling in strong nitric acid or in aqua regia, a rather more lengthy process is necessary for the preparation of really pure samples. The following method is recommended by Camp and Hanna[32];

(1) Dry the sample and break into 5 to 10 mm pieces;

(2) Add strong HCl to about three times the volume of the sample and boil for 15 minutes to an hour;

(3) When as much mineral matter as possible has been taken up, pour off the HCl and add a similar amount of strong HNO_3. Boil again to take up mineral matter. (Aqua regia sometimes gives better results);

(4) Pour off the liquid and wash very thoroughly with several changes of distilled water by centrifuging and decantation;

(5) Add strong H_2SO_4 and boil gently to remove carbonaceous matter. The time varies from a few minutes to an hour or more, depending on the amount of organic matter present. When the mixture has cooled add a few crystals of $NaNO_3$ or $KClO_3$ to remove any colloidal carbon;

(6) Pour off the acid and again wash very thoroughly with several changes of distilled water;

(7) If the treatment so far has not disintegrated enough of the sample, cover with about three volumes of distilled water, add a few flakes of NaOH and boil for a few minutes. (Strong alkali and prolonged boiling must be avoided.) If iron compounds are precipitated or suspended material flocculated, pour off the alkali and boil for a few minutes with HCl again. It may be necessary to repeat the alkali stage several times;

(8) Wash again thoroughly with distilled water and concentrate by centrifuging and decanting;

(9) Pipette a drop of the sample containing the concentrated fossils onto a clean No. 0 or No. 1 cover-glass. Dilute with a little distilled water and allow the fossils to settle, distributed evenly over the cover-glass;

(10) Evaporate the water with gentle heat (do *not* boil);

(11) When quite dry, add a drop of warmed Styrax (or Hyrax) free from air bubbles. Evaporate the solvent gently from the mounting

medium until it hardens on cooling. Now place the cover-glass, mounting medium side down, on a clean slide and heat gently until the mountant flows to the edges of the cover-glass. Keep the slide raised at one end and apply gentle pressure while the mountant is still fluid to remove any air which may be trapped in the diatom frustules. Then allow to cool.

The diatoms will be in optical contact with the under side of the thin cover-glass and can be examined with a 1/12th oil immersion objective.

Impressions, Casts and Moulds

Since little or no organic matter remains in these kinds of fossil, methods of examination are limited to the inspection of surface features by reflected light. Unilateral illumination can be used to make full use of surface relief. In general, little actual preparation of the fossil itself is possible, but the treatments described below sometimes give improved results.

Surface features are often well preserved but hidden by a layer of coal, which can be removed by mechanical means or often more effectively by cautious heating in a red fire.

A white coating of NH_4Cl, employed in conjunction with unilateral lighting, accentuates relief features for photography. The coating can be applied simply by condensing on the surface of the fossil the fumes given off when NH_4Cl is heated in a tube (Hoskins and Cross[33]) or by using a simple 'smoke-producing apparatus' in which the fumes of HCl and NH_3 are blown together over the fossil.

If an appreciable quantity of carbon remains on the fossil, an improved appearance is often obtained by complete immersion in xylol or paraffin. The effect of these media is to increase the contrast between the rock and the carbonaceous fossil, so that the outline of the latter is seen better. Aniseed oil has been used for the same purpose, as it evaporates more slowly and there is less fire risk.

Fossil plants which are preserved as Casts and Moulds can often be used to prepare the complementary Moulds and Casts by using plaster of Paris, paraffin wax, or liquid rubber and then removing the rock mechanically or with a suitable acid. In 1941 Hoskins and Cross[33] described a method of making rubber casts and moulds. They applied 'air-drying liquid rubber' to the specimen in the form of a paint and, when sufficient thickness had been obtained, they incorporated a backing of cheesecloth in a further coat of rubber to make the mould retain its shape. Such a mould, first strengthened with a plaster backing, was used to prepare a plaster cast. The same authors describe an enlarging process in which the rubber moulds were prepared without the incorporation of cheesecloth. When placed in paraffin these moulds expanded uniformly to about $1\frac{1}{2}$ times their original size. From such an enlarged mould, supported on sand, an enlarged plaster cast was prepared. The process of enlargement with alternate casts and moulds immersed in paraffin can be repeated several times.

When the form of the original fossil will not permit the removal of a rigid cast, the method described by Hopping[34] in 1956 can be used. This method employs a 'hot melt compound' (a synthetic plastic which is fluid when hot, elastic when cold) to prepare an elastic cast. This also can be used to make a rigid plaster cast by first preparing from it a wax mould.

Incrustations

Many different methods of examination are available for compressions of this type where some of the original organic material remains. The specimens can, of course, be examined superficially with reflected light (either dry or immersed in xylol, as described above) and without prior development, but much more valuable information, often critical data, can be obtained by using one or more of the methods outlined below. All of them involve separation of the fossil from the matrix.

Direct excavation method

When the incrustation is not confined to one bedding plane there is no entirely satisfactory way of removing the complete fossil. A great deal can be done, however, by careful excavation ('development' or 'dissection') using a microvibratory machine. If such a machine is not available, or if the fossils to be examined are very small, the work can be done with a small hammer and fine steel needles or very small chisels. The specimen should be firmly supported on a sand bag and the development carried out preferably under a binocular dissecting microscope. The method is time-consuming but often gives excellent results, as Leclercq and Andrews[35] have recently demonstrated.

Transfer methods

These methods all involve transfer of the entire specimen from the rock, usually by dissolving the matrix in an acid which leaves the fossil intact. They are particularly valuable when the fossil lies flat in the bedding plane or when it is too delicate for removal by other means.

Several variations are available, each suited to a particular purpose. The various methods, together with the name of the discoverer, are given in chronological order below.

The Walton Canada balsam transfer method (1923)—This is the original transfer method. It is used when the fossil is brittle or consists of comparatively thick carbonaceous material and when it is desired to expose the undersurface for investigation of its relief features.

Walton[1] gives the following stages, which are also illustrated diagrammatically in *Figure 6.7*:

(1) Trim the rock to a convenient shape and size by carefully chipping with hammer and chisel or cutting with a hacksaw. Remove as much rock as possible from the back of the specimen;

(2) Mount the specimen, fossil side down, on a slide in hot viscous Canada balsam as described in the *Ground slice method* (*Ground Rock Sections*, page 221);

(3) Remove surplus rock from the back of the specimen by cautious grinding on a glass plate with carborundum powder. Do not grind too near to the fossil;

216

1

2

3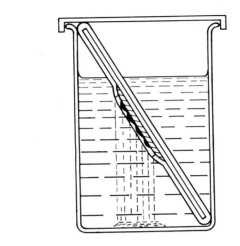

Figure 6.7. Diagrammatic representation of four stages in the Walton transfer method of examining Incrustations.

1. The specimen is cut to a convenient shape and mounted, incrustation side downwards, in Canada balsam on a slide. (Incrustation shown in black, balsam by line shading)
2. The preparation is protected with a coating of paraffin wax, except the surface to be etched by acid.
3. The preparation subjected to the action of the acid.
4. The completed transfer after removal of the paraffin wax coating.

(4) Wash the preparation in water and, when quite dry, coat both specimen and slide by immersion several times in melted paraffin wax at a temperature just above its melting point. When hard, cut away the wax from the back of the rock on the side opposite to the incrustation. This is facilitated by moistening the rock with a little dilute glycerine just before coating with the wax;

(5) Immerse the whole preparation, fossil side downwards, in commercial HF contained in a polythene beaker, until the rock is converted to mud by the solution of the silica it contains, and the incrustation is left attached by the balsam to the microscope slide. The time needed varies from several hours to several days. It can be shortened by changing the acid from time to time and by carefully removing the disintegrating rock with a needle. (Calcareous rock can usually be removed easily with HCl, when no protection of the slide by wax is necessary. If, however, the rock contains silica as well as calcium carbonate, a short additional treatment with HF may be necessary to clean up the transferred incrustation);

(6) When the action of the acid is complete, wash the preparation thoroughly with several changes of water, and complete the removal of any adhering fragments of rock using a soft brush under water.

(7) Finally, cut away all wax and excess balsam, wash the preparation again in water and allow to dry. Protect the newly-exposed surface of the transferred incrustation and keep it dust-free by constructing a small glass case over it with a cover-glass supported on strips of glass of suitable thickness.

The *Walton transfer method* can also be used to isolate large pieces of incrustations for the preparation of their cuticles. To do this, simply dissolve away the balsam with xylol and subject the isolated fragments to oxidative maceration (see *Mummifications, Andrews Method*, page 231).

The Ashby cellulose film transfer method (1926)—This is used when the incrustation is very thin or consists of small scattered objects such as sporangia. The main advantage of the method is that the final preparation is a flat film which can be examined by transmitted light.

Lang[19] gives the following steps:

(1) Coat the surface of the fossil and the immediately adjoining rock surface with a solution of cellulose nitrate in amyl acetate (for details of solution, see *Peel-section method*, page 226). Allow to dry and repeat the treatment until a strong film is obtained;

(2) Remove surplus rock from the back of the specimen by careful grinding;

(3) Immerse the specimen in 25 per cent HF (or HCl for calcareous rock) until the cellulose film is free and cleared of mineral matter;

(4) Wash the transfer thoroughly in water, completing the removal of any adhering rock fragments with a soft brush;

(5) Dehydrate in 95 per cent alcohol (*not* absolute alcohol);

(6) Clear in terpinol or oil of bergamot (*not* clove oil);

(7) Mount in balsam, if necessary applying slight pressure with spring clips. Keep the preparation in a warm oven until the balsam is hard;

If the rock matrix is not affected by HNO_3 the fossil can often be macerated and made translucent before it is transferred from the rock. After treatment with HNO_3 and $KClO_3$ (see *Mummification, Andrews Method*, page 231) gently wash the specimen free of acid with water, dehydrate at once with alcohol, soak in amyl acetate and coat with cellulose nitrate solution. Allow to dry and proceed as in stages (2) to (7) above.

The combined Walton-Ashby transfer method (1928)—Walton[20] gives the following details:

(1) Trim the specimen to a convenient shape and size;

(2) Coat the surface of the fossil and adjoining rock with a cellulose ester solution as described above;

(3) Proceed as in stages (2) to (7) in the *Walton transfer method*;

(4) The preparation formed in this way now offers a choice of two further treatments. If surface features are the more important, keep the preparation for examination by reflected light, as in the original *Walton method*. If however, surface features are relatively unimportant and the specimen can be examined more advantageously by transmitted light, dissolve away the balsam in xylol and mount the cellulose film with its attached incrustation in balsam under a cover-glass as in the *Ashby method*.

The Abbott transfer method (1950–1952)—In 1950 Abbott[27] described a more rapid way of making transfers from incrustations. The method differs from earlier ones in that acids are not employed to dissolve the rock matrix. In effect, the method consists of coating the fossil with a solution of a cellulose ester, much as in the *Ashby method*, and when this coating is sufficiently strong and dry it is stripped from the rock, bringing the incrustation with it. Later modifications by Abbott and Abbott[28] in 1952 make it possible to transfer incrustation as large as six inches by four inches by this technique.

The incrustation is coated several times with a solution of a proprietary American brand of nail varnish. While the last coating is still moist, a sheet of cellulose acetate is incorporated or alternatively a further coating of a mixture of the nail varnish with ordinary decorator's varnish is added. After drying, the strengthened film is removed by firm, steady pulling. Andrews[8] states that the modified method gives excellent display preparations and also that it is useful for preserving incrustations in fragile rocks. The method does not appear to be of general application, however, because the particular American brand of nail varnish is not readily available in Europe and substitutes in the form of thin solutions of various cellulose esters have not been entirely satisfactory.

The Danzé transfer method (1954)—This method has been devised by Danzé[29] for the examination of the extremely fragile carbonaceous incrustations that are found in the north of France. The treatment falls into two parts; the softening ('plastification') of the fossil, obtained by using a solvent for the carbon; and transfer proper, using a specially prepared film with strong adhesive properties.

The steps in the rather lengthy process are as follows;

(1) Place the specimen, previously reduced to a thickness of about 2 mm, in a bath of pure pyridine and leave there for about eighteen hours;

(2) Remove the specimen and allow it to dry at room temperature until the pyridine has completely evaporated;

(3) Coat the incrustation with a layer of Bakelite Varnish 35/35. Allow to dry for fourteen hours at room temperature;

(4) While the film of varnish is still soft and plastic, pour on it a solution of cellulose nitrate in amyl acetate and allow to dry for twenty-four hours at room temperature;

(5) Place the prepared specimen in HF (0·1N) until the surface of the fossil previously hidden in the rock is exposed;

(6) Continue the treatment in HF (0·05N) until the rock is completely dissolved;

(7) Wash thoroughly and remove any remaining particles of rock with a fine soft brush;

(8) After drying, mount the film obtained in balsam under a cover-glass in the usual way;

Experiments with a wide range of specimens from several different countries have given good results in about 80 per cent of cases.

Maceration methods

When the incrustation is strong enough to be handled without the use of a transfer base such as Canada balsam or a cellulose ester, it can be freed from the rock matrix either by mechanical means or by the process known as Bulk Maceration, which involves solution, or breaking down, of the rock with a suitable reagent. The isolated fragments can then be subjected to oxidative maceration to obtain their cuticles.

In the case of Bulk Maceration the oxidation stage may be incorporated at the outset or applied subsequently (for details of Macerations methods, see *Mummifications*, page 230).

The microtome method

As applied to Incrustations this method involves the isolation, softening, demineralization and embedding of the specimen. The following is a generalized procedure:

(1) Remove the specimen from the rock by direct excavation (page 216), balsam or cellulose transfer (page 216), or bulk maceration (page 230);

(2) Soften and demineralize. Several methods have been used to achieve this, for example, Hollick and Jeffrey[26], working with Cretaceous lignites, boiled the specimens for several days in 1 to 3 per cent NaOH and then placed them in HF. For Jurassic material, Hamshaw Thomas[24] used boiling saturated alcoholic KOH for periods of up to five weeks, also followed by desilicification with HF. For harder specimens of Carboniferous age, Halle[25] used much the same method as Thomas, but heated his material in alcoholic KOH under high pressure in specially constructed gun-metal vessels. This prolonged softening treatment with hot alkali causes considerable swelling of the incrustation. Preparations made in this way often have the advantage that they give an idea of the original size and shape of the plant organ;

(3) After thorough washing, dehydrate with alcohol, embed in paraffin wax or celloidin and cut thin microtome sections as with modern plant materials.

(4) If desired, the sections can be macerated and stained before finally mounting under a cover-glass in the usual way. Canada balsam, glycerine jelly or Karo syrup can be used as mountants (for details, see *Mummifications*, page 230).

Petrifactions

Four methods, with various modifications, are available for the examination of fossils of this type where the internal structure is preserved. The older methods will be described first, followed by the more recent.

The ground-slice method (about 1830)

This is the classical method of preparing thin rock sections of petrified plants. It has been in use now for more than a century and a quarter but is still very useful; indeed, with certain kinds of petrifactions it remains essential. In principle, the method has hardly changed since the time of Nicol and Sanderson but there have, of course, been great improvements in the machines and accessories used. At the present day high speed circular saws (or cutting wheels), edged with industrial diamonds, are used to cut

Figure 6.8. A modern rock-cutting and grinding machine. (By Courtesy of the Cutrock Engineering Co. Limited, London)

slices of the specimen and these are then ground on power-driven laps until they are thin enough for examination by transmitted light. The necessary equipment can be obtained in a combined rock-cutting and grinding machine, of which a number of different types are available. An example of a modern machine, manufactured by the Cutrock Engineering Co. in Britain, is illustrated in *Figure 6.8.*

The use of these rock-cutting machines is essentially the same for petrified plants as for other geological materials. The stages in the process are as follows:

(1) First cut the petrifaction into pieces of a manageable size. This will naturally vary with the kind of specimen;

(2) When the part to be investigated is revealed, cut off a slice about 3 mm (1/8 in.) thick in a plane parallel to the desired section. Petrifactions of large area will need thicker slices;

(3) Smooth one side of the slice by hand on ground glass plates using carborundum powder and water. Use a sequence of progressively finer

grades of abrasive (for example, from No. 300 to No. 600) on separate glass plates and wash the slice carefully between grindings with different grades. Finally impart a high polish to the slice, using emery flour, knife powder, chromium oxide or Aloxite.

(4) Warm both the slice and a glass slide on a hot-plate, melt resin on the slide, then place the slice, *polished side down*, in the melted resin with gentle pressing and rotating movements to eliminate air bubbles. Allow the mounted slice to cool for a few minutes until the resin hardens. As mountants, commercial resins, such as Lakeside 70, are recommended as they are specially prepared to harden to the correct viscosity. Natural Canada balsam can be used for the same purpose but must be cooked at about 125°C until a small drop drawn out between the points of forceps or with a needle forms a quickdrying brittle thread. (If a viscous solution of balsam in xylol is used, heating must be continued until the xylol has been driven off);

(5) When quite cold, grind the exposed surface of the mounted slice with coarse abrasive (No. 100) on a revolving lap until it is thin and just translucent. Wash thoroughly and continue grinding on a second lap with finer abrasive (No. 400); finally, complete the grinding by hand on ground glass plates as described in stage (3) above;

In the final stages of grinding, the preparation must be washed and examined under a microscope repeatedly until the appropriate thinness is obtained. The whole procedure needs some skill, and uniformly thin sections are produced only with experience. A grinding instrument which greatly facilitates hand-polishing is available (see *Precision grinding*, page 235).

(6) Now warm the preparation, specimen uppermost, on a hot-plate at about 100°C. At the same time, heat melted balsam or synthetic mounting medium on a cover-glass until any bubbles formed have dispersed. Invert the cover-glass and, with the mountant accumulated at one edge to act as a hinge, lower it carefully over the specimen. Press it down gently and keep the preparation on the hot-plate for about an hour;

(7) After cooling, remove excess resin from the preparation, wash it in soapy water and set it aside to dry.

Modifications—If the material to be sectioned is very soft, fragile or porous one or more of the following modifications can be adopted.

(*a*) Immerse the specimen in melted resin for a few minutes and allow to harden again before cutting.

(*b*) Prepare a polished surface on the petrifaction, as described above, but fix the whole specimen to the slide first, instead of cutting off a thin slice. Then clamp the specimen, *not* the slide, in the jaws of the cutting-machine and cut the slice off as near to the slide as possible.

(*c*) Strengthen the specimen by coating the polished surface with a cellulose ester film before grinding. This can be done before fixing to the slide, whether the slice method is used or the whole specimen attached before cutting. To coat the specimen, etch the polished surface (the one to be fixed to the slide) very slightly with a suitable mineral acid, then pour on a solution of cellulose ester (for details of solutions, see *Peel-section method*, page 226). After this treatment continue the ground-slice method as already described.

The section protected with the cellulose film backing between the slide and itself does not chip so readily in the final stages of grinding and also it can, if necessary, be removed from the slide by soaking in the solvent appropriate to the mountant used.

The chief disadvantages of the ground-slice method are that it requires considerable time and skill to produce good sections, that it is wasteful of material, and that the finished sections are several millimetres apart. Important information may be lost in the cutting and grinding processes. Some of these drawbacks can be partly offset by making thinner sections closer together. Hoskins and Cross[33], and Andrews[8] describe methods of cutting using a fine wire instead of a cutting-wheel. Steel wire or copper wire, gauge No. 30, is drawn backwards and forwards over the specimen, using a paste of Carborundum or Aloxite as abrasive.

The serial-grinding method (examination of polished surfaces)

Some petrifactions and small fragments of some compressions are structurally preserved in iron sulphide (usually pyrite) or iron hydroxide (hydrated iron oxide). The ground-slice sections described above and peel-sections (see pages 221–224) are generally of very limited use because the specimens are more or less opaque. All the same, such specimens should not be neglected, as valuable information can often be obtained by examining serially polished surfaces. The method consists simply in grinding down the specimen on glass plates with an abrasive and water, as already described in the ground-slice method. At the requisite intervals a high polish is imparted to the surface, which is then examined with reflected light. Camera-lucida drawings, or photographs of the successive polished surfaces, are made and in this way the complete structure can be worked out.

Modifications—The serial-grinding method is probably as old as the ground-slice method, if not older, and like the latter has undergone little change. During the last few years, however, techniques have been developed to overcome the difficulty which is sometimes experienced in trying to obtain a high polish on the surface of specimens which have a tendency to crumble. Pyritized specimens are particularly liable to do this. As a remedy, a variety of natural and synthetic resins and plastics have been used as embedding substances.

In 1950 Leclercq and Discry[36] used a relatively simple process which involved immersing the pyritized specimens in xylol for twelve hours, then in a solution of Canada balsam in xylol for three hours, and finally evaporating the xylol during a further four or five hours.

Subsequently Leclercq and her collaborators[36,37] used styrene and the synthetic liquid plastics known as Marco 26C and Markon 7 as transparent embedding substances. A small amount of the prepared plastic solution is poured into a glass or porcelain tray and allowed to set to form a supporting layer, 2 to 3 mm thick. The specimen is then placed on the supporting layer, covered with the remaining plastic and allowed to harden overnight. Finally, the transparent block with the embedded petrifaction is cut to the desired form and polished with a series of progressively finer abrasives. The actual preparation and use of these plastic solutions is complicated and the reader is referred to the original descriptions for details of the steps involved.

More recently Beck[38] has recommended the use of a solution consisting of one part of Canada balsam or of Harleco Synthetic Resin (HSR) in three parts of toluene. Beck gives the following instructions. Boil a thin slice of the specimen gently in the balsam or HSR solution on a hot-plate until most, but *not* all, of the toluene has evaporated. (If evaporation goes too far the resin becomes brittle, but the fossil can be re-immersed in the solution and the process repeated without risk of damage.) Then remove the section, clear away excess resin while still hot, or with a hot needle after cooling, and polish both surfaces with No. 600 Carborundum, followed by chromium oxide. (Since the fossil is only slightly penetrated by the resin, keep the polishing to a minimum.) Wash the section, dry it, rinse in xylol or toluene and mount on a slide under a cover-glass in balsam or in a fast-drying mountant such as Permount. Both sides of the finished preparation can be examined by reflected light.

The Walton peel-section method(1928)

This method is used where an appreciable amount of the original plant material is still present and where the preservation is largely in calcium carbonate or silica. In those cases where none of the original substance of the plant persists, and also in heavily pyritized or dolomitized specimens, the ground-slice or serial grinding methods, already described, must be used.

The peel-section method has many advantages over these earlier two methods. It is rapid, close serial sections can be prepared, there need be no waste of material, the size of sections is limited only by the dimensions of the cutting-machine used in the preliminary preparation of the specimen, and the finished sections, commonly called 'peels', are durable and easily stored.

As originally devised by Walton[22] the method involves the following stages (also illustrated in *Figure 6.9*);

(1) *Preparation of the specimen*—Cut the petrifaction on a machine, or grind by hand with coarse abrasive, until the required part is exposed. Smooth the exposed surface using the finer grades of abrasive, observing the precautions mentioned in the ground-slice method (page 221). A highly polished surface is *not* necessary. Paint the surface of the petrifaction, except that to be examined, with a thin solution of shellac in alcohol. Allow to dry to form a protective coat.

(2) *Etching*—Place the prepared specimen, smooth surface downwards, in a suitable mineral acid. Calcareous specimens should be raised slightly at one end (on small pieces of glass or siliceous gravel) to permit the free escape of carbon dioxide bubbles. Alternatively, petrifactions of large area can be levelled, with the smooth surface uppermost, on a sand tray or on a levelling table with three adjustable screws. Use a spirit level in order to ensure that the smooth surface is horizontal. Then build a rim of plasticine round the edge of the specimen to prevent the acid from running off and add just sufficient acid to cover the surface to be etched.

The exact acid strength, or combination of acids, and the etching time depend on the nature of the rock matrix and on the thickness of the sections required. They must be ascertained by preliminary experimentation in

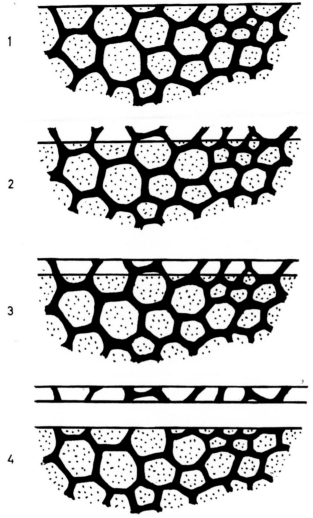

Figure 6.9. Diagrammatic representation of four stages in the peel-section method of examining Petrifactions.

1. The prepared specimen. The surface is ground smooth in a plane parallel to that from which a section is required.
2. After etching away the rock matrix with a suitable acid the carbonaceous plant material projects slightly above the general surface.
3. The specimen coated with cellulose ester.
4. When dry, the cellulose film is carefully removed bringing with it a thin section of the fossil plant material. (After Wesley, 1954[49])

each case. The following concentrations and times, adapted from Darrah[39] are given as a guide:

(*a*) *Calcified specimens.* Cold 2 per cent HCl, 30 seconds to 10 minutes.
(*b*) *Partially dolomitic specimens.* Cold 2 per cent HCl, 30 minutes or longer, or hot 10 per cent HCl for several minutes.

225

(*c*) *Silicified specimens.* Cold commercial HF, 30 seconds to 3 minutes. (25 per cent HF for about 2 minutes generally gives satisfactory results).

(*d*) *Silicified and calcified specimens.* 25 per cent HF for 1 or 2 minutes, followed by 10 per cent HCl for 2 minutes.

When HF is used, extreme care is necessary. Coat the prepared petrifaction (except, of course, the surface to be etched) with paraffin wax, use closed polythene or wax vessels, work in a fume-cupboard (or, failing this, out of doors) and wear the protective clothing recommended for this type of work. HF is a dangerous chemical and must be treated with respect.

In the etching process a thin layer of the rock matrix is removed, but the carbonaceous plant material is not affected and is left standing in relief (see *Figure 6.9.2*).

(3) *Washing*—Wash the etched surface free of acid by immersion several times in large volumes of water or in a very gentle stream of running water. Do not touch the etched surface.

(4) *Drying*—Dry the etched surface in dust-free air. This can be accelerated by flooding with 70 per cent alcohol, followed by 95 per cent alcohol.

(5) *Pouring*—Place the petrifaction with the etched surface uppermost and horizontal, using a sand tray or levelling plate. Moisten the etched surface with a few drops of amyl acetate and then pour or carefully smear a fairly thick solution of cellulose nitrate over it to form a layer 2 to 3 mm thick. Remove any air bubbles which may appear.

There is no one universal or ideal cellulose ester mixture; a rather large number of formulae has been suggested by various authors for different purposes (see, for example, Walton[22], Leclercq[40], Koopmans[41], Duerden[42], Graham[43], Darrah[44], and Andrews[8]). The following formula is the one recommended by Andrews[8] in 1961.

Parlodion (*a form of nitrocellulose*)	28 g
Butyl acetate	250 ml
Amyl alcohol	30 ml
Xylol (*xylene*)	10 ml
Castor oil	3 ml
Ether	3 ml

This mixture is allowed to mature for a week before use.

Instead of the Parlodion, commercial nitrocellulose can be used and some kinds of photographic film, with the emulsion washed off, also give good results.

(6) *Peeling*—Leave the preparation to dry in a dust-free place for twelve to twenty-four hours, when the cellulose ester solution dries to a thin but tough film enclosing the fossil that was formerly left standing in relief by the etching process. (Drying can be accelerated in an oven, but the temperature should not exceed about 35°C.) Next immerse the preparation in tepid water for ten minutes to facilitate removal of the film, ease up one edge of the film with a scalpel or old razor, and finally remove the whole film with careful steady pulling. The fossil material is thus removed as a thin section encased in and protected by the cellulose film. If there are any adhering rock particles remove these by gentle rubbing on a ground glass

plate or by immersion for a few moments in dilute acid, wash in water and finally dry the film ('peel-section' or 'peel') between filter-papers under pressure to prevent curling.

The petrifaction is now ready for repetition of the process. The only preparation necessary is to lightly polish the surface with a fine abrasive in order to prevent the differential etching which, if continued, would eventually produce a deeply pitted surface.

If desired, the whole petrifaction can be converted to close serial sections or, if closely placed sections show little or no change, rock can be ground away between successive peel-sections. It is also possible to prepare the transverse and longitudinal sections of a specimen in a single peel. Smooth and etch both surfaces, as described above, but coat one surface with the cellulose solution and allow to dry first; then turn the petrifaction and coat the second surface. When dry, the two peels will remain attached at their adjoining edges. They can be removed and mounted as one peel.

The finished peels can be trimmed to any desired shape and size with scissors. They can then be either cleared in terpinol, rinsed quickly in xylol and mounted in balsam under a cover-glass in the usual manner, or kept unmounted in envelopes stored in boxes or drawers of the card-index type. Unmounted peels are ideally suited to dispatch by air mail. They can also be mounted between glass plates and used directly as lantern slides.

Modifications of the peel-section method

During the thirty years or so which have elapsed since Walton first devised the peel method, there have been many additions and refinements in the technique. Some of these modifications, such as the staining of peels, are not now in general use. Nevertheless a brief description of all the modifications is provided in order to indicate the amount of experimentation which the peel method has undergone.

The use of gelatine for large peels (1930)—To prepare peel-sections two square decimetres or more in area, Walton[23] recommends the use of gelatine instead of cellulose esters. In this way the use of expensive, harmful or inflammable materials is avoided. The procedure is as follows:

(1) Before etching, place the petrifaction with the smooth surface (that is, the one to be examined) uppermost and horizontal. Build up the edge of the petrifaction with a rim of plasticine.

(2) Etch and wash the petrifaction as described in the peel-section method, stages (2) and (3), pages 225–226, but before the surface is dry from the washing carefully pour a hot gelatine solution over it. A solution sufficient for about two square decimetres of etched surface is prepared and poured in the following way: (a) mix 1 ml of pure glycerine in 100 ml of water and heat to about 80°C (b) add 4 grams of pure gelatine and stir until dissolved; (c) with the mixture at 60° to 80°C quickly stir in 1 ml of formalin and pour immediately, while still hot, over the wet etched surface of the petrifaction.

(3) After drying in dust-free air, peel off the thin gelatine film, clear in xylol and mount in balsam.

Stains for peel-sections (1936, 1945)—The claim has sometimes been made that peel-sections can be improved for photographic purposes by staining

227

with solutions of organic dyes, such as safranin. Whether such staining really adds much to the value of the peel-method is a debatable point, but it is a fact that peel-sections can be readily stained. The staining can be carried out at several stages in the peel method.

Where the peel-section has already been made, it can be stained by immersion in aqueous dye before mounting, or the fossil material can be transferred from the cellulose film to a slide before staining. In the latter case the peel-section is fixed to a slide with Mayer's egg albumen, in the manner described by Barnes and Duerden[45], or with gelatine solution as described by Walton[46] (see *flattening of wrinkled peels*, below). When the albumen has dried and the peel is firmly attached, the cellulose ester is removed with the appropriate solvent, leaving the fossil attached to the slide. This is then stained in aqueous dye, washed, dehydrated, cleared and, mounted in balsam.

Alternatively, the petrifaction can be stained after etching and washing and before pouring the cellulose ester solution. Several authors have tried this. Darrah[44] finds that 2 per cent aqueous solutions of the dyes are satisfactory, but Kosanke[47] recommends the use of strong dye solutions in warm water for 30 seconds to one minute. After staining, the petrifaction is washed again and the procedure is as in the normal peel-section method.

Flattening of wrinkled peels (1952)—The following procedure is given by Walton[46]:

(1) Prepare a 3 per cent solution of gelatine in water, heat to 60° to 80°C, mix in about 0·5 to 1 ml of formalin and immediately pour a small pool onto a slide;

(2) Lay the wrinkled peel onto the pool of hot gelatine and set aside to cool;

(3) When the gelatine is set, dissolve away the cellulose ester with the appropriate solvent, leaving the fossil attached to the gelatine;

(4) Allow the preparation to dry completely, when a very thin film of solid gelatine will be formed, and variations in thickness due to wrinkles in the original peel will become negligible.

The use of embedding substances (1952–1955)—In preparing fragile petrifactions for the peel-section method it is often useful to impregnate the specimen with some strengthening substance. Sometimes it is sufficient simply to soak the specimen in a thin alcoholic solution of shellac and allow it to dry before polishing for each successive section. Or impregnation with balsam or other resin in the manner described by Beck[38] (see page 224) may be employed.

Walton[46] has described a more elaborate procedure which not only strengthens the petrifaction, but greatly facilitates levelling prior to pouring the cellulose solution.

(1) Place the petrifaction, polished surface downwards, on a levelling table provided with three adjustable screws. Accurately level the table using a spirit-level.

(2) Surround the specimen with a parallel-sided collar of celluloid and fill the space between collar and specimen with plaster of Paris. Level the top surface of the plaster with a ruler and allow it to set.

(3) Remove the celluloid collar and impregnate the plaster with shellac. The specimen is now embedded in a block of plaster whose lower and upper surfaces are parallel.

(4) After etching and washing in the normal way, place the plaster block on the levelled table with the etched surface uppermost, when it is clear that this surface will also be level. This ensures that a film of even thickness is produced from the cellulose ester solution, and if the latter is allowed to spread beyond the petrifaction onto the surrounding plaster, any thick edge which may form in the film is not on the surface of the section. This plaster embedding process has another advantage. If several small specimens of the same etching rate are to be examined, they can be embedded in one block of plaster and sections prepared from them simultaneously, thus saving a considerable amount of time and handling.

The use of cellulose acetate solution (1952)—Mixtures employing cellulose acetate have been found to possess several advantages over those using nitrocellulose. The materials used are more readily obtainable at lower cost; the peels produced are less inflammable than those produced from cellulose nitrate, and they show none of the discoloration with age that characterizes cellulose nitrate peels.

Walton[46] gives the following details for preparing the cellulose acetate solution:

(1) Make a stock solution of cellulose acetate by dissolving 20 g in 130 g of acetone and keep well stoppered to prevent loss of the solvent by evaporation.

(2) Immediately before use, dilute one part of the stock solution with about one part of tetrachlorethane until an easy-flowing fluid is obtained.

(3) Filter the mixture through gauze or muslin and apply to the etched surface of the petrifaction. Proceed as already described in the original peel method. (Tetrachlorethane is unstable and its vapour noxious in high concentration. It should be stored in dark bottles away from strong light and the preparation of the peels should be carried out in a fume cupboard or in a separate room. The complete mixture of cellulose acetate, acetone, and tetrachlorethane loses its fluidity after some weeks and should therefore be prepared afresh each time it is required.)

The use of preformed cellulose acetate sheet (1956)—Joy, Willis, and Lacey[30] have described a highly satisfactory technique which uses cellulose acetate sheet instead of a solution of this ester. There are numerous advantages to be gained by using this modification of Walton's original fluid method. The materials used are relatively cheap, no elaborate solutions and no levelling apparatus are required, the peels produced are absolutely uniform in thickness and there is a great economy of time. As many as a dozen or more peel-sections can be made from one petrifaction in one day.

The stages are as follows:

(1) Prepare the petrifaction through the stages (1) to (4) of the original peel-section method, that is, until it is ready for 'pouring' (pages 224–226).

(2) Place the petrifaction with the etched surface uppermost and nearly horizontal. Add sufficient acetone to moisten the surface and to form a small pool at one side.

229

(3) Lay a piece of cellulose acetate sheet, 0·05 mm (0·002 in.) thick and of appropriate size, quickly and gently across the surface of the petrifaction. This is most easily done by slightly bending the sheet and applying it first to the pool of acetone in such a way that excess acetone is pushed before the sheet as it flattens and excludes air bubbles. A little practice soon makes it possible to apply the sheet deftly. If too much acetone remains beneath the sheet, quickly and gently smooth it down with the finger. The sheet may wrinkle a little but becomes smooth again as the solvent evaporates. A small overlap of the sheet all round the petrifaction is an advantage as it provides a convenient handle for subsequent peeling.

(4) Set the preparation aside in a dust-free place to dry, allowing about two hours at room temperature or thirty minutes in a 35°C oven. Do not touch the surface once the sheet has settled in position as it may become tacky.

(5) Finally, remove the peel-section as in the original liquid method.

The microtome method

As in the case of Incrustations already described (page 220), the preparation of microtome sections of petrifactions involves demineralization and embedding of the specimen. The application of these processes to petrifactions is not new. As long ago as 1918, Marie Stopes demonstrated that it was possible to completely demineralize Cretaceous silicified wood and recover the tissues in an excellent state of preservation. Despite this early beginning the microtome method has been little used with petrifactions, but deserves more attention than it has hitherto received. Andrews[8] has recently given details for the preparation of microtome sections of silicified wood in which the cell structure is well preserved:

(1) Cut cubes of about 1 cm side (using rock-cutting machine);

(2) Observing all the necessary precautions, stand the cubes in 25 per cent HF for a few days. Test the specimen from time to time with a needle to determine when the mineral matter is all dissolved away;

(3) Wash very thoroughly by leaving in running water overnight;

(4) Embed in celloidin and cut microtome sections as with modern plant materials. (Consult standard text-books of botanical technique for details of the embedding procedure);

(5) Mount in the same manner as microtome sections of modern plants, except that staining is usually not necessary.

Mummifications

In the account of the ways in which plants are preserved as fossils (pages 202–208), four examples of different types of mummification were given. The methods of examination which are applicable to three of these, namely, mummification in fine-grained sediments, peat and coal are discussed below. (The fourth type, preservation in amber, is rather specialized and is omitted from the present review.)

Mummification in fine-grained sediments

These are examined by bulk maceration methods. Several variations have been described, depending largely on the nature of the enclosing rock. Two widely used techniques are given below. They are also applicable to incrustations.

The Harris method (1926)—The steps given below are slightly modified from the method as originally described by Harris[21]:

(1) Break the shale into pieces about 5 cm (2 in.) square and immerse in concentrated HNO_3 containing 5 per cent $KClO_3$. Leave for several days;

(2) Decant off the acid and wash the shale well with numerous changes of water;

(3) Add dilute caustic soda; the shale breaks down to a fine mud, some of the organic matter forms a dark-coloured solution, and the remaining plant fragments are reduced largely to their resistant cuticles;

(4) Separate off the cuticle fragments by passing through a nest of sieves and wash very thoroughly with water;

(5) Finally, clean up the specimens (cuticles) with 25 per cent HF and again wash thoroughly with plenty of water.

This oxidative maceration is most effective with relatively soft shales. With hard rocks it is often better to remove the mummified plant fragments from the rock matrix before subjecting them to oxidation. In this case, the following method can be employed.

The Andrews method—The procedure given here is a modified and amplified version of the method described by Andrews[8]:

(1) Place the fossiliferous rock in 25 per cent HF for a period which may vary from a few hours to several days. (In the case of calcareous rock, use HCl);

(2) Wash the sludge containing the plant fragments very thoroughly with several changes of water to remove the acid:

(3) Separate out the larger plant fragments by hand and the smaller pieces by washing through a nest of sieves. (The material passing the finer sieves will be likely to contain microfossils and can be retained for separate study);

(4) From this point the method becomes one of oxidative maceration and is equally applicable to mummifications and incrustations. Plant fragments isolated from the rock matrix by mechanical dissection, transfer, or bulk maceration methods can all be treated in the same way. Place the isolated pieces according to size in a cavity slide, small watch glass or specimen tube and cover with Schulze's macerating fluid (concentrated HNO_3 to which a little powdered $KClO_3$ is added). Allow time for the oxidation of the plant materials to take place. Overnight maceration is generally sufficient, but the actual time required may vary from an hour or less to several days, depending on the size and nature of the specimen.

(5) When oxidation is complete (usually indicated by the plant fragment becoming translucent and pale brown in colour) remove all traces of acid by thorough washing with water.

(6) Add dilute alkali to extract the brown non-cuticular substances from the plant fragments. It is usual to employ very dilute ammonia solution for this, but it is also possible to use 2 per cent to 5 per cent solutions of NaOH, KOH, or Na_2CO_3. The alkali stage must be carried out carefully. Watch

the process of the extraction by examining the cuticle fragment from time to time under a microscope.

(7) After complete extraction with alkali, wash the cuticle fragments throughly with water.

(8) If desired, stain the cuticles with safranin or other dye.

(9) Finally, mount on a slide under a cover-glass or between two cover-glasses. Canada balsam can be used as a mountant but, of course, necessitates dehydration of the fossil with alcohol and treatment with xylol. This sometimes makes the cuticle hard, brittle and difficult to handle. Glycerine jelly is much easier to use but may dry out in a warm climate or liquefy in a damp one. Addition of a little formalin will cause the jelly to set irreversibly but ringing should also be used.

Other mountants are available. Radforth[48] has used 'pure corn syrup' while Wesley[49] strongly recommends Karo syrup diluted with water or with dilute alcohol to the consistency of 50 per cent glycerine. Karo syrup is a mixture of dextrose, dextrins and maltose. It requires no dehydration and hardens at higher temperatures, eventually becoming as hard as balsam.

When the plant fragments to be macerated are very delicate, they should be handled as little as possible. The whole maceration process can be carried out on a microscopic slide. Mount the fragments directly in HNO_3 with a little $KClO_3$ on a slide and under a cover-glass. Increase the rate of oxidation by keeping at 60°C for about 15 minutes. Then remove the oxidized organic matter by drawing sodium hypochlorite solution or very dilute ammonia solution through, under the cover-glass, with filter-paper, and finally introduce warm glycerine jelly in the same manner.

Peat

Peat can be examined both for its macroscopic and for its microscopic content. In the first case, the compressed masses of mummified plant fragments can usually be separated sufficiently by simple agitation in water. If necessary, mineral matter can be removed and the peat softened by treatment with 10 per cent HCl or HF. The macroscopic remains are then sorted by screening and selected by hand for examination. They can be subjected, if desired, to further treatments, such as microtome sectioning or oxidative maceration for cuticles.

For the examination of microscopic remains (spores, pollen grains, cuticle fragments, *etc.*) many methods are available, mainly due to the work of L. von Post, G. Erdtman, and H. Godwin during the first thirty years or so of the present century. The original techniques devised by these and other early workers consist essentially of subjecting the peat sample to either an alkali hydrolysis or an acid hydrolysis, or a combination of both of these two treatments. These basic techniques have been modified in various ways by later investigators. It is probably no exaggeration to say that nowadays there are available for palynological studies (that is, the study of both recent and fossil spores and pollens) almost as many variations of the basic techniques as there are workers in this rapidly expanding field. It is quite beyond the scope of the present chapter to attempt a review of all of these methods and variations. For full information of this sort the reader is referred to the excellent book *Palynological Techniques* published in 1960 by

Clair A. Brown[50]. This work collects together and supplies practical details of most of the techniques, old and new, not only for the examination of microfossils preserved in peat, but also for those in soils, clays, coals, shales, oils, bitumens, ice, and honey. Two methods only will be described here.

Alkali hydrolysis—

(1) Powder dry peat through a 100-mesh sieve;

(2) Place about 1 g of the powdered sample in 50 ml 5 per cent KOH or NaOH and keep gently simmering for several hours. This process removes humic materials;

(3) Centrifuge for several minutes to compact the residue and discard the supernatant liquid;

(4) Add distilled water and wash the residue by centrifuging and decanting, this process being repeated several times;

(5) Mix the residue with glycerine jelly prestained with safranin. Mix thoroughly, spread thinly on slides and cover with large cover-glasses. (If the slides are inverted before the jelly is set the microfossils will settle on or near the cover-glass and can be more easily examined.)

Acid hydrolysis—

(1) Dry the peat in a vacuum or over concentrated H_2SO_4.

(2) Rub the sample through a fine sieve (100 meshes/sq. cm);

(3) Add a small amount (about 0·2 g) of the powdered peat to a mixture of 4 to 5 ml glacial acetic acid, 1 to 2 ml concentrated HCl and five drops of saturated $NaClO_3$ solution. Keep the mixture for several minutes, with occasional careful shaking. Lignin is oxidized by this process;

(4) Centrifuge the mixture and discard the supernatant liquid. Wash with distilled water and centrifuge, repeating several times. Finally wash with glacial acetic acid, centrifuge and decant the acid;

(5) Add to the residue a mixture of 5 ml acetic anhydride and 2 ml concentrated H_2SO_4. (Exercise care with this step.) Place in a water bath and warm very carefully until bubbling occurs. Keep thus for a few minutes. By this process cellulose is removed;

(6) Thoroughly wash the residue by centrifuging with distilled water and decantation, repeated several times;

(7) In the last washing, stain the residue with dilute aqueous safranin. After staining, centrifuging and decanting, add glycerine jelly. Mix thoroughly, spread thinly on slides and cover with cover-glasses. Allow to set as described above.

Coal

The preparation and examination of coal constitute a highly specialized branch of applied palaeobotany. In the present review it is possible to give only a very brief indication of some of the very many methods which have been employed by different investigators. The following methods, already described, can all be utilized:

(1) *Ground-slice sections* for examination with transmitted light (see *Petrifactions*, pages 221–223).

(2) *Polished surfaces* for examination by reflected light (see *Petrifactions*, pages 223–224). According to Seyler[51], slight etching of the polished surface

with a mixture of saturated chromic acid and strong sulphuric acid sometimes emphasizes the detail. The two foregoing methods usually necessitate
embedding of the coal in a strengthening material. The method described
by Leclercq and Noel[37] is particularly useful for this.

(3) *Peel-sections* (see *Petrifactions*, pages 224–230).

(4) *Microtome sections.* E. C. Jeffrey developed a technique many years
ago which involved demineralizing, softening and embedding the coal in
nitrocellulose, so that it could be sectioned with a microtome. The method is
lengthy and time-consuming. Details of Jeffrey's method are given by
Darrah[52] and by Brown[50], to whom reference should be made.

(5) *Maceration preparations.* The methods used in the maceration of coal
are essentially the same as those applied to the study of mummifications in
shale and in peat.

The techniques used depend to a large extent on the nature of the material
to be examined. Lignites and brown coals, for example, are usually prepared
by alkaline hydrolyses, by acid hydrolyses, or by a combination of these two
methods, very similar to those used in the case of peat. Bituminous and hard
coals, however, are more often subjected to oxidative maceration with HNO_3,
either alone or in combination with other oxidizing agents such as $KClO_3$
(Schulze's macerating fluid) or bromine (Zetzsche method), followed by
treatment with alkali (ammonia or KOH). Far too many variations of
these techniques have been described to permit their enumeration here and
the reader is again referred to Brown's *Palynological Techniques*[50] for a complete list. The book by Raistrick and Marshall[53] dealing specifically with
coal should also be consulted.

As an example of a coal maceration method in current use, the Zetzsche
Method in the form employed by Dijkstra[54] is given here:

(1) Take 10 grams of the coal sample and crush in a mortar to pieces 3 mm
to 5 mm in diameter;

(2) Place the crushed coal in a 1·5 litre glass-stoppered, wide-mouth
bottle and add 3 to 4 ml. of liquid bromine. Place the glass-stoppered bottle
in a special wooden rack with screw device to keep the lid in place. Shake
vigorously and leave for several hours (usually overnight);

(3) The next day, turn the bottle on its side and reduce the pressure to
loosen the lid and allow bromine to escape (this should be done in a fume
cupboard or out of doors);

(4) Place the bottle in a container of cold water, with crushed ice added;

(5) Carefully add, in small quantities at a time, 125 ml. of fuming nitric
acid (1·52 sp. gr., 97 per cent) and leave for some hours, shaking occasionally.
(The time depends on the hardness of the coal. Brown coal requires about
$\frac{3}{4}$ hour, coal with 30 per cent volatile matter, 2 to $2\frac{1}{2}$ hours; 27 per cent
volatiles, 3 to 4 hours; below 25 per cent volatiles the method is not very
satisfactory);

(6) Add ice inside the bottle at first to prevent boiling and to dilute the
mixture, then after a few minutes fully dilute by filling the bottle with cold
water. Shake the mixture;

(7) Strain through a 100-mesh (or about 200 μ mesh size) silk sieve.
Wash thoroughly with water several times. Retain the filtrate (that is,

the fine mud that passes through the sieve and the washings) for microspores. Concentrate by centrifuging and washing. Add 5 per cent NaOH to the residue in the centrifuge tube, heat gently, centrifuge again and remove all traces of the alkali by repeated washing, centrifuging and decanting. Transfer the residue to the mounting medium (glycerine jelly, prestained with safranin) and mount on slides in the usual way;

(8) Transfer the larger fragments, including megaspores, to a metal sieve by inverting the silk sieve and washing through from the reverse side with water;

(9) Wash the fragments several times with 5 to 10 per cent NaOH for about one minute;

(10) Wash quite free of alkali and allow the fragments to dry on the metal sieve;

(11) Pick out the megaspores by hand under a binocular microscope and mount as free dry objects in white background cardboard cells with cover-glass lids.

In all work on fossil spores and pollen contained in shales, peat, coal, and other deposits, great care must be taken to prevent contamination by recent plant material. The samples for maceration should be collected from freshly exposed surfaces wherever possible. As a precaution against the possible infiltration of recent material some investigators actually decontaminate the surface of shale and coal by searing with a flame. All reagents and apparatus must be kept scrupulously clean, distilled or filtered water used for washing, and all reactions carried out in covered vessels (preferably in a fume cupboard fitted in a sterile room) to exclude the possibility of pollution by airborne spores and pollen.

Miscellaneous Developments

In order to give as complete a picture as possible of the development of palaeobotanical technology, brief reference must now be made to the many additional aids which have been described from time to time by various authors. Several of these procedures have a general application in palaeontology, others are specifically palaeobotanical, but the majority were primarily developed for other purposes and later adopted by the palaeobotanist.

Precision grinding

Croft[55,56] has described a simple 'parallel grinding instrument' which is available commercially. This apparatus not only makes possible the preparation by hand of uniformly thin sections in the ground-slice method, but also facilitates the accurate spacing of successive levels in the serial-grinding and peel-section methods; it thus adds considerably to the value of all these methods.

Construction of scale models from serial drawings

Lacey, Joy, and Willis[57] describe a method utilizing sheets of dental wax. Camera lucida drawings are prepared in the usual way from ground-slice

235

sections, polished surfaces or peel-sections. Each drawing is protected with a thin sheet of cellulose acetate, then a sheet of translucent dental wax, about 1 mm thick, is laid over the drawing and the outline of the latter is traced by cutting through the wax with a needle. The portions thus cut out are numbered, stacked in order and sealed together using a very fine gas flame from a glass capillary. Using the Croft grinding instrument (described above) or a micrometer gauge, the distance between sections is adjusted to correspond in scale with the thickness of the wax used, and the resulting model is to scale in all dimensions.

Photography of fossil plants

Photography has, of course, long been in use in palaeontological work but the last few years have seen marked improvements in photographic materials and technique. In a particularly useful paper published in 1960, Wienert[58] has described the use of New Coccine (a water-soluble red dye for the local control of negative densities), 'ring-lighting' for even illumination of fossils, colour filters, and interchange of varying exposure and development times. Reference should certainly be made to the original paper for details of the first three techniques. With regard to the last, it is given as a general rule that dark objects should be overexposed and underdeveloped, light objects underexposed and overdeveloped to improve the quality of the negative.

Stereophotography

Wienert[59] has also described an ingeniously simple single-lens device for stereophotography of palaeontological specimens.

Infra-red photography

Leclercq[60] and Walton[61] have both utilized infra-red light to photograph opaque transfers of incrustations. Such specimens are appreciably translucent to infra-red rays and considerable detail of the venation and other features is revealed.

Phase-contrast photography

Danzé[29] reported in 1954 that the use of phase-contrast equipment sometimes proved valuable in the examination of certain transfer preparations which showed little contrast.

Electron microscopy

Wesley and Kuyper[31], and Wesley[49] have given instructions for preparing plant petrifactions for examination with the electron microscope. The method consists of making a very thin peel-section in cellulose nitrate. The underside of the peel is then coated with a layer of 'Formvar' dissolved in dioxan and when this coating is dry the cellulose nitrate is dissolved away with amyl acetate. The fossil material remains attached to the 'Formvar' base and in this form is placed on the grid of the electron microscope for observation. Darrah[6] refers very briefly to Wesley and Kuyper's work with the electron microscope and comments that 'the method has not proved practical', apparently because of the complicated apparatus and procedure involved. While this may well have been true ten years ago and when working with petrified palaeozoic material, a paper published in 1959 by Ehrlich and Hall[62] dealing with Tertiary pollen has shown that the electron microscope is undoubtedly of value in elucidating the fine structure of the cell walls of certain kinds of fossil plants.

x-ray photography

Darrah[6,63] has experimented with x-ray photography as a means of identifying structures in certain petrified specimens. The main objective was to be able to locate the position of the various structures, so that the specimen could be orientated to best advantage and critical features not destroyed or passed by in cutting the petrifaction preparatory to making peel-sections. It is not clear from Darrah's descriptions whether this objective was completely achieved.

Double cover-glass mounts for microfossils

Schopf[64] has described a method of mounting plant microfossils dispersed in Canada balsam between two cover-glasses, instead of directly on a slide under one cover-glass. The double cover-glass preparation is then supported on an ordinary glass slide and secured in place with strips of adhesive masking tape. When it is necessary to examine the fossils from both sides the tape can be removed and the preparation turned over. Lacey, Williams, and Hibbert[65] employ a slight modification of the technique for mounting the double cover-glass preparation. A so-called 'bifacial' slide (of the type originally devised by Lyon and Sims[66]) is used. This simply consists of a 3 by 1 in. duralumin slide provided with a central cavity into which the double cover-glass preparation can be fitted. A circular hole, slightly smaller than a $\frac{3}{4}$ in. circular cover-glass, is cut in the slide. This hole is then counter-sunk at a diameter slightly larger than the cover-glass until a small thin flange remains at one face of the slide. The double cover-glass preparation is placed in the cavity in the slide and rests on this flange. After fixing in place with mountant or masking tape, the preparation can be examined from either side, if necessary with an oil-immersion objective. The spores or cuticle fragments should preferably occupy the central portion of the double cover-glass preparation, so that the supporting flange does not foul the objective or mask any of the fossil material.

Ultrasonic separation

During recent years the ultrasonic generator has been used in the processing of samples containing fossil spores and pollen. This equipment can be used in two ways; either in the disaggregation of certain kinds of rocks or, more commonly, in the clearing of organic débris and small mineral particles from microfossils which have been first extracted by chemical methods.

Brown[50] gives some practical details of the latter application of ultrasonic vibrations.

Flotation methods for the separation of microfossils

After the microfossils have been freed from the rock matrix by maceration, with or without the subsequent application of ultrasonic treatment, a

237

complete separation can often be achieved by flotation methods. A sample containing the microfossils is shaken up with a liquid of high specific gravity and then allowed to stand; the mineral fraction sinks but the organic remains float and can be readily separated. A variety of heavy liquids has been used for this purpose; for example, Thoulet's solution (potassium and mercury iodides), sulphuric acid, bromoform, zinc bromide, zinc chloride, ethyl iodide, potassium and cadmium iodides. Brown[50] gives details of the use of some of these reagents. He concludes that the KI/CdI mixture is the most generally useful in the separation of microfossils from the sediments derived from sandy rocks, clays and peats.

Oil flotation methods have also been utilized for separating microfossils. They are less easy to apply, however, and appear to be less generally useful.

Other chemical and physical methods

All the techniques which have been described so far in this article relate to the preparation of palaeobotanical material for subsequent examination or illustration. There are, however, several other sources of information about fossil plants, for various methods are available which permit the identification of some of the organic constituents of the plant or an approximate determination of its age. As examples may be mentioned the spectroscopic methods which have made it possible to recognize various derivatives of chlorophyll in coal and other carbonaceous sediments; and the carbon-14 (radiocarbon) method of dating. The latter has been used hitherto mainly for dating specimens of archaeological significance, but some attempts to date the fossils contained in more ancient sediments have also been made. The reader is referred to *Radiocarbon Dating* by Libby[67] for further information in this specialized field.

SUMMARY AND CONCLUSION

The history of the development of palaeobotanical technology has been briefly outlined and a description given of the many techniques which are now available. It will be apparent from what has been said that the palaeobotanist of today is very much better provided with research tools than were his predecessors of less than forty years ago. He looks to the future splendidly equipped with an impressive array of techniques to aid him in his work, and the field of work which lies before him is very wide. Some general idea of its scope and possible lines of advance may perhaps form a fitting conclusion to this article.

In the study of compressions preserved as incrustations the intensive application of transfer techniques to fertile fronds and other reproductive structures, coupled with maceration preparation of their cutinized membranes, may be expected to yield information of the first importance bearing on the identification of early representatives of the various groups of plants. Radforth[48], for example, has used transfer methods to establish beyond doubt that Schizaeaceous ferns were already in existence in Carboniferous times. More recently Wilson and Yates[68], using the same techniques, have demonstrated the essential characters of the sorus in two Dicksoniaceous ferns from the Yorkshire Jurassic. They are the first investigators to do this successfully with Mesozoic fern compressions. This satisfactory result was due to the application of Walton's balsam transfer method.

Apart from work on fructifications, the study of the cuticles of coal-measure compressions is almost an untouched field. In Britain the earliest work of this kind was done by Wills[69] in 1914 and followed up many years later by Dix[70], but there is scope for much more work in this direction.

In the case of petrifactions, the development of the rapid peel method, using cellulose acetate sheet instead of solution, will greatly accelerate the output in this field. The new method has been very favourably received, especially by palaeobotanists in America, and it is already in general use in that country. But petrifactions have not been neglected in Europe. In Britain at the present time research is concentrated on the rich petrifaction-bearing deposits in the Lower Carboniferous of southern Scotland. In this connection attention is particularly drawn to the fascinating results achieved by Long[71] and Barnard[72] in their studies of pteridosperm cupules and seeds. In the Soviet Union Snigirevskaya[73] is also using the rapid peel technique to investigate Carboniferous petrifactions from the Donbass.

There is one aspect of the study of petrifactions which has remained curiously neglected. This is the preparation of cuticles from petrified plants by total solution of the rock matrix with acids. This is rather surprising in view of the fact that it has been known for a long time that well-preserved plant fragments can be isolated in this way. The examination of cuticles prepared from structurally-preserved plants should prove to be very useful in correlating the latter with those preserved as compressions. A start in this direction has already been made recently with material of palaeozoic age. This is evidenced by the interesting work of Harms and Leisman[74] on the cuticle structure of *Cordaites* leaves preserved in American coal-balls.

Very few attempts have been made to obtain cuticles from Mesozoic petrifactions. Harris[14] has already pointed out that petrified *Cycadeoidea* seeds have never been studied by maceration. It might well be worth while trying to prepare their cuticles in this way.

Research on mummified plant remains contained in shales, peat and coal has made very rapid strides in recent years. The very thorough studies of peat deposits carried out by workers in many countries has led to the establishment of Quaternary palaeobotany as a discipline in its own right. It now rests on a very firm basis. Godwin's *History of the British Flora*[75] can be cited as one example of the outcome of this kind of work pursued over a long period of years.

The investigation of coals and shales has been concerned largely with the spore and pollen content. Hitherto this has been the province of the geologist rather than the botanist, for, as is well known, the geologist can use plant microfossils as very valuable indices for stratigraphical purposes, without necessarily concerning himself about the botanical affinities of his fossils. The botanical aspect of this kind of work has, until quite recently, been hampered by the lack of knowledge of the parent plants providing the dispersed spores. The solution to the problem lies in the making of spore preparations from authentically named fructifications preserved as incrustations or petrifactions, in the same way that it was necessary to study recent

239

pollens from known parent plants before progress could be made in the palynological investigation of quaternary deposits.

As Felix[76] has recently pointed out, the opportunities for research in relating plant microfossils to megafossils are almost unlimited. Felix makes a plea for more work of this kind to be undertaken, for the task is indeed enormous. As this work proceeds, more and more isolated spore types will be related to the parent plants and spore floras will begin to take on a new importance from the botanical point of view. Much has in fact already been done in this direction and the position has now been reached where, as Chaloner[77] has shown, certain spore types whose parent plants are known can be used to provide information bearing on palaeoecological and palaeo-geographical problems. Harris[78] also has recently indicated that attention could be profitably paid to the study of Mesozoic microfloras, in Greenland.

Enough has been said then to show that there is no lack of palaeobotanical problems awaiting solution, and that the techniques of investigation available are more than adequate to the task. Even the most unpromising material which a few years ago would have been regarded as useless and discarded can now be made to yield valuable results. More than this, the impressive advances that have been made during recent years suggest that techniques will continue to undergo modification and improvement. It may be confidently expected that palaeobotanical knowledge will continue to advance rapidly in all its many aspects.

REFERENCES

1. WALTON, J. 'On a new method of investigating fossil plant impressions or incrustations'. *Ann. Bot., Lond.* 1923, **37**, 379–391
2. WALTON, J. *An Introduction to the Study of Fossil Plants* 2nd edn: A. and C. Black, London, 1953, p. 201
3. CROOKALL, R. *Coal Measure Plants* Arnold, London, 1929, p. 80
4. ARNOLD, C. A. *An Introduction to Paleobotany* McGraw-Hill, New York and London, 1947, p. 433
5. LACEY, W. S. 'Methods in palaeobotany'. *North W. Nat.* 1953, 234–249
6. DARRAH, W. C. *Principles of Paleobotany* 2nd edn: Ronald Press, New York, 1960, p. 295
7. ANDREWS, H. N. *Ancient Plants and the World they lived in* Comstock Publishing Co., New York, 1947, p. 279
8. ANDREWS, H. N. *Studies in Paleobotany* Wiley, New York and London, 1961, p. 487
9. WALTON, J. 'On the factors which influence the external form of fossil plants'. *Phil. Trans.* 1936, B **226**, 219–225
10. WALTON, J. 'Carboniferous Bryophyta. I. Hepaticae'. *Ann. Bot., Lond.* 1925, **39**, 563–572
11. WALTON, J. 'Carboniferous Bryophyta. II. Hepaticae and Musci'. *Ann. Bot., Lond.* 1928, **42**, 707–716
12. NICOL, W. 'Observations on the structure of recent and fossil Coniferae'. *Edinb. New Phil. J.* 1834, **16**, 137–158
13. SCHULZE, F. 'Uber das Vorkommen wohlerhaltener Cellulose in Braunkohle und Steinkohle'. *Abh. preuss. Akad. Wiss.* 1855, 676–678
14. HARRIS, T. M. 'Mesozoic seed cuticles'. *Svensk. Bot. Tidskr.* 1954, **48**, 281–291
15. THOMAS, H. H. and BANCROFT, N. 'On the cuticles of some recent and fossil Cycadean fronds'. *Trans. Linn. Soc. Lond. (Bot.)* 1913, **8**, 155–204

16. BATHER, F. A. 'Nathorst's methods of studying the cutinised portions of fossil plants'. *Geol. Mag.* 1908, Dec. 5, **5,** 454–459

17. NATHORST, A. G. 'Einige paläobotanische Untersuchungsmethoden'. *Paläobot. Z.* 1912, **1,** 26

18. THOMAS, H. H. 'On some methods in palaeobotany'. *New Phytol.* 1912, **11,** 109–111

19. LANG, W. H. 'A cellulose-film transfer method in the study of fossil plants'. *Ann. Bot., Lond.* 1926, **40,** 710–711

20. WALTON, J. 'Recent developments in palaeobotanical technique'. *C. R. Congr. Strat. Carb., Heerlen, 1927* 1928, 749–754

21. HARRIS, T. M. 'Note on a new method for the investigation of fossil plants'. *New Phytol.* 1926, **25,** 58–60

22. WALTON, J. 'A method of preparing sections of fossil plants contained in coal-balls or in other types of petrifaction'. *Nature, Lond.* 1928, **122,** 571–572

23. WALTON, J. 'Improvements in the peel method'. *Nature, Lond.* 1930, **125,** 413–414

24. THOMAS, H. H. 'The Caytoniales, a new group of angiospermous plants'. *Phil. Trans.* 1925, B **213,** 299–363

25. HALLE, T. G. 'The structure of certain fossil spore-bearing organs believed to belong to Pteridosperms'. *K. Svenska Vetensk Akad. Handl.* 1933, **12,** 1–103

26. HOLLICK, A. and JEFFREY, E. C. 'Studies of Cretaceous coniferous remains from Kreischerville, N.Y.' *Mem. N. Y. bot. Gdn.* 1909, **3,** 1–76

27. ABBOTT, M. L. 'A paleobotanical transfer method'. *J. Paleont.* 1950, **24,** 619–621

28. ABBOTT, R. E. and ABBOTT, M. L. 'A simple paleobotanical transfer technique'. *Ohio J. Sci.* 1952, **52,** 258–260

29. DANZÉ, J. 'Une nouvelle méthode de transfert des limbes fossiles carbonifères'. *Ann. Soc. géol. Nord.* 1954, **73,** 142–153

30. JOY, K. W., WILLIS, A. J., and LACEY, W. S. 'A rapid cellulose peel technique in palaeobotany'. *Ann. Bot., Lond.* 1956, **20,** 635–637

31. WESLEY, A. and KUYPER, B. 'Electron-microscopic observations on the xylem elements of a fossil plant'. *Nature, Lond.* 1951, **168,** 137–140

32. CAMP, C. L. and HANNA, G. D. *Methods in Paleontology* Univ. California Press. Berkeley, California, 1937, p. 153

33. HOSKINS, J. H. and CROSS, A. T. 'Techniques useful in the study of fossil plants'. *Trans. Ill. Acad. Sci.* 1941, **34,** 107–108

34. HOPPING, A. C. 'A note on the leaf cushions of a species of Palaeozoic arborescent lycopod'. *Proc. roy. Soc. Edinb.* 1956, B **66,** 1–9

35. LECLERCQ, S. and ANDREWS, H. N. '*Calamophyton bicephalum,* a new species from the Middle Devonian of Belgium'. *Ann. Mo. bot. Gdn.* 1960, **47,** 1–23

36. LECLERCQ, S. and DISCRY, M. 'De l'utilisation du plastique en paléontologie végétale'. *Bull. Soc. géol. Belg.* 1950, **73,** 151–155

37. LECLERCQ, S. and NOEL, R. 'Plastic—a suitable embedding substance for petrographic study of coal and fossil plants'. *Phytomorphology* 1953, **3,** 222–223

38. BECK, C. B. 'A technique for obtaining polished surfaces of sections of pyritised plant fossils'. *Bull. Torrey bot. Cl.* 1955, **82,** 286–291

39. DARRAH, W. C. *Principles of Palaeobotany* 1st edn: Chronica Botanica, Leiden, 1939

40. LECLERCQ, S. 'La méthode J. Walton pour la préparation des lames minces'. *Ann. Soc. géol. Belg.* 1928, **52,** 24–25

41. KOOPMANS, R. G. 'Celluloid preparat anstatt dunschliff'. *Jvrsl. géol. Bur. Heerlen* 1929, 131–132

42. DUERDEN, H. 'On the preparation of cellulose films of fossil plants'. *Ann. Bot., Lond.* 1931, **45,** 376–378

43. GRAHAM, R. 'Preparation of paleobotanical sections by the peel method'. *Stain Tech.* 1933, **8,** 65–68
44. DARRAH, W. C. 'The peel method in paleobotany'. *Harvard Univ. Bot. Mus. Leaflets* 1936, **4,** 69–83
45. BARNES, B. and DUERDEN, H. 'On the preparation of celluloid transfers from rocks containing fossil plants'. *New Phytol.* 1930, **29,** 74–76
46. WALTON, J. 'Notes on the preparation and permanence of peel sections'. *C. R. 3ième Congr. Strat. Géol. Carb., Heerlen,* 1951/1952, **2,** 651–653
47. KOSANKE, R. M. *J. Paleont.* 1943, **19,** 658 (original not seen, quoted from Wesley[49])
48. RADFORTH, N. W. 'An analysis and comparison of the structural features of *Dactylotheca plumosa* Artis sp. and *Seftenbergia ophiodermatica* Goeppert sp.'. *Trans. roy. Soc. Edinb.* 1938, **59,** 385–396
49. WESLEY, A. 'A short synopsis of some microscopical methods in palaeobotany'. *Proc. Leeds phil. lit. Soc.* 1954, **6,** 168–179
50. BROWN, C. A. *Palynological Techniques* Privately printed, Baton Rouge, Louisiana 1960
51. SEYLER, C. A. 'The microstructure of coal'. *Fuel,* 1925, February, p. 56. (Original not seen, quoted from Walton[2])
52. DARRAH, W. C. *Textbook of Paleobotany* Appleton-Century, New York, 1939
53. RAISTRICK, A. and MARSHALL, C. E. *The Nature and Origin of Coal and Coal Seams* English Universities Press, London, 1939
54. DIJKSTRA, S. J. Personal communication
55. CROFT, W. N. 'A parallel grinding instrument for the investigation of fossils by serial sections'. *J. Paleont.* 1950, **24,** 693–698
56. CROFT, W. N. 'A simplified parallel grinding instrument'. *Ann. Mag. Nat. Hist.* 1953, **6,** 915–918
57. LACEY, W. S., JOY, K. W., and WILLIS, A. J. 'Observations on the Aphlebiae and Megasporangia of *Stauropteris burntislandica* P. Bertrand'. *Ann. Bot., Lond.* 1957, **21,** 621–625
58. WIENERT, H. W. 'Techniques in the photography of fossilized plants'. *Contr. Mus. Paleont. Univ. Mich.* 1960, **15,** 125–132
59. WIENERT, H. W. 'A simple device for single-lens stereophotography of paleontological specimens'. *Contr. Mus. Paleont. Univ. Mich.* 1960, **15,** 121–124
60. LECLERCQ, S. 'Application de la lumière infra-rouge à l'étude microscopique des végétaux fossiles'. *Ann. Soc. géol. Belg.* 1933, **56,** 351–356
61. WALTON, J. 'An application of infra-red photography to palaeobotanical research'. *Nature, Lond.* 1935, **135,** 265
62. ERLICH, H. G. and HALL, J. W. 'The ultrastructure of Eocene pollen'. *Grana Palynologica* 1959, **2,** 32–35
63. DARRAH, W. C. 'The materials and methods of paleobotany'. *Palaeobot.* 1953, **1,** 145–153
64. SCHOPF, J. M. 'Double cover-glass slides for plant microfossils'. *Micropaleont.* 1960, **6,** 237–240
65. LACEY, W. S., WILLIAMS, P., and HIBBERT, F. A. (in MS) 'A note on the use of "bifacial" slides in palaeobotany'.
66. LYON, A. G. and SIMS, A. L. Personal communication
67. LIBBY, W. F. *Radiocarbon Dating* 2nd edn: Univ. Chigago Press, Chicago, 1955
68. WILSON, S. and YATES, P. J. 'On two Dicksoniaceous Ferns from the Yorkshire Jurassic'. *Ann. Mag. Nat. Hist.* 1953, **6,** 929–937
69. WILLS, L. 'Plant cuticles from the coal-measures of Britain'. *Geol. Mag.* 1914, Dec. 6, **1,** 385–390
70. DIX, E. 'Mummified plant remains from the Etruria Marl Series, Warwickshire'. *Proc. Geol. Ass., Lond.* 1943, **54,** 115–116

71. LONG, A. G.   A series of papers (continuing) on petrified seeds from the Calciferous Sandstone Series of Berwickshire.   *Trans. roy. Soc. Edinb.* 1959–1961, **64,** 201–215, 261–280, 281–295, 401–419

72. BARNARD, P.   *Calathospermum fimbriatum* sp. nov., a Lower Carboniferous Pteridosperm Cupule from Scotland'.   *Palaeont.* 1960, **3,** 265–275

73. SNIGIREVSKAYA, N. S.   'The genus *Botryopteris* in Donbass coal-balls'.   *Bot. Zh. S.S.S.R.* 1961, **46,** 1329–1335 (in Russian)

74. HARMS, V. L. and LEISMAN, G. A.   'The anatomy and morphology of certain Cordaites leaves'.   *J. Paleont.* 1961, **35,** 1041–1064

75. GODWIN, H.   *The History of the British Flora* Cambridge University Press, Cambridge, 1956, p. 384

76. FELIX, C. J.   'Some neglected aspects of plant microfossil research'.   *Ohio J. Sci.* 1960, **60,** 88–93

77. CHALONER, W. G.   'Palaeo-ecological data from Carboniferous spores'.   *Recent Advances in Botany* University of Toronto Press, Toronto, 1961, 98–983

78. HARRIS, T. M.   'The Rhaeto-Liassic Flora of Scoresby Sound, Central East Greenland'.   *Geology of the Arctic* University of Toronto Press, Toronto, 1961, 269–273

INDEX